THE
ADVOCACY

MELISSA FISCHER

THE
ADVOCACY

Foreword by

Professor Daniel B. Oerther

Kilometer Thirteen
Los Angeles   2019

ISBN: 978-0-9802170-7-0
Library of Congress Control Number: 2019946977

Grateful acknowledgement is made for the following permissions:

The District and Obuasi maps are transformative adaptations of the map, "A. W. D. A. AREA S1230ᴬ," by Ashanti Goldfields Company Limited. Copyright © 1993 Ashanti Goldfields Company Limited. Reprinted by permission of AngloGold Ashanti Company Limited.

Excerpt from *Journal of a Solitude* by May Sarton. Copyright © 1973 by May Sarton. Reprinted with the permission of W.W. Norton & Company, Inc.

Excerpt from *A Bend In The River* by V.S. Naipaul. Copyright © 1979 by V.S. Naipaul, used by permission of The Wylie Agency LLC.

Excerpt from *A Bend In The River* by V.S. Naipaul, Copyright © 1979 V.S. Naipaul. Reprinted by permission of Vintage Canada/Alfred A. Knopf Canada, a division of Penguin Random House Canada Limited. All rights reserved. Any third party use of this material, outside of this publication, is prohibited. Interested parties must apply directly to Penguin Random House Canada Limited for permission.

Excerpt from "Introduction. Urban Theory and Performative Streetscapes," in Oxford Street, Accra, Ato Quayson , pp. 1-36. Copyright, 2014, Duke University Press. All rights reserved. Republished by permission of the copyright holder. www.dukeupress.edu.

Excerpt from *The Forest People* by Colin M. Turnbull. Copyright © 1961 by Colin M. Turnbull; Renewed 1989 by The United Negro College Fund, Inc. Reprinted with the permission of Touchstone, a division of Simon & Schuster, Inc. All rights reserved.

Excerpt from *What Will My Mother Say: A Tribal African Girl Comes of Age in America* by Dympna Ugwu-Oju. Copyright © 1995 by Dympna Ugwu-Oju. Reprinted with the permission of Rowman & Littlefield.

Excerpt from *Spirit Possession: Modernity & Power in Africa* by Heike Behrend & Ute Luig. Copyright © James Currey Ltd 1999. Reprinted with the permission of James Currey Ltd, an imprint of Boydell & Brewer.

Excerpt from *The Mind of Africa* by W. E. Abraham. Copyright © 1962 by W. E. Abraham. Reprinted with the permission of The Orion Publishing Group, London.

Excerpt from *Invisible Governance: The Art of African Micropolitics* by David Hecht and Maliqalim Simone. Copyright © 1994 Autonomedia, D. Hecht & A.M. Simone. Reprinted with the permission of Autonomedia.

A portion of the description of the Severan Basilica at Leptis Magna is reprinted from a website of the United Nations Educational, Scientific, and Cultural Organization (UNESCO). Copyright © 2011 by UNESCO. Facebook. Reprinted with the permission of UNESCO. https://www.facebook.com/unesco/photos/a.10150138085998390/10150142369658390/?type=1&theater.

Direct quotation of Bessie Head is an excerpt from *Bessie Head: Thunder Behind Her Ears – Her Life and Writing* by Gillian Stead Eilersen. Copyright © Gillian Stead Eilersen 1995. Reprinted with the permission of James Currey Ltd, an imprint of Boydell & Brewer.

The Nyame Nti adinkra symbol is excerpted from *Adinkra Symbols Font* by Marie Flaherty. Copyright © 2012 SymbolMinded. Reprinted with the permission of SymbolMinded, a Foundry of MyFonts Inc. Monotype Imaging Inc. 20 July 2019. https://www.myfonts.com/fonts/symbolminded/adinkra-symbols/

The title font is *Yellow Magician* by Érico Lebedenco. Copyright © 2009 Érico Lebedenco. Reprinted with the permission of Érico Lebedenco, FontSquirrel. 26 July 2019. https://www.fontsquirrel.com/fonts/Yellow-Magician?q%5Bterm%5D=yellow+m&q%5Bsearch_check%5D=Y

Cover Art: Staff of Office: Ceremonial stool, chain, and swords motif (ɔkyeame poma), ca. 1930s. Akan peoples, Asante group. Wood, gold foil. H. 63 7/8 x W. 4 3/8 x D. 3 5/8 in. (162.2 x I I.Ix 9.2 cm). Drs. Herbert F. and Teruko S. Neuwalder, 1987 (1987.452.2a-c). The Metropolitan Museum of Art, New York, NY, U.S.A. Image copyright © The Metropolitan Museum of Art. Image source: Art Resource, NY

Design by Indigo Editing
Kilometer Thirteen, Los Angeles, CA; info@kilometerthirteen.com

Printed in the United States of America

For Joann

FOREWORD

In their debut novel, Melissa Fischer opens a door into the mind and spirit of Louisa "Lou" Lehmann, a civil engineer and Peace Corps volunteer in Ghana's mining belt. As I walked through that door I was compelled to read page after page of a story that does justice to the challenges, disappointments, and triumphs of engineers. Fischer's convicting prose elevated the read to something spiritual.

As engineers, we are too often pigeonholed as neurotic, socially inept, excelling only within a narrow range of mathematical gymnastics. Fischer doesn't pretend that this is myth. They embrace the engineer stereotype, giving Lou foibles that we can all recognize. But Fischer doesn't settle for caricature. While reading *The Advocacy*, the term that came to mind over-and-over was, *cura personalis*; a Latin phrase taught with tenacity by every Jesuit influenced institution. "Caring for the whole person"—body, mind and spirit comes screaming through the pages of every chapter.

Employing a Faulkner-like stream of consciousness, Fischer intertwines seemingly disparate threads—feminism, obsession-compulsion, *The Rifleman*—until the pattern, at first incomprehensible, yields whole cloth.

I've worked to bring clean water and adequate sanitation to villagers along the equator. I've spent time in Ghana. And yet, *The Advocacy* introduced me to vital nuance I was missing in my views. I can still remember my first meal of fufu; the patience that was shown by my host in re-teaching me how to eat. "If you like fufu, you like Ghana," my host explained with a grin, the memory of which I cherish.

Fischer has a gift for honoring such moments of connection, for taking us back to a time before cell phones and iPads, to the vital necessity of seeing and being seen. Lou is an engineer like me. Her career—as a woman succeeding in a "man's" profession—is inspirational. I'm excited that my students will come into their own with bold Lou blazing the way. *The Advocacy* is a must read for every engineer; for everyone who knows, works with, or loves an engineer; for everyone who knows or has curiosity about Ghana; and for all concerned with environmental and social justice.

If you are a development professional, you'll find insight into the creativity of the engineer's mind. We aren't the same as the scientists that Lou knows, and we aren't the same as the businessmen and politicians of Lou's world. We're engineers. And as Fischer shows beautifully, that means we have the ability to build bridges and appear to be two things at once.

—Professor Daniel B. Oerther, PhD, PE,
Missouri University of Science and Technology;
Three-time Fulbrighter; former Senior Science
Advisor at the U.S. Department of State; and
incoming President of the American Academy
of Environmental Engineers and Scientists

July 2019

KRADIN

Akan children are often given several names, including a traditional Akan name, a religious or Western name, and a kradin or "soul name" correlating with their day of birth. Kradin follow this convention:

Day/English	Day/Twi	Soul Name	
		Female	Male
Sunday	Kwasiada	Akosua	Kwasi
Monday	Dwoada	Adwoa	Kwadwo
Tuesday	Benada	Abena	Kwabena
Wednesday	Wukuada	Akua	Kwaku
Thursday	Yawoada	Yaa	Yaw
Friday	Fiada	Afia	Kofi
Saturday	Memeneda	Ama	Kwame

The soul name is not just a nickname for children. It may be the preferred name in adulthood. The spellings of kradin may vary depending on the bearer's heritage or the dialect of Akan they speak.

LANGUAGE

There are at least seventy-nine indigenous languages spoken in Ghana. Together with their respective dialects, Ghana boasts of more than two hundred fifty tongues. Akan is the most spoken indigenous language, native to the Akan people, and used as a second language by a majority of the populace. Twi is one of the main dialects of the Akan language, with different sub-varieties as Asante Twi and Akuapem Twi. Asante Twi prevails in the Ashanti Region, including in and around Obuasi. The migration to the mining area of people from other parts of Ghana, Africa, and the world contributes to a rich expression. Inconsistencies in spelling are deliberate reflections of the variability found within the local milieu.

Asante Twi, just like the English language, employs the Latin script in its orthography. Twi, however, has two vowels, "ε" and "ɔ," which are absent in the English alphabet. For readers who possess no familiarity with Twi, it is simplest to consider "ε" as the sound of the letter "e" in the word "pen," and "ɔ" as the sound of the letter "o" in the word "pot." Consonant clusters and digraphs may be simplified as follows: "gy" as "j"; "ky" as "ch"; "dw" as "djw"; and, "hy" as "sh." Some useful pronunciations:

Adwumadiem   A djoo' ma dee yem

Agyeman   A' je mai *(with the last /i/ pronounced as in 'pit')*;
              /adʒɪmaɪ/

Akua	A koo' a
akye	a' chi *(with /i/ pronounced as in 'pit' /atʃɪ/)*
akyire	a chee re *(with the last /e/ pronounced as in 'eight')*
cedi	si' di
Ghanaian	Ga nay' un
Gyimi	Jimmy
Gyimiso	Jimmy soo
hyia	shee' a
Kakraba	Ka kra' ba
Kwadwo	kwa jo /kwædʒo/
kyɛw	cho
maadwo	ma' a djo /adʒʊ/
Takyi	Te' chee
Tekyiman	Te' chee mai *(with the last /i/ pronounced as in 'pit')*

The spellings of places reflect spellings that were in use at the time of the story, which, in many instances, were anglicized. For example, "Ɔboase" is the Twi spelling of the anglicized "Obuasi." Residents of the town spelled the name as, "Obuasi"; similarly, formal documents retained the anglicized version. "Adanse" is Twi, while "Adansi" is anglicized. Both spellings are in use. The use of "Adansi" in the novel reflects the practice of the District Administration, which spelled its name as, "Adansi West."

A glossary is provided at the back of the book.

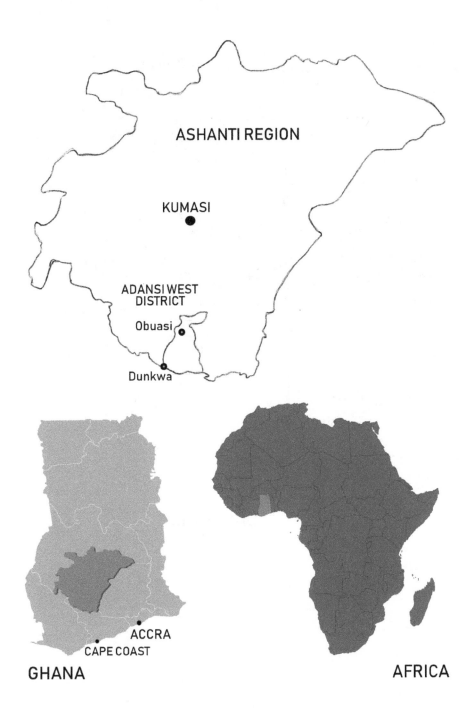

ASHANTI REGION

KUMASI

ADANSI WEST
DISTRICT

Obuasi

Dunkwa

GHANA

ACCRA

CAPE COAST

AFRICA

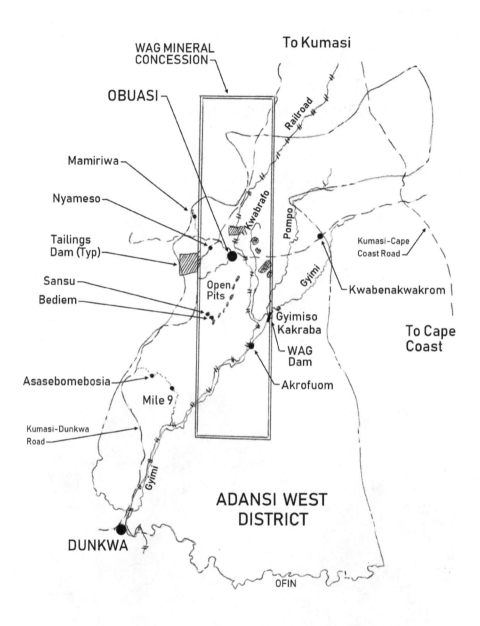

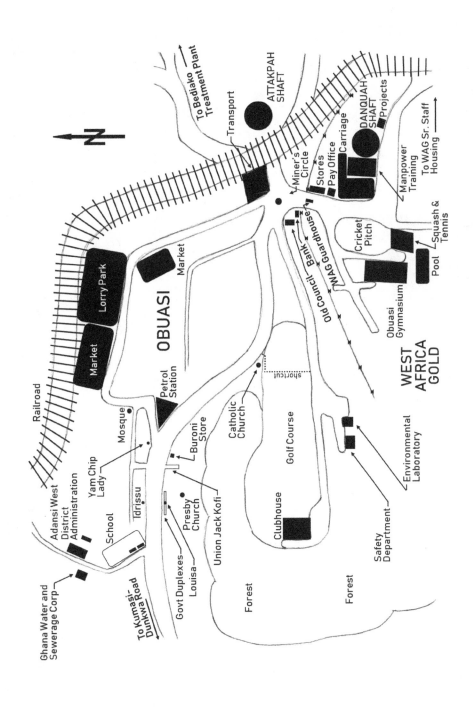

CONTENTS

1

THE MINE CONCESSION

If one looks long enough at almost anything . . .
Something is 'given.'

—Sarton, *Journal of a Solitude*

Always walk your site twice a day.

—The Old Man

CHAPTER ONE

No one is interested in an engineer's tale, but everyone needs a civil engineer. Humanity can live without airplanes and missiles, cars and computers. But a shelter within which to sleep and harbor one's children, a cistern or well for drinking water, a road to travel in the harshest weather, a bridge to cross a river, a sanitary means to dispose of waste—these necessities bestow upon the civil engineer a universal passport.

The small boy sits to my right. On my left, Takyi, one of four Ghanaians who comprise our health team, alternately mops his brow and nods off in the heat. I stare at Ghana's red earth.

Earth is the source of all things. I taste the scent of damp iron, so strong that iron grains must pepper the air. The rich smell feels fertile. Iron—the scent of structural beams hoisted for erection, the aroma of the birthplace of humanity—construction and procreation—the twin phenomena by which possibility is manifest, in the outer world and within.

The boy rests a light hand upon my thigh. I look down. He meets my gaze then looks away. I appreciate his ease. I could be his aunt, a familiar presence that is accepted and does not require words. The boy wears no shirt and is barefoot. Though his hair is growing in, his shaven head bears scars from the razor.

Takyi's head drops and he wakes with a start. Rarely do Takyi and I make the village rounds alone. Today, the other men had business in Obuasi town.

Before exhaling, I savor the eros that satisfies my intellect and my heart. This place that most would refer to as, "nowhere," a village of subsistence farmers, feels to me the center of all things. Because I'm embarrassed by my writing, it's only to Carol that I attempt to express the depth of my sentiments. A tear springs at the recollection of my first letter.

Africa compels me to pay attention. Since my earliest years, I have known Africa as the place where two worlds come together. Unlike the place of my birth where one struggles to pierce the veil, in Africa the world behind the world animates every stone, every word, every act.

In America, when a stranger nods as they pass, they are saying, "Hello." In Africa, when a stranger speaks, they open the mouth of God.

Carol has been my dearest friend since junior high school. Her response overwhelmed me. "So beautiful, Isa. Where have you been hiding your poet? I would love to hear more from her." Tears come and I turn away from Takyi. In one open-handed motion, I wipe the sweat from my brow along with the flow of emotion.

"Akua," Takyi utters my local name with warmth and respect. The men have never referred to me by my American name, Louisa. I turn to my colleague. Seeing that he has risen to acknowledge the arrival of a village elder, I stand for the introduction.

"Akua, this man is the CDR Chairman." Takyi enunciates each word. "He says they are rousing the people now and he begs us to be patient." The gentleman has buttoned an old suit coat over a tee shirt. In some villages, we are met by the chief. In others, the Committee for the Defense of the Revolution or "CDR" acts as proxy. The title lands in my ear as an anachronism. I can't picture what it means that this is part of the present order.

From his pressed lapel, the man's hand trembles in a slow arc to meet mine. I extend my hand and offer a slight bow of my head. He says nothing and does not make eye contact. Tugging on the hem of his coat, the Chairman takes a seat beside the boy. Though showing wear, his coat is neither frayed nor dirty.

Takyi and I resume our seats. We all stare at the bare red earth of the meeting ground. I think every movie I've ever seen about Africa is rooted in red earth. This ground and the pungent vapor of damp iron must bind this continent. I brush sweat from my eye. Pushing the rolled sleeves of my tee shirt above my shoulders, I cast a glance at the Chairman, suffering within the cocoon of his respectability.

I am an engineer. I know the world that can be measured and predicted. I once flirted with the other world. Wondering if my profession was manifesting an arrogance of absolutism, I asked a colleague, "In the end it's all theory, isn't it? $F=ma$ is an approximation. It happens to align with all that we know. But one day, we will know much more and $F=ma$ will be inadequate. These things appear true because of what we don't know."

My colleague hid his scorn behind a polite response. "No, I think it's true. Force equals mass times acceleration. . . . Unless you're referring to the theory of relativity?"

I wasn't and that is why I'm not a physicist.

I was referring to simpler math. One plus one does not always equal two. For instance, a man and a woman conceive a child, one plus one equals one. Or, depending on how you view it, one plus one equals three. Or, if you believe in souls, one plus one plus one equals one (. . . or . . . three).

The boy leans toward the Chairman. His long torso boasts the nicks and cuts of boyhood. The Chairman speaks into the child's ear. I scuff my sandal across the top of the baked ground. Takyi mops his brow with his handkerchief.

If I were a poet, I could speak of souls. The truth is I am my father's daughter. He is a geologist and can tell you the truth of rocks. He lives in the empirical world and does not concede the existence of any other.

The truth is I have always wanted to be my mother's daughter. She is a psychologist and can tell you what you feel. When the empirical world is not to her liking, she denies its existence.

It is this heresy that makes me suspicious. I love the tangible world. It is the root of all things. One must always begin with what the senses perceive.

I wish Carol were here with me. She laughs at the way I inventory my surroundings. "Next time I'll remember to skip to the end of your letter. Only after every detail is recorded do you become human."

Her words sting, even though I know she understands. Better than anyone, Carol knows my embarrassment at living a split life. She knows my frustration at my own thought process, my inability to waver from thorough observation. I have to jump the track to find my emotions, set a deliberate intention to release myself from the obligation to be rational. That is what has led me back to Africa. I can remember a time when there was no split.

A slight pressure moves over my leg. I look down to find the boy's brown eyes upon me. He is not smiling and not afraid. More than anything, I feel calm in this boy. Unlike the children in Obuasi, he does not make me feel like a novelty for his amusement.

How would a poet speak of the monotony of waiting in this humidity? I let my mind jump the track—it's so much easier to do in Africa. A long, sanded bench of wawa wood. Upon which in damp silence wait Takyi, Akua, the boy, and the CDR Chairman. Families summoned from their plots. Constellation of subsistence farmers, potency growing unseen. The durbar mound, red dust, vacant. My heart slows to an ancient rhythm.

If I were my mother, I could dismiss that last equation. Mom knows the mind and emotions, but has no concept of a soul. "One plus one plus one equals three." Mathematical logic requires the existence of a soul to balance the equation. This is the beauty. If followed to its logical ends, the quantifiable world demands what cannot be measured. But engineers do not speak of souls.

Sometimes I am my mother's daughter, in the best sense. I do feel things and love that civil engineering puts me in situations where I can touch life, where I feel life touches me. This is the richness of my profession. It saddens me that my voice does not sing in the telling—or so I am told.

There must be ground before one can stand. There must be a place and a situation before one can have feelings about it. It is the logical way to convey information. Why do people despise order?

It is my profession that grants me the privilege of sitting on this bench with this boy beside me. I take his presence as a gift. In the resonance of our shared tempo of waiting, slow, eternal, I feel I might know him just from looking, from the communication of our silence.

"Ei, Akua," Takyi cries. The high pitch of the Ghanaian, "Ei," confuses my ear. Even after nine months, I don't expect this falsetto from adults, especially not from men. How would Takyi survive on a construction site? "Did you ever imagine Ghana could be so hot?"

Without intention, heat had been my litmus test. I had questioned whether Ghana would be the same Africa where I had left my childhood. When our Peace Corps flight landed in Accra, the smothering, equatorial heat dissolved all doubts. At last I was home. This continent, where I have always felt most alive, finally I was free to experience through clear eyes, without parental filters, with nothing to protect my bare hands from touching the rawness of life. "Oh, yes. You know I grew up in Libya, and I come from a very hot place in America."

Takyi's kind eyes widen. "Really, Akua? You come from a place as hot as Ghana?" Takyi has the weakest constitution of the men. He is not tall and his waist narrows to a stalk. Despite his frailty, Takyi knows the villagers and brings an unmistakable sincerity to our mission. "As hot as Africa! Really, Akua?" The damp air mutes his surprise.

"Well, not this hot. Southern California gets very hot in the summer, but we don't have your humidity." Takyi's gentleness feels a balm. His simplicity soothes the ravages of a past rife with a violence of the intellect.

It is part of why I came here, to walk away from the coercion to be smart and fast. I had grown to hate my own speech, every articulation delivered as a cut to the jugular or blocking the blow of the unforgiving, critical mind of my father, my teacher, my boss. I felt confused by the passion injected into my answering of technical questions. How could engineering stir so much emotion? Why was I willing to fight to the death to show I was right? I felt as if my survival hung in the balance.

I came here to lay down the sword of reason. To be clear, I have no quarrel with rational thought. I detest its perversion as a claim of supremacy or proof of self-worth. More than anything, I hate my inherent obedience to this savagery. That is the gift of Ghana. People are valued. There is that fundamental courtesy extended to every person, in every exchange, the imperative to acknowledge another's existence—regardless of performance. As a human being, one has value.

At home, my heart is not strong enough to counter the tide of a culture that worships intellect. I submit to the tyranny of cherishing a correct answer above all else. At what cost? What is sacrificed? In Ghana, I feel buoyed by a culture whose existence depends upon its appreciation of what cannot be seen. My breathing slows. My heart calms. I am no longer under attack, no longer fighting for my life.

"It is dry and hot in Southern California." Takyi turns this over in his mind. "Dry and hot. Like the Sahara?"

"Like the Sahara. Like the North of Ghana."

"Ah, yes." Takyi chuckles and drags his handkerchief across the back of his neck.

The Chairman rises and speaks in Twi to Takyi.

"Akua, the Chairman apologizes for the slowness of the villagers. Many had gone to farm without realizing we would come today. As we bring important matters, the Chairman feels it is necessary that we wait for all the people to gather. Akua, the Chairman apologizes for the slowness, but the people have gone to farm."

"It is no problem," I reassure the Chairman.

No longer reticent, the Chairman stands before me and asks in English, "Do you like Ghana?"

"Yes, I like Ghana very much."

He studies me with a male eye. "How long have you been in Obuasi?"

"Seven months. I came in March."

"Are you married?" He leans his grizzled head close to mine to impress upon me the seriousness of his question.

"No."

"You are strong." The Chairman raises his head, to express satisfaction with his appraisal. "How old are you?"

It's obvious where this is heading. "I'm twenty-nine," I say, turning to Takyi. My colleague intervenes in Twi, at which the Chairman bows and returns to his seat.

Though glad to have preempted his marriage proposal, I concur with the Chairman's observation. I am stronger than the typical Peace Corps volunteer. Before signing on, I worked in construction. My outlook is more pragmatic than most. Of the roughly seventy volunteers in our group, few have ever held a professional job or attempted the basics of maintaining a household and feeding themselves. I stand on the shoulders of feminists who fought for my right to be here. My freedom is born of my profession.

Although our bench is sheltered by the fronds of a banana plant, the damp air presses the heat upon us. It may be my mother's Lebanese blood or my youth spent swimming in the Mediterranean—my skin loves this climate. Ghana is a fertile country. Food and export crops are grown here in the central belt of tropical forest. Thick, lush vegetation towers over the perimeter of the meeting ground. The habitations of Gyimiso Kakraba lie hidden beyond the vivid green of the forest. No sounds of the life of the village reach us through the thick air. Even mosquitoes and flies find it too much effort to lift a wing.

"Ah, these villagers are slow." Takyi shakes his head at the few young men and women who dot the open ground.

The men wear shorts and short-sleeved Western-style shirts, unbuttoned in the heat—or no shirt at all, revealing healthy torsos muscled from farming and mining. The young women are immaculate, their wraps ironed to a crisp, headcloths accenting their personal styles. One woman points at me. Leaning into her sister's ear, with a shrewd narrowing of her eye and jutting of her lip, she pronounces her verdict. I don't need to hear her words to know she thinks she's solved the riddle of my gender. One quality common to Ghanaians and Americans is the compulsion to categorize by gender.

I cut off all my hair just before entering the Peace Corps. Carol had honored my request under the oak that we had frequented in our adolescence. I remember the earth shuddering from the stallion's thunderous gallop down the half-mile length of pasture to assess our threat. Carol hesitated too many times. She had tried to leave the front and one side long to preserve some vestige of attitude. She held up the mirror. I shook my head. Carol bit her lip and trimmed away the last remnant of style. Accustomed to the bright dyes of our teen creations, the stallion raised an inquisitive muzzle. "Shorter?" Carol asked, thrusting the mirror at me. Holding my gaze on the contrast of white mane and slate coat, I ran my fingers over my temple and confirmed, "More." Finally, Carol set down the scissors. When I stood, she placed a hand on my shoulder and I brushed a tear from her cheek.

The defoliation, along with my thick, black eyebrows gives me a harsh appearance. I've tried asking expat wives to cut my hair, but they are reluctant to go so short. I've found I can accomplish the requisite shearing with the scissors on my Swiss Army knife. It feels a rite necessary to why I came.

Thin, scratched, dusty boy legs on the bench beside me. One scratch is a red, crusty sore, at which the boy picks till it bleeds. The surrounding nicks and scrapes come into focus—how did I not notice? His legs, arms, and belly are speckled with sores. I nudge Takyi, who looks at the boy, wipes his handkerchief across his eyes, and peers closer. Incredulity spreads over his face. I presume he, too, cannot believe he sat here this long while without noticing.

Takyi turns to someone, drawing my attention to the large crowd that blocks the red earth from view. Their presence is a mystery to me, something from nothing, as I never saw anyone come. Perhaps fifty people press forward to hear Takyi. How was there no sound, movement, or feeling to intimate their arrival? This way of being, of moving in the world makes me feel that we sit amongst gods.

The Chairman stands as spokesman. Clasping both lapels, he elocutes, "It is the dam. Ever since they built the dam, the water in our stream is not good. Everyone has sores and itching." His dignified bearing epitomizes the oratorical tradition of the Ashanti.

"Everyone? Who else? Show me," I say.

No one moves. I'm certain it's an exaggeration. West Africa Gold, referred to by locals as "WAG," needs vast quantities of water for its refining operations. This year's goal to mine a million ounces necessitated infrastructure improvements, including a dam built on the Gyimi River.

A man steps forward and removes his shirt, revealing sores across his belly and chest. He extends a palm to the side to show the pink marks on the inside of his forearm. A woman steps forward and raises the hem of her cloth, exposing her legs. At home in Obuasi, I have a copy of *Where There Is No Doctor*, Peace Corps standard issue. It makes fascinating reading when the fever breaks a hundred and one, or when a new diarrhea regime appears, but I haven't ventured to the pages describing skin infections.

Child after child is presented to me, their sores darker, often crusted.

"The adults are able to keep from scratching," Takyi observes.

If Takyi and I report the epidemic to the Ministry of Health, we run the risk that no one will follow up and the villagers will perceive that we—the Adansi West Rural Water, Sanitation, and Health Advocacy—did nothing.

I look down at my young friend. There's something perfect about this small boy, gentle and poised, unconcerned about the epidemic. Cocoa-skinned, with soft features, the boy's quiet attentiveness reminds me of myself at ten. That was the year I flew out of Tripoli. I've wondered how different my life might have been if someone had been there for me. Perhaps my poet would not have absconded deep underground. 1973, the year I took refuge in the cold workings of my mind.

Takyi and I walk to the truck followed by a trail of villagers. The boy matches my stride. Of all days for the other men to be diverted. In particular, I miss Agyeman. He possesses an attuned political sensibility and usually serves as my sounding board. Bringing people to Obuasi for examination could open our health team to the hostility of West Africa Gold. If we bring infected villagers to the mine, it might imply guilt by association. If, however, we bring villagers to the health clinic, WAG might take offense at not being given the first option to handle the matter.

If they were Kwasi's children, he would want to know what is wrong. Dr. Kwarteng-Badu or "Kwasi," as he prefers to be called, is the senior environmental officer at the mine who administers WAG's funding of the Advocacy. Although environmental engineering is a specialty of civil engineering, Kwasi and I share no professional camaraderie.

His discomfort with his public relations role overshadows any possibility of a meaningful friendship. Within West Africa Gold there is no precedent for the types of decisions Kwasi is called upon to make. By virtue of our daily contact with the villages, the Advocacy acts as a conduit for grievances. In a backstabbing organization like WAG, any poor move on Kwasi's part comes at a high cost.

Resigned to the inevitable repercussions, I open the door to the back seat of the twin cab, catch my small boy's eyes, and nod toward the interior of the truck. He looks at the seat which sits at an elevation as high as his chin and back at me. Clutching his waist with both hands, I lift the boy onto the seat. Disbelief and excitement break over his face. Takyi ushers in a sore-speckled girl and the Chairman from the other side of the cab.

CHAPTER TWO

Gyimiso Kakraba . . ." Kwasi is of American football player proportions, though of softer tone. Black glasses jut from an egg-shaped face framed by hair trimmed close to his scalp and greying at the temples. He wears khaki pants and a striped sports shirt. While looking down at his desk, he tugs at his open camp collar.

I sit beside Kwasi, wanting to push him into action. Knowing that will be counterproductive, I catalog colors instead: Wide stripe—blue, thin stripe—white, temple hair—grey, frames—black, skin—brown, pants—khaki, desk—wood brown, walls—white. Blue—white—grey—black—a Ghanaian shade . . . Kwasi's hesitation sucks the air from the room. His fear of a misstep is probably the greatest factor impeding the formation of a plan. Blue-white-grey-black-brown-khaki-wood grain-white-suffocating paralysis.

Jim Hansen slides open the small window in the wall separating their offices. I'm relieved to see his piercing blue eyes and snowy beard fill the opening.

"Couldn't help but overhear," Jim clips in a British accent. "Greetings, Louisa. Don't you go without me giving you something."

I feel buoyant in anticipation of his gift and in relief at his intercession. Jim is concentrated energy on behalf of the good, the environment, the planet. He is not the superior Kwasi fears. It is the upper tier of management at the mine, European and Ghanaian, that is known for abrupt dismissals of staff who fall into disfavor.

Jim asks, "Didn't we order a water tanker?"

"Ah, yes . . ." Kwasi chews his lip. "I've been trying to get a water tanker for Gyimiso Kakraba. The problem is two tankers are broken down. I've been calling Mr. Owusu about the status of the repairs." He rubs his chin. "He is supposed to call me. Perhaps I should go to see Mr. Owusu." Kwasi looks at me. "Could you give me a lift to Carriage?"

The Environmental Laboratory sits on the side of a hill that flanks the southern edge of WAG's golf course. From the landing outside the lab, Kwasi looks down on our truck in the parking lot.

Making out the heads of Takyi, the children, and Chairman, he says, "O, your truck is full."

"They are from Gyimiso Kakraba. I didn't know if you would want to see them." I had wanted the leverage of human suffering to mitigate any backlash against the Advocacy.

"No, that's not necessary." Kwasi adjusts his glasses.

"They could wait here while we go to Carriage."

"No. I'll borrow another car." Kwasi drops his gaze to the concrete walk. He doesn't seem angry. I suspect the presence of the villagers, even from this distance, has had its effect. Kwasi turns his barrel of a body away from me. I feel a wisp of compassion. Perhaps I underestimate his motives. He is an intelligent man. Kwasi trudges off with head bowed and I wonder if his heart aches for his people, if he feels anger and shame as an environmental engineer to be party to this.

Before descending to the truck, I check with Jim. I dare not hope what he might have for me.

"Back so soon?" Jim responds to my appearance at his door.

"Kwasi decided to take another vehicle."

"Ah. Well, without further ado, let me present you with the

object of your desire, lo, these many months." Jim hands me a roll of blueprints.

"Truly, this is happening?" Unrolling the prints, I lay them out on Jim's enormous table. I'm a bit confused by what I find—roads, mountains, village names, but no demarcation of a boundary. There is a second sheet with a narrow printing of the same types of symbols.

"Well, that's the southern bit," Jim says, sliding the narrow strip to match the bottom of the full print.

"Aha, yes, I see." I'll study this later. Everyone's waiting in the heat in the truck. "Jim, thank you for your persistence. I cannot tell you how much it will put me at ease to know where I'm going."

Jim tugs the tip of his van dyke. "It's for my own well-being, actually. It grieved me to see an engineer so lost, unable to triangulate her location. I hope this will end your suffering and mine."

I shake his hand, meeting his fine eyes. He's a character. One that our cultures, our ages, his marriage, and the archaic social construct of Obuasi prevent me from knowing in any depth. "I've got people waiting." I nod toward the door.

Jim waves me off, already returning to his work.

As I close the door, I look back through the glass. Jim sits reading papers in his lap, his pen raised. I would have liked him as a university professor. Every few seconds, he clicks the pen taking us one step closer to the revolution.

Family members of patients line the halls of the Obuasi clinic, their worries inducing a silence atypical of Ghanaians. Takyi leads us through the stench of antiseptic to an exam room. A nurse says something to my small boy, whereupon, to my shock, he lowers his shorts to reveal crusted sores on his genitalia. I look away. The others inspect the boy. Dampness in the corners of my eyes summons the Rifleman to the fore, my hero after Libya. Owning the stoic set of Chuck Connor's jaw, I force my gaze on the boy's groin to prove I am not too delicate.

I catalog the geography of the boy. His skin—cocoa, powder streaks across his legs—earth dust red, lowered shorts—blue, scabs on his scrotum—crusty purple, the ring around each thick scab—ghost white, raised eyes—deep, unwavering brown. Cocoa-dust red-blue-crusty purple-ghost white-unselfconscious brown.

The nurse sends us along to the next of the many exam rooms we will visit. The boy stands, dropping his shorts before nurse after nurse. Cocoa-dust red-blue-crusty purple-ghost white-non-accusing brown. Without comment, each nurse examines him before directing us to another's jurisdiction.

The calm face of a ten-year-old boy. No expectation, no shame, no fear as he stands exposing himself. This is a child who can afford to trust. He is raised not only by his mother, but by every older relative—brother, sister, aunt, uncle. He moves in a sea of family, passed from one hand to another, knowing that he is cared for. His trust need not be broken in a lifetime. In the Akan culture, he will always have his place.

After two hours at the Obuasi clinic, we leave with a promise that the epidemic will be reported to the District Health Officer. As we round the Miner's Circle, I glance at the children—"smalls," as they are called—in the rear-view mirror. The boy and girl hold hands, entranced by the world passing outside their window.

I brake as a haul truck lays on its horn and cuts in front of me, spewing its murky exhaust. So much particulate matter is thrown into the Obuasi air—diesel exhaust, dust, arsenic trioxide—it might be possible to harvest gold from our lungs. I check again on the smalls. This is probably their first ride in an air-conditioned vehicle. It's probably the first time they've traveled not squeezed on their mothers' laps or stuffed between a chicken and a food basket. Perhaps I should buy them frozen yogurt. Perhaps I am an idiot for imagining this as a joy ride.

At Tutuka Junction, we'll take the feeder road south to Gyimiso Kakraba. Before reaching the turn, I pull over. Takyi looks surprised.

"Fanyogo," I say.

"Fanyogo?" he replies, as if trying to make sense of the word.

"Yes, Fanyogo." I point through the windshield.

Takyi considers the bustling scene at Tutuka Junction. Market women in their stalls and street hawkers crowd this major cross-roads in the Obuasi suburb of Tutuka. Miners on foot, on bicycles, in taxis, crowd the intersection. They often stop here for a meal, street chop, on their way to and from one of the three shifts at the mine. Takyi scans the throng of commerce till he spies the Fanyogo boy.

"Ah, Fanyogo." He chuckles, but still does not move.

"May we buy Fanyogo for the smalls?"

"Akua, you want to buy Fanyogo for the smalls?" Takyi awaits my clarification with solemn patience, as if the peace of nations depends on his comprehension of my meaning. I love him for this, for the care he gives to the smallest detail, for surviving in this world without guile.

"It is all right?" I ask, nodding toward the backseat.

Takyi consults in Twi with the Chairman.

"Akua, I have spoken to the Chairman. I have informed the Chairman that you would like to buy Fanyogo for the smalls. I have told the Chairman that you would like to buy Fanyogo for the smalls and the Chairman agrees that this is all right. You may buy Fanyogo for the smalls," Takyi reports. He watches my reaction for reassurance that he has done the right thing.

I smile and hand over several two-hundred-cedi notes. Takyi picks his way through a crowd of miners pressing upon two popular kiosks serving hot chop at the road's edge. He pays the Fanyogo boy, who pulls two frozen yogurts from the wooden box nestled between his handlebars.

I open my door and stand on the threshold, raising my head above the roof of the cab. "Buy five!" I yell to be heard, thrusting my outstretched palm in Takyi's direction. Of course, he did not want to presume.

I wave to the backseat, indicating all should join me in meeting Takyi at the hood of the truck. The Chairman urges the children out the door farthest from the chaotic road. Takyi hands each a treat, cautioning the smalls about the cold and cupping his hand under theirs. Wide-eyed, the smalls stare at the strange food, but do not eat. I suppose they've never indulged in frozen yogurt. I show how to suck from the corner of the plastic bag sliced open by the Fanyogo boy. The smalls make no attempt to imitate.

"Ɛyɛ pa ara!" I encourage them.

Both children let their gaze fall to the ground. The passivity inculcated by the local culture infuriates me. Staring at the sores on the boy's neck, I try to control my irritation at the growing sense that I am failing, once again, to make the simplest human connection.

Takyi asks, "What is it, Akua?"

I respond in a low voice, "Why don't they eat?"

Takyi speaks to the Chairman. I feel tired and would like to get in the truck and drive away. I don't care what explanation they give.

In his infinite good humor, Takyi offers, "Akua, the smalls and the Chairman will bring the Fanyogo home to their families. Their mothers will share it with everyone in the home. The Chairman knows that his grandchildren will be very happy when they see what he has brought. O, they will be very happy. Akua, they are grateful for this happiness."

I wave an impatient hand. "Yɛnkɔ."

As I move toward the truck, something brushes across my wrist. Annoyed, I glance down, unprepared for the gentle countenance of my small boy. I flush at the presence of his hand in mine.

CHAPTER THREE

I have conducted a thorough inspection of the ceiling plaster. Every crack and crevice beckons. From my vantage on the couch, thin ridges shaved by the mason's trowel cast shadows, mouths of crevasses that penetrate time and place. Random contours yield whole forms to a patient eye, characters caught in mid-act. After seven months, hours spent every day, I've come to understand this ceiling holds my life—all that I ever was and all that I could be.

In the near corner above the bookcase, several parallel plaster ridges roil in a cock's comb. One thin claw of the scrawny rooster clutches a stick. I ponder the meager fowl, discovering in the mason's gift, Tripoli, a memory that has lain dormant for decades: a jauntier cock crowing from the center of a wagon wheel. The bright restaurant logo, hand-painted, announcing our arrival at *Chicken On Wheels*. The Tripoli landmark served real Italian gelato.

I loved the green pistachio flavor, letting the ice melt on my tongue. The Libyan proprietor stood in starched white shirt and black bow tie announcing our orders in Italian. As if naming award honorees, he raised each bowl off the tray at his shoulder with a flourish. I squeezed Art's hand in excitement. My little brother did not squeeze back. Whatever gratification he found in his chocolate gelato he kept to himself.

Though traffic thins after sunset, mine operations continue. Intermittent haul trucks terrorize any sense of peace at night. In the relative cool, I close my shutters to the incessant dust and thunderous rumble of Obuasi. Out of habit, I surrender to the sofa. The automatic recitation of the color choreography of this corner flies through my head—dirty beige-thread grey-sworl brown-CAPITAL green black red white-Gere grey. Dirty walls, cobweb, bookcase wood grain, bold titles of engineering texts, the grey spine of Gere and Timoshenko's, *Mechanics of Materials*. A trove of engineering problems to be solved.

I had thought I would be posted to a small village where I would while away the idle hours calculating moments and deflections. I would revel in honing my discipline. Stress and strain, modulus of elasticity, Mohr's circle. I would relearn it all, comprehend it better in my isolated village, where few other intellectual challenges would exist. But, I didn't get the village in the brochure. Peace Corps sent me to Obuasi, where I work with the same dedication as I would on a construction site.

Peace Corps had asked me to visit Obuasi during our training. They needed someone to replace Lynn. She'd been a volunteer in Obuasi for three years and had just received a two-year commitment from the mine to fund the Advocacy. Peace Corps had to provide another volunteer to manage the health team. I took one look at this place—the winding gears atop the shafts, the miners in hard hats, the stinking sewage in open gutters, the massive cranes and backhoes, the bustle of people drawn from all over Ghana, from all over the world, the dirt and dust everywhere—one look and I knew it was mine.

It is ugly and it is mine.

I look up at Bessie. She knew ugly and wrote about it. If I could write as well as Bessie . . .

Photos of Bessie Head and Barbara McClintock grace the far wall. Carol mailed them to me the day I left for the Peace Corps. "So you know extraordinary women are racing to meet you," she had said. Bessie and Barbara claimed their place in the world. Seeing them gives me sustenance.

I put a cassette in the boom box, so glad I didn't bring some piddling Walkman. The small end table yields dessert in the form of roasted groundnuts. I made the little cupboard and am proud of the snug fit of the hinged door. Breaking one twisted cellophane ball, I pop the contents into my mouth. Groundnuts roasted today by a woman somewhere in this town. The flavor of the food beyond anything called "fresh" in America. I play with the string of cellophane balls, each holding a serving of groundnuts, dragging the chain across the surface of the table.

Everything happens at this table. Here, I write, draw, eat, read. There is eroticism in a table. A clean, hard surface ready and waiting to support creation. I push the nuts aside and press my palms into the grain of the wood. Anything is possible.

The stillness of the room prompts me to open the front door and the shutters to the tropical air. Enjoying a rare moment of quiet, I gaze above my compound at the few lanterns glowing from the distant porches of uphill neighbors. Leveraging the half-wall that encloses my porch, I breathe into a set of pushups. One very nice thing about the pace of this life is time for my body. While resting, I pour boiled water into the filter. Another set, then a break to sweep the front room. Rolling back my one luxury, a circular carpet that covers most of the floor, brings memories of Lynn and her fiancé, Jeff Fogerty. They gave me the carpet when they closed their house and left Ghana.

A circle of dust hides the red concrete floor where the carpet had lain. Lynn had grown distressed when I spiked a high temperature for several days upon arriving in Obuasi. I was staying with her and Jeff at their house on the mine. "Take your medicine," Lynn had advised. Every volunteer is given a bottle containing two anti-malaria pills to take in an emergency. Lynn was distraught at my fevered state and probably none too pleased to be sharing a toilet with me.

The Obuasi dust smears under the broom. I'd dragged myself to a sitting position, my back against Lynn's sofa, my butt on this carpet. Contracting malaria ranks as one of the worst risks of being a Peace Corps volunteer. My lips were chapped. I couldn't bring myself to eat. I had lacked the strength to replace the clammy wrap of my sweat-soaked bedclothes.

Mopping with a wet rag brings out the shine in the red concrete. Malaria can kill and the cure is worse. I roll the carpet back into place, grateful that I hadn't succumbed to Lynn's fears, hadn't thrashed my body with the harsh pills. Drugs are not my preferred means of coping.

One more set of pushups, followed by dusting the tight, double-layered mesh that serves as a window in the front room. It overlooks the standpipe just outside my gate. To this window, Idrissu sometimes comes to talk to me. Volunteers in small villages often live with a family or have a professional colleague designated by the nananom to attend to the volunteer's welfare. Owing to its origins, Obuasi seems to lack the traditional village structure. I have never heard reference to an Obuasihene, nor mention of a local durbar.

It is said that over a hundred years ago, when Ghanaian entrepreneurs Ellis and Biney arrived, Obuasi was no more than a few huts in the bush. Today, its ninety thousand inhabitants are supported by a mine workforce ten thousand strong. Governance of Obuasi falls under the jurisdiction of the Adansi West District Administration, while the town's stratified social hierarchy reflects the colonial legacy of British-born West Africa Gold. In this community void of any unifying chief, Idrissu has made it his business to look out for me.

A final set at the wall and I return to the couch. It's not easy to cultivate the one skill omitted from Peace Corps training—how to endure the unrelenting presence of time. I can work and visit neighbors, shop, cook, read, write, and still there are hours left in a day. There is no escaping oneself.

A wadded up dishcloth forms the shape of a hand. A blobby hand that never possessed delicacy or sensitivity. I peer at this hand trying to see a different one, a child's hand. The hand of my small boy light upon my thigh. The hand of my little brother in his lap beneath the tassels of the crisp white tablecloth. My small boy's tense grip at the shock of the frozen yogurt. Art's hand closing into a fist as I reach to take it. I feel a constriction in my chest. My small boy's presumption of welcome, sliding his hand into mine.

I didn't even ask his name. Dirty beige-thread grey-sworl brown-CAPITAL green black red white-Gere grey.

The ceiling is high, a good ten feet. Long before there existed anyone called an engineer, Ghanaian builders appreciated the thermodynamics of heat dissipation, thank goodness. My eyes follow the shallow relief of ceiling plaster. Slight ridges and flat pans are traversed by cracks that wind like fine rivers across the plain.

Spanning one of these rivers is a bridge in California that I worked on years ago. A man had claimed that while crossing the bridge his car was showered with something that had pitted his windshield. My inspection confirmed his windshield was pitted. We had been sandblasting traffic stripes.

Weeks later, I met the man in small claims court. My defense was the inability of the plaintiff to prove that we had pitted his windshield and the fact that no one else had lodged a similar complaint. I may have implied that the plaintiff, who appeared down on his luck, might have been fishing for a payoff from my company's deep pockets. The judge ruled for the plaintiff.

Many rivers etch the ceiling. One dies into a dam of thickened plaster. A stagnant river upon which a village depends.

An epidemic. A gold mining operation. Subsistence farmers. Multinational mining corporation. Who judges? Who rules for the plaintiff?

I don't wallow in outrage at the arrogance that leaves a village without water. I don't wonder why this injustice isn't a headline. Just as I don't dwell upon the chronic unsanitary conditions that plague a large portion of Ghana's population. Without a gold mine to blame, many villages drink unsafe water. They often drink from the same river in which they bathe and launder. Rain washes human waste into the rivers. Even without a dam, such rivers are not safe for drinking.

Mom would say, "Don't be your father. You are better than that."

My eyes rest on the cock's comb. I see my brother's fist and feel the sting of my failure to connect. Am I better than my father? Engineer-mind takes the helm without my noticing. It seems normal to be rational. What is wrong with that? I thought it was logical to propose partnership. I thought if WAG believes its own propaganda, I could swing them, swing the Advocacy away from the draconian contract, away from confrontation and calamity, toward productive collaboration. Did I fail to hear my mother's idealism creep in? Is it possible WAG will take up the call for something better than cliché? Or have I pissed off the lion?

It comes always without warning, the clamor of steel upon steel. A bolt of fear shoots through me. The raucous persistence of mining operations rips me from slumber nearly every night. The sudden onslaught when I am most undefended strips away any remaining pretense. I press my hand to the center of my chest. Something is broken in me. I push my face into the pillow and cry.

Impossible to gage time on a road where the trucks never stop. How long have I lain here unable to soothe myself? I get out of bed and pull an engineering pad from the small cupboard. Sitting at the table, I click lead to the tip of the pencil. I press my palm into the grid. Only rational things are possible. I print: WT OF HAUL TRUCK. My breath trembles and tears come. I focus on each stroke of impeccable lettering: VOLUME OF HAUL TRUCK. A whimper escapes my throat. I can always trust the solid heft of the mechanical pencil: DENSITY OF ORE. I fill my lungs and preempt the poverty of helplessness by forcing out sound, low, hollow. Lead etches paper. Parameters materialize: LIVE LOAD, DEAD + LIVE LOAD, TRIPS/DAY. The regimen of problem-solving wraps me in safety. My body forgets fear. If I know the ratio of gold per ton of ore, I'll know the number of trucks to produce one million ounces.

CHAPTER FOUR

The daily operation of the mine is overseen by a thin tier of Europeans bolstered by a strong senior staff of Ghanaians. These top managers and senior staff live within the fenced perimeter of the main mine. Their residences and surrounding grounds are a transplanted English countryside. The lawns and billowing shrubs create a sense of peace that defies the grit of Obuasi town.

I occupy an indefinable social position. I am white and appear to many locals to be no different from the hundreds of expatriates working under contract to West Africa Gold. The primary difference is that I am paid a salary in local currency that is paltry in comparison with the income of an expatriate miner. Ghanaian cedis are very real to me—whereas, the exchange rate of six hundred fifty on the dollar renders them meaningless to expatriate contractors. They toss around cedis like play money and are easy marks for beggars.

I live in town, not at the mine. To expatriates, this sets me apart as a generous-hearted aid worker willing to brave the local squalor. "Squalor," is a relative term. I have a seven-room compound to myself. A family of eight Ghanaians could occupy the same space. Because Obuasi has electricity, Peace Corps has provided a small refrigerator. Although I don't have running water, the standpipe for the neighborhood is right outside my gate. I do have a private room for bathing and a real, sit-down toilet. The old bucket latrine was replaced with a septic tank weeks before I arrived. By Peace Corps standards, I have first-rate accommodations, luxurious relative to the high-density living of most of Obuasi's ninety thousand residents.

Although I am not employed by the mine, I enjoy many mine privileges. As far as I can tell, this is due to the inroads made by my predecessor, Lynn Lubic. Lynn was a health education volunteer who dated Jeff Fogerty, who was the mine exploration manager. After a brief stay at the house that I inherited, Lynn moved into Jeff's house on the mine and partook of the amenities offered to senior staff families. She could enter and exit the mine at will. She could dine at the Obuasi Gymnasium and make use of their facilities, which include a cricket pitch, squash courts, tennis courts, and an Olympic-sized swimming pool.

I caught a glimpse inside the Obuasi Gymnasium the day Lynn introduced me to the staff as her replacement. A broad portico overlooks the cricket pitch and must be crossed to enter the grand bar. I've never returned, as it feels contrary to why I joined the Peace Corps. Lynn also introduced me to the guards at the mine gate, who let me pass without question. I don't socialize a great deal with the mine community. Occasionally, a wife takes pity on me. Tonight, I have been invited to a dinner party as, "Lynn's replacement."

Lounging on cushions and leaning against sofa fronts, clusters of couples close the perimeter of the living room. Among these senior managers and their wives, the people I know are Finn Harrigan and Jim Hansen. Finn has appointed himself bartender in celebration of his five-month anniversary as manager of the new Safety Department. He is a stocky fellow who comes to West Africa Gold from a lengthy career in South African mines. Tonight's occasion was inspired by the arrival of Finn's wife, who has taken her final leave of Johannesburg. Audrey Harrigan stands near the altar where her husband ministers the needy, who extend their empty chalices in welcome.

Jim Hansen has the compact build of a serious runner. He glides over with a liquid smile, stroking his pure white van dyke beard. "Good to see you, Louisa."

"Hello, Jim, it's nice to see you away from the lab. I was hoping to see Flora."

"She's in Zimbabwe with the children. Visiting family." Jim was hired a couple of years ago to found the mine's Environmental Department. He's passionate about his vision for cleaning up operations. It was Jim who encouraged Lynn to investigate water sources in the villages to determine the impact of mining on local water supplies. Her research led to the formation of the Advocacy.

"Thank you for the map. It makes a huge difference."

"My pleasure," Jim responds with a shallow bow. "Have you put your hands on a tennis racquet, yet?" He's an avid player.

"No, I'm thinking of asking my parents to send one of their old racquets."

"We'd love to get you out on the courts. There's plenty of opportunity to play. You need something to distract you."

"Thanks. I'll work on it."

"Do it!" he says with gusto. In response to a hand pulling his shoulder, Jim tips an imaginary hat and turns away.

Jim's authority is eroding with the subsuming of Environmental under the auspices of the new Safety Department. Although Jim hired Kwasi, both now retain the same title, senior environmental officer. Finn has displaced Jim as Kwasi's direct superior.

A man wearing a plaid shirt raises a smooth wooden block, and proclaims in a Scottish accent, "'s something ye canna find anywhere else in the world. Every piece is 'andmade. Each piece is unique, 's what makes this game work. Ye canna' mass produce these."

Those of us who don't own a set, catalog Takoradi Blocks as something distinctive to leave on the shelf for curious friends in years to come. I wonder whether the rectangular blocks, no longer than a hand span, are only made in the port city of Takoradi and why that would be.

I settle against the wall sipping Squash, a lemon-lime soda, and resting my eyes on the Scot's plaid. I can look at it without feeling disoriented. That would not be possible in America, where the myriad bright rectangles would send me spinning. It's another way I know that I belong here.

The only other single person, by my estimation, claims the ottoman close by. I've seen Terry around and know he's new on the mine, a South African pilot hired to fly the gold from the mine's new airstrip. Our eyes meet. I perceive him as a tepid individual of banal character. Just the sort to kowtow to the WAG establishment in full force tonight. A burst of Audrey Harrigan's warm laughter drifts our way. With a sideways lean in my direction, Terry offers, "She has all the charm Finn foregoes."

"I'd vote for her right now, if she were on the ticket," I say, sharing his admiration for Mrs. Harrigan's political acumen. In my surprise at his willingness to impugn Finn, I came across larger than I'd meant to.

Terry doesn't waste the opportunity. He extends his hand with a wide smile. "I don't believe we've met. I'm Terry Mathers."

"Louisa Lehmann," I respond, giving him a firm shake.

"I'm new," he says. "I'm a pilot. Have you been here long?"

I pick up his implicit reference to the impersonal, isolating nature of Obuasi. "Seven months. Nine total in Ghana. I had a two-month training in Koforidua."

"I can't imagine." Terry raises his brows. "Isn't six months the longest? Are you into your second contract? . . . Are you a mine geologist . . . or a solicitor?"

"No." I smile at his attempt to place me. "I'm a Peace Corps volunteer. I'm here for two years."

"Wshoo." Terry pulls back, letting out a soft whistle. "Two years." He pronounces it like a court sentence. "Are you here with your husband?" His distress suggests that a spouse could be the ameliorating circumstance that renders the obligation bearable.

Obuasi is hard and fast. It feels less hospitable to expatriates whose mission was never to know the local culture. Their impossible quest for the comfort of home propels their sense of alienation. Local amenities guarantee disappointment when stacked against the bounty of home.

"I'm not married." My voice comes soft and even. I hear flirtation. I'm certain that's what he hears, too. It is not my intention. I resent the pull I feel to be closer to Terry . . . to touch him. I'm not here to be his security blanket.

Terry pivots toward me a little more. "You're from America. Right. I've got nothing against the Yanks." I hear a British accent and he must see the question on my brow. "I'm originally from England," he says in a pleasing rhythm. "My girlfriend and I drove the eastern seaboard all the way down to Florida. This was years ago. We were living out of a car. We were kids." He speaks into his drink, occasionally peering my way with hungry brown eyes.

A boisterous hail of many voices pulls me into the warm circle of the party proper. I take my turn at constructing a tower from the slender wooden blocks. Smooth wood. Unlike the coarse two-by-fours with which my brother and I played. We built forts, laying long blocks flat for the floor. Shorter blocks we used for the walls, saving an arch for the door. For the roof, we employed a transverse bevy of mid-length blocks. We'd sit back to marvel at our creation, then on a silent cue, we'd cry in mock rage and dash the fort to pieces.

In truth, I can't remember Art handing me a block. He is there, but has turned his attention elsewhere. I don't have an explicit memory of him building the fort with me. I can see Art building a fort by himself, the excitement on his face. I can see the two of us on the ground with the pile of blocks. But I can't see us, together, building anything.

My inability to connect, especially with children, sinks my spirits. The Fanyogo episode leaps to mind. The block I'm holding becomes a frozen yogurt. I encourage the smalls, "Ɛyɛ pa ara!" to no avail. The bar of yogurt falls from my hand. Picking up the block and placing it in exact alignment helps me push away the memory.

Every tier of the tower is made of four parallel Takoradi blocks set on edge. Each successive level is set at ninety degrees to the previous one. When my construction tops out, I check that the corners of each block line up with the edges of the lower tier. Someone dubs me a conservative engineer. I beam with pride.

Most people have removed their shoes. The women wear thin garments in this tropical climate, casual and sexy. They lean against their men, who wear their shirts unbuttoned because of the heat, revealing the hair on their chests. The men smile too large and too long. Their laughter booms from a place deeper than any they can find in daylight.

I recall, as a child, the endless succession of expatriate dinner parties. Geologists and their wives shared outrageous tales of run-ins with the locals, clutching their liquor, while homemade tapes of Jimmy Buffet and Carly Simon blared from the reel-to-reel. We children ran in and out of the house, daylight or darkness, swinging often through the kitchen for ample helpings of cake. In bed, I fell asleep to intermittent crescendos of laughter, dreaming of a day when I would stand with my own band of worldly mates.

Takoradi Blocks is a party game. People take turns removing a block from the tower. For a while, there's enough redundancy that missing blocks don't matter. Later, as pointed out by the Scot, the uniqueness of handmade blocks comes into play. Because of their irregularities, with careful study, one can identify a block of lesser depth, upon which no load is bearing. Removing it will have no effect. The game ends when the tower collapses.

Structural failure. The failure of systems, claimed a professor I once had, does not result from crises; crises expose the weaknesses that already exist. The peril lies in those unacknowledged defects. Before hearing that, I had attributed my neuroses to the crisis engendered by leaving Libya. The wisdom of my professor's observation induced doubt that has plagued me. Would I have become the same person regardless of which continent I lived on? Were my neuroses rooted and ready to bloom during what I perceive as the happiest period of my life? Was I doomed to be an engineer, trapped in the implacable cycling of my mind?

Tapping one last block into alignment completes my tower. I feel both satisfied with my precision and weary of an engineer's discipline. Nine months is a long time. Couldn't I just relax into Terry, into what this night brings? Barbara McClintock would find the notion superfluous. I don't care to embrace her reclusiveness. Bessie Head wouldn't approve of a one-night stand. My desires have been denied long enough. I settle against the wall, ready to welcome fate.

Terry eases off the ottoman and stretches out on his side, propping his head on his hand next to my shoulder. From that angle, he looks up at me and seems younger, accessible. In the rush of recalling something, he presses his hand to my thigh, then flicks that hand high. "Dire Straits! We listened to their album during our trip down the coast." He brings his fingertip to rest below his nose, lost in recollection. "The truth is," he leans closer to confide, his hand light on my thigh, "a teenager cannot fully appreciate their music."

I'm lost in the warm sensation spreading through my leg and into my groin, in the gentle roll of his voice in my ear, the warmth of his breath on my neck. How long has it been? I tug the shorn lock behind my ear. I feel feminine and wish I looked it.

Our intimacy is interrupted by Finn Harrigan staring at me from the distance of a vodka wrapped in a warm grip. Finn has a pudgy face cropped by dark bangs. He is squatting to position his eyes on level with mine, his middle-aged gut propped up by a low coffee table. He holds his drink against his chin. I wince at his breath.

"You've got one tough job filling Lynn's shoes." Finn's warning reeks of a B western. "She did one hell of a job. Before Lynn, there was no trust between the villagers and West Africa Gold. She won the respect of both. She earned it and you've got to maintain it."

The mythical status of my predecessor has even saturated the imagination of this Johnny-come-lately. My face freezes in neutrality. Inside me, the Rifleman strides to the center of Main Street, twirling his Winchester.

"Those villagers are sitting pretty. They can have anything they want, as long as they don't go too far. As long as they don't ask for too much. That's your job—to make sure they don't screw it up by asking for too much."

My body goes rigid. I imagine a few stray townspeople diving behind watering troughs.

Finn drops to one knee. "There's two hundred thousand dollars earmarked for those villages and you get to decide how to spend it. They've got it good, as long as they are mindful."

It's difficult to not take a shot. The Rifleman stands silent, gaze steady.

"In the end, no one cares about a few subsistence farmers. WAG owns this land. We're just letting the villagers live on it, but we can kick 'em off, anytime. The government knows that."

The Rifleman clenches his jaw and closes the distance to the trigger. The town drunk staggers into the line of fire.

Finn turns an ear and puzzles over pleas for the bartender. Flagging his glass above his head, he cries, "I'm that chap!" With a belated sense of cordiality, Finn winks a soggy farewell.

The Rifleman watches till the villain is out of town, uncocks his gun, and stows it in the scabbard on his horse. There is no love lost between Harrigan and me. When he arrived at WAG some months ago, he approached me as a father. That veneer has worn to a gruffness that can verge on hostility. Finn's aggressive tack tonight must be fallout from our altercation over the Advocacy contract. Unlike most engineers, I don't shrink from conflict. I can take Harrigan at his game any day of the week.

Terry's brown eyes are wide with intrigue, his brows arched, at my exchange with Finn.

I try to pick up the thread of our conversation. "But, you cannot blame the teenager for trying!"

"Hear, hear." He raises his glass and nurses. "Do you work for Finn?"

"Oh, no. I manage a watsan—water and sanitation—organization that works in the villages. We're funded by the mine."

"Very good. And what, exactly, do you do?"

"Oh, nothing so beautiful as it must be to fly over Ghana and get paid for it."

"Well, now, I have seen some sights. Let's see, and they do pay me well . . ."

I envision my private tour of the corporate plane, Terry flying me over Ghana's forested hills. He points out features of the landscape, spins tales of other skies, recounts the details of that near miss . . .

". . . my wife . . ." the engine coughs.

Fuck.

". . . my beautiful wife, whom I love very much . . ." Terry continues in his docile voice, peering into his drink, as if he can see his wife's beautiful face. I get up for another Squash.

Harrigan holds an uncapped Gordon's in one hand and Merlot in the other. The spirit of Bessie, conjured by her drink of choice, comforts me. At this juncture, Bessie might dive into a stiff one. Would Barbara, in her college heyday have preferred the Merlot? She would not have wasted a moment on Terry. Glowing from the seduction of her wine, Barbara would have sidled over to Audrey Harrigan for a tête-à-tête with the most interesting personality in the room.

Finn tilts both bottles toward me with a questioning look.

I lean over the bar like an old friend and announce, "You worked South African mines."

"Sixteen year," he says with pride.

"It's a fascinating business. I'm mesmerized by what it takes to move so much ore. Those trucks are huge! How much do they weigh?"

"These here trucks are newer models. The fleet was just expanded to handle the increase in tonnage. I dunno, well, the chassis could run 200-260 ton. The body, aah, well, you could see 70 ton, the body could."

"Huh. I used to be aghast that the road isn't in better shape. But when you think of the weight on that surface, it's a wonder there's any pavement at all."

"What's your poison, dear?" He jiggles the Merlot and Gordon's.

"Squash, please."

He roots in the ice chest and pops the cap for me.

"Thank you."

"Anythin' for you, luv," he replies with fatherly affection.

I savor the tart-sweet bubbles fizzing in my throat while panning the gallery of guests. With crude humor, the Scot carries the room. Plaid. A dark-haired woman of ample proportions kneels before the Takoradi tower, her blouse hanging open, desperate for signs of a loose block. Brunette. Coarse laughter accompanies the raising of bourbon and Guinness. Amber. Where are the charming, insightful, eclectic personalities with whom my parents howled at the moon? Aside from Jim—van dyke white—there's not a soul I would trust. Have I come this far for naught? Grimacing, the woman extracts her selection. Smooth, sanded wood beneath nail polish pink.

The excited trill of many voices hails the collapse of my tower. Plaid-brunette-amber-van dyke white-sanded wood-polish pink. Plaid-brunette-amber-van dyke white-sanded wood-polish pink. Plaid-brunette . . . I shake my head and find Terry sitting against the wall squinting at me.

Dropping onto the ottoman, I extend my bottle, against which he taps his tumbler. "Cheers," we toast in unison.

"How did you meet your wife?" I ask, eager for any conversation to displace the cycling.

CHAPTER FIVE

Everyone who knows Obuasi knows the tailor across from the Presbyterian church. For twenty years, Idrissu has sat at his sewing machine witnessing Obuasi's celebrations and scandals churning their glories and obscenities into this road. About a meter inside Idrissu's shop is a wall behind which he lives with his family. It is the image of this husky man working the tool of his trade, framed by the open doors of his shop that everyone thinks of when they hear, "the tailor across from Presby."

A covered concrete slab occupies the small distance between the shop and the road. On his tiny porch, with haul trucks rattling past, the world comes to Idrissu. Friends stop to visit, some daily and for hours at a stretch. Some iron fabric while discussing the day's events. The porch to the right of the doors belongs to Idrissu's wife. It is here that Fathia will set up her charcoal stove or lay out aluminum basins to wash dishes or laundry.

Idrissu is a stout man, around five feet-four inches, half a head shorter than me. He has bulk in a Ghanaian way that does not seem unhealthy. His heft emphasizes the rootedness of his station. Despite his constancy, zinging gestures emphasize his impassioned arguments. Idrissu is ready to meet any situation.

From my customary seat on the bench beside the doorway, I answer Idrissu's questions. Usually, I omit details involving West Africa Gold. I don't want to breach any confidence that might cause Kwasi or Jim to refrain from sharing information. In this case, I forfeited confidentiality when I brought the Chairman and smalls to Obuasi. I would love to get Idrissu's advice on how to bring about a lasting solution to Gyimiso Kakraba's problem.

Idrissu turns off his sewing machine to ponder the rash epidemic and broken water tankers. Shaking his head, he says, "I feel sorry for Africa if de white man never come. I feel sorry for Africa if de white man never come."

Idrissu's self-abasing assessment comes from a place too deep for me to address. I turn my attention to the road. Because of the slope of the hill, the edge of the asphalt sits on par with my hip. I hear the click and whir as sewing resumes.

Just three feet from where I sit, the back of the gutter trough doubles as a retaining wall to support Obuasi's chaotic flow. It rises more than a foot higher than the near leg of the u-shaped gutter, allowing for an elevation offset. We hunker in a pocket of domesticity, Idrissu at his craft, Fathia fanning the flames of her charcoal stove, me unwinding from my day, as taxis, pickups, and haul trucks grind past, spiced with an array of foot traffic—a woman with a headpan calling out her wares, children dallying on their way home from school, a pregnant goat oblivious to the fatal speed of gold, a businesswoman looking smart in local costume.

Idrissu's hand flies up. "Dis would not happen in America. Akua, dis would not happen in America."

I chew the inside of my cheek. Dropping my voice, I say, "Oh, yes. This happens in America."

He is already shaking his head. "How can dat be, Akua? A great nation like America has good water. For all de peoples, America has good water."

Fathia removes cooked vegetables from the pot and sets them on her mortar, which rests on the concrete. I don't know how much she comprehends of the English. She never contributes to our porch discussions. A pedestrian dodging a vehicle apologizes as he leaps down to the corner of Idrissu's porch.

"Well, that is how it should be. You are right. America is a great nation. It has the capacity to provide water for all its people. But, what is possible and what is are not always the same."

"Dat cannot be so, Akua. America is a great nation. America sends grain to feed people all over de world. America is a great nation. All de peoples have water."

An aqua haul truck thunders past. I watch the beautiful color until it disappears. Using a stone pestle, Fathia reduces her vegetables to liquid.

Grateful for a diversion, I greet Kwadwo, who takes a seat on the stool opposite me. He's a good friend of Idrissu's and a driver for WAG. Kwadwo's a stocky man with a moustache and beard, and glasses that wrap around his cube-shaped head. I'd guess he's in his forties. He holds a notebook in his lap.

"You are not working, today?" I ask.

"Yes. Today is the first day of safety training. We are learning first aid for the body."

Idrissu hunches over his cloth with an ear to our conversation. "Is this new?"

"Yes, first time. All the drivers must attend."

It must be part of Harrigan's programme. "Is it a good course?" I ask. "Are you learning?"

"Oh, yes." Kwadwo's two hands open the notebook as if it is a sacred text. "Here is the human respiratory system. These are the lungs, this is the tracheal tube, this is the larynx, this . . ." Kwadwo takes care to point to each part. The sketches are meticulous copies of anatomy pictures, the lettering that of a scribe.

"You draw beautifully. You are an artist," I say.

Kwadwo caresses the page.

"Look at this, Idrissu," I insist.

Idrissu leans over his sewing machine. "Yes, yes." He smiles, his head bobbing, his palms floating on the fabric, keeping the alignment.

"I was a good student," offers Kwadwo, "but, there was no one to pay my school fees."

"I am sorry. Kwadwo, do you drive the haul trucks?"

"No. Not often. When I started, I drove haul trucks. But now I am established and don't do that."

"You used to drive haul trucks. How many drivers do you think there are driving trucks every day?"

"Oh, there are many. I cannot say."

"Is it difficult to drive on this road?"

"No. This is one of the best roads."

"The best?"

"Yes. Yes, look. Akua, you see it is paved. It is a good road."

"Yes, but there are so many potholes. Doesn't that make it difficult for you?"

Idrissu and Kwadwo speak in Twi. Kwadwo returns to me with approval. "Akua, you are trying to fix the road. That is nice. The potholes do not stop us. We are not allowed to slow down the gold. But, it is true that it is not safe to speed through Obuasi town."

"I am amazed there are not more accidents with pedestrians."

"We are good drivers," Kwadwo acknowledges. "Can you fix the road?"

"I don't know. But, designing the road would be the first step, and we must know the loads upon it."

"I see." Kwadwo scratches his neck through his beard.

"Is there a way to know how many trucks pass over the road each day?"

"No."

Idrissu's Twi sounds angry. Kwadwo folds his arms across his chest and gives Idrissu a strong response. Turning to me, he says,

"It is difficult. Ore comes from the five shafts. There are drivers going to every shaft. Some to more than one shaft each day."

"But they all go to Bediako Treatment Plant?"

"That is true."

"So, we can simplify our task by finding the number of trucks that arrive at Bediako each day."

Kwadwo covers his mouth with his hand. Idrissu gives him an expectant look. "Ei," Kwadwo sighs. "Akua, you are determined. Ei, I cannot promise, but I will try."

"Medaase pa ara."

A horn blast snaps our heads to the road, where a truck pulls into the curb. Kwadwo balances his sandaled foot on the high, road-side lip of the gutter and leans into the open window. When he reclaims his stool, Kwadwo flourishes a newspaper, from which he relates a story.

> A man in Mpraeso District was digging a well. He cried out in distress. His friend began pulling and had the man part way up when there was a pull from the other end of the rope. The man went down to the bottom of the well. He did not speak again. The friend knew he was dead and called to others to lower him in to retrieve the body.
>
> They lowered the friend, who tied his rope, also, about the waist of the dead man. When they were halfway out of the well, there came a great tug on the rope and both fell to the bottom. Two dead. The people called for the fire department. The fire department could not come until the next day. No one else dared to enter the well. The people made offerings at the well that night.

"Do you get it, Akua?" Idrissu rises, squeezing his burly frame through the gap between his sewing machine and the doorjamb.

45

He raps the newspaper with his knuckle. "It is not right in dat place. Wote aseɛ? Dat place is not right."

Idrissu and Kwadwo stare at me.

"Juju," I say, letting the word hang in the air.

"Juju!" Idrissu exclaims.

We all remain still for a few moments.

Kwadwo speaks in earnest. From amidst his Twi, I catch the name, "Kofi," an oblique reference to Amadu Kofi al-Attar. I cannot imagine what this local legend would have to do with events in Mpraeso District. Amadu al-Attar, if you believe he exists, can be encountered in the streets of Obuasi. No one knows his true name. Everyone rejoices when they hear him called. No one has seen him. Representations of religious encounters with Amadu adorn various corners of Obuasi. It is disrespectful to speak his name. It is profane to describe his appearance. Idrissu does not translate.

"What happened when the fire department arrived?" I ask.

Kwadwo studies the paper for a long moment. "To be continued."

"Dat place is not right," declares Idrissu, before returning to his niche.

It's getting dark. Kwadwo heads home to study his safety lesson.

I received a crash course in safety at age ten and know the one lesson one needs to remember: "There is safety in numbers." Numbers bear accuracy, certainty, predictability. After Libya, I learned to cherish the sanctity of quantifiable relationships over social ones with peers who had never left their small town. Asking them to distinguish Lebanon from Libya was pointless. My ideas were not understood, my sincerity mistaken for humor.

Idrissu smooths the fabric and turns on the lamp in his alcove.

I left a world where the differences in each friend's manner of speech and dress stirred interest and enjoyment, and I could trust that my classmates appreciated my eccentricities. Bakersfield was not intolerant so much as incapable of comprehending. My clothes, the way I spoke and walked were foreign, and not in a cool way. Kids my age seemed immature. I had no rapport with them and found refuge in math.

Fathia returns her vegetable slurry to the pot.

Being the best student was my redemption. In a culture obsessed with right answers, supplying them nonstop won me respect. My numbers strategy had the unintended effect of removing me from my family. I retreated to my room to do homework, then continued solving unassigned problems. I may have felt grateful to avoid witnessing the strain between my parents. Or maybe I always had it in me to drop connections. Maybe that is the weakness exposed by my crisis of continents.

Idrissu clips a thread and scratches his cheek through a full beard. An aqua haul truck rumbles past. Even in the dark, the bright paint brings cheer to the drab road.

By junior high, I began reading math textbooks like novels. I thrilled in transforming word problems into coherent equations and solving for the unknown. I was well ahead of the class and turned in solutions to every problem in every chapter.

Report cards full of As won my parents' approval and neglect. Intellectual prowess is the ultimate pass card in America. Both my family and my profession succumb to this bias. It matters not what social ineptitude one exhibits, if one can play the trump card of brilliance. To be fair, I'm a master at masking my ticks. I want to hide my peculiarities, yet feel neglected when no one notices. Except Carol, she always knows when my mind is cycling. Her laughter, even when she's laughing at me, feels such a relief.

Idrissu's youngest daughter, Laila, arrives from the maze of domiciles behind the frontage row of shops and hands her mother a small paper package. She gives me a shy glance but in the presence of her parents does not greet me. Fathia unwraps a small block of meat to dice for the stew.

Fractions, then algebra, then geometry became my allies. I loved that I could solve problems. I felt safe in the certainty of numerical outcomes. I never erred and developed an imperturbable confidence in the workings of my rational mind.

Idrissu feeds cloth under the drill. I don't know many details of Idrissu's life, but imagine he has not had much schooling. His understanding is based on the oral tradition, in which he partakes in abundance. Though I don't perceive him as cunning, it seems Idrissu has some agenda for my education.

I stand.

"Worekɔ he?" asks Fathia from her low stool.

"Mekɔ fie."

"What will you do?" asks Idrissu.

"Ah, mekɔ fie, menoa aduane, na mekɔda."

"Yes. You go to cook food and sleep. Yes."

Fathia fans the flames and calls, "Da yie."

"Yoo." Hanging onto the low reverberation, I head across the road.

Juju is why I came to Ghana. I was uncertain whether sub-Saharan Africa was the same place I had known as a child. But, when I stepped off the plane into the heat and humidity, I knew I was home. I felt the submission of my body, right there on the tarmac yielding to an ethos that spurns control. Logic is no longer paramount. Every person acknowledges larger, incomprehensible forces that disrupt and undo life. Nailing down every detail is not necessary because it is not possible. In place of fanaticism for perfection, lives an honoring of the unpredictable, of adaptability, of community, without which survival is not possible against such unconquerable odds.

My home is in a row of District-owned duplexes that front the main Obuasi road. My gate sits opposite Idrissu's porch, but is elevated due to the slope of the hill.

Juju. That which gives people value. I cannot explain it, but I felt it when we left Libya. I was ripped from a world where people value people and deposited in an American suburb, where people are selective about how they spend their time and with whom. I came to Ghana to be reduced to a state in which I find joy in the company of another human being, just about any other human being. To experience the pleasure of a conversation that distracts me from my utter aloneness. Away from television and telephone, away from the illusion of control that drives the culture of my birth and the egotism of my profession.

Bessie Head knew that joy. The gift of a guest in Serowe. Bessie's photo swims in a sepia wash. She is speaking to someone off camera. I imagine her in Jackson, enlivened by the respect and adoration of her audience. There are photos Carol did not choose. One with wide, fearful eyes, baring her vulnerability. Another in which I mistake her for a man—wearing a stern expression and gesturing with a cigarette in front of her mouth. I love Bessie's range. She feels human.

McClintock never sought to escape her profession. She holds an ear of maize. Dark, knobby kernels look like they were carved from the same piece of wood as McClintock's creased face and gnarled knuckles. Her stiff form belies the light in her eyes, the radiance of a brilliant mind. I understand. It takes that rigidity to contain the light. Her creativity needs a vessel. She never let a person hold her. She fashioned her own body into the structure she required.

Am I weak to want human connection? I love solitude. I have no issue occupying myself for long periods—though Obuasi has stretched my limits. But I want more. I want solitude and connection.

No one lives behind the duplexes, though some homes dot the hill farther up. Presby church sits above the far end of our row. In the darkness, I can make out the forms of people high above, sitting on their porches, watching the town.

I adjust the wooden shutters to encourage a breeze, then sit at the table and flatten my hands across the fiber of the wood. I open a notebook and pass my hands over the smooth page. Gratitude comes with the swell of words:

> Two men and a buroni
> A worn concrete porch
> Long, obnoxious horn invading our circle
> Ignore
> Honor the anatomy artist
> Nothing special,
> That gift strangers give each other
>
> Staccato blasts popping in my ear
> Listen from my heart
> Talent discarded by life's impunity
> Acknowledgement of our day
> Nothing tangible
>
> A single, sharp blast
> How do we know?
> Detritus of racket pouring off that road
> Three necks crane in unison
> What connects us?

Here, in Ghana, the world forgets I'm an engineer and sends me poems without prejudice. I remember such magic from my childhood. This is why I came.

All de people have water
Corporations cherish integrity
Conduct bears dignity
Government spurns indecency
Civil engineers sanctify water
. . . in a great nation
. . . called "America"

It is impossible to challenge Idrissu's tautology. Even the
Rodney King case could not tarnish America's image. Idrissu
loves to read the *Newsweek* magazine that is given gratis to every
Peace Corps volunteer. I watched the videotape of the beating
on the *Voice of America* at the American House in Accra. Idrissu
read of the acquittal of the officers just a few weeks ago, such is
the time it takes for the magazine to make it to Ghana, to Obuasi,
through my thorough reading, and into his hands.

He took my breath away when he said, "Dey released de officers. Akua, dey released de officers, who did nothing wrong." It
is not my place to strip Idrissu of what evokes his passion for the
highest good.

I know how rudderless I would be if someone took Africa
from me.

Drums from Presby beat dusk into dark into dream. Around
two a.m., sounds of destruction send me bolt upright. My pet-
rified mind expects to see a truck smashing through the wall of
my bedroom. There is a transverse strip missing from the road
near my house, perhaps a utility crossing whose patch crumbled
under the punishment of mine traffic. Haul trucks hit that gash
at full speed, unleashing a malevolent screeching of steel striking steel, smashing the night. Frozen wide, my eyes register the
wall, whole.

I get out of bed and pull out the engineering pad. I press my palm into the grid with a long inhale. Tears erupt. Beside, WT OF HAUL TRUCK, I scratch, 200-260 → 230 TN. My next breath comes as a series of truncated chunks of air. I stare at the grid. Only rational things are possible. I press my palm into that certainty. Beneath the truck weight, I list, CHASSIS 70 TN. I draw a firm line under that, warning my terror not to cross over. Summing the numbers yields, 300 TN, which I box for emphasis. The motion to draw the four sides of the box takes me back to college. The distilled essence of every problem, four to six problems per set, one set per class per week, five classes. Twenty-five boxes per week announcing a right answer. The certainty with which my pencil draws that box, top line—left to right, etching the paper; right side—a crisp downward stroke, cavalier; the bottom—left to right, a loud flourish; and, the left side—slicing the ends off the horizontals. Three hundred tons. The value is cut off from external influences. Nothing can change it. Six hundred thousand pounds. A right answer. That's just the tare weight.

The trickiest moment is getting back to sleep. It's high risk for cycling. I close my eyes and pray for mercy. My mind analyzes recent events and races through things to do tomorrow. Is it true that the government has sold the land from under the villagers? Does Gyimiso have no legal standing? Bediem and Sansu tomorrow. We need to get the truck early . . . I try to interrupt my thoughts, but fear grows that I will forget something. The sequence recycles. My breath comes in gasps. It will never stop. I press my hand to the center of my chest and cry.

Ah! I see the boxed number. The error. I blow my nose, feeling the insight vindicate my anguish. Pulling the pad from the cupboard, I add, IMPERIAL after 300 TN, and extend the box to capture the correction. Harrigan was speaking in long tons. An engineer has to know where she is in the world. Two thousand two hundred forty pounds in the imperial ton. Six hundred seventy-two thousand pounds per truck. A twelve percent discrepancy. What if I hadn't caught that?

CHAPTER SIX

Before heading to the office, I unroll the map and search for today's villages. Driving the unmarked, winding dirt roads I lose all sense of direction. It's a source of great aggravation to me to not know where I am or where I'm heading. There are no published road maps. What does this say about the condition of my profession in Ghana?

Since arriving in Obuasi, I've begged Hansen to get me a map from West Africa Gold's Survey Department. What a joy to see the lay of the roads, the inclination of the open pits, and the relative proximity of the villages. WAG's concession cuts a five-by-twenty mile swath down the center.

I study the oblong circles representing the elevation to which the open pit mining operation has reduced the range of hills that extends southwest of Obuasi. There is no "pit," per se. One day the hills will be gone and the term will apply. Meanwhile, I have incorporated into my vocabulary the vernacular reference to the disappearing hills as "open pits," though the rankling misnomer contradicts the quest for accuracy that is the duty of every engineer.

"Oh, today, we will be beaten," Thomas moans.

The others giggle. My ear, attuned to the low tones of male voices, has difficulty reconciling this high pitch from Ghanaian men. Osei makes an urgent point in Twi. I listen to more giggling as I navigate potholes. Just outside Obuasi, dust from the open pits powders the roadside vegetation.

"Akua, I think you may turn here." Agyeman indicates a paved road to the left.

"These people are difficult pa ara." Takyi drags out the "pa ara" in a way that I love. At twenty-eight, Charles Yaw Takyi is the youngest member of the team. He is Ashanti and grew up in Mampong. In his eight years with the Department of Community Development, Takyi has come to know the villages in the district.

After their last visit to Bediem and Sansu, the team reported that the villagers had threatened to beat them and smash their truck. They refused to return without protection. I made certain that I could join them, today.

We stop first at Sansu to remind the residents we will return later for a durbar. Though small, the village has a town feel. Many well-dressed people congregate in and along the main drag, where homes and businesses perch on the side of a steep hill.

"Is that the chief's car?" asks Takyi.

We all follow his gaze through the dull haze of saturated, grit-laden air.

"You are lucky," says Agyeman, "the Sansuhene is here today. He will control his people. He is a powerful chief. We have not met him before." Agyeman Isaac Theodore is a born poet and a beautiful, very dark-skinned man. His passion for improving his country seems always to lead him into predicaments. Agyeman's insight into local politics is essential for our team's survival. He comes to us from the Department of National Mobilization.

We turn onto a rutted, dirt road and drive past the school to a junction obscured by an enormous mudhole. I try to guess where the road emerges. A phrase of my father's comes to mind, ". . . scratching their lives from mud." Dad had tilted his head with a grin and taken a deep sniff of wine, sending that wave of confusion that often colors his vignettes. This story of a family that came to his aid in some remote terrain—it was delivered to us, my brother and me, as an education in life's realities, delivered with the slap of smugness, delight in upsetting our innocence with the harshness of poverty.

A voice calls through my open window, "This way to Bediem." A man wearing a tie and carrying a large zippered, leather folder points the way, then disappears into the bush to circumvent the mudhole.

"The school headmaster." Agyeman offers.

Unable to drive through the bush where the headmaster has gone, I let the truck ride the edge of the mudhole. The men let their nervousness rise and tumble in jokes about our peril. What is the life at the end of this so-called road? How battered are Bediem's residents by life's realities? My father roams the world searching for oil. I roam Obuasi's streets and the bush roads of the district seeking a child's grace, that innocence that courts poetry and simplicity, the riches of my heart long ago lofted upon Libyan winds and cast into the desert.

A few villagers observe us pulling into Bediem. No one approaches. We get out of the truck and wait. One sour-faced man comes within range and discharges a few gruff words in Twi.

"Akua, we are going just there." Agyeman points out a home to the left. "It is wise of you to park the truck closer, so we can see it."

Our truck is a white twin cab. Identical to about a hundred other trucks that recently replaced West Africa Gold's dilapidated fleet. The distinguishing feature of ours is the blue Advocacy logo on the doors.

We are led to a large courtyard and given chairs on a slim ledge of concrete under a low overhang. We wait for the chief and people to gather. Low buildings of mud block construction define the four sides of the courtyard. It is typical of the Ghanaian homes we see in the villages, except that it has four open corners. Most homes have one access—a doorway or an open corner. The low buildings consist of a string of rooms, each with a door opening onto the courtyard. A well-built home will have interior porches, walls painted in a fading pink or blue emulsion, and the yard, hosting the life of the family, may be earth or concrete. The walls surrounding us have never been painted, never plastered. The exposed blocks have eroded in the rains.

Without fanfare, Nana—an appellation accorded to all chiefs—takes the chair to my left. He is a short, bald man in casual Western dress. While Nana confers with his linguist, I survey the growing crowd, thirty to forty people mute near the walls of the compound. Several have brought their own chairs. Like the chief, most wear somewhat lackluster Western attire. Though the silence and informality is atypical, I feel no sense of danger.

I sit beside Thomas Anyidoho, who is a tall, copper-skinned man of the Ewe people of southeastern Ghana. He was assigned to the Ministry of Health in Obuasi after completing his health certificate at Korle-Bu Hospital in Accra. When the Advocacy was formed Thomas was seconded to the team.

Children stare at us from across the courtyard. One small dresses his younger sister. His short fingers struggle to fasten the large buttons of a blouse that falls to her knees. When he reaches the bottom, one unmatched button hangs low. He grabs the short side and tugs. He tugs again, harder. The scene catches Thomas's eye, too, and we laugh. The girl stands still while her brother starts over.

Nana shifts his chair to within the narrow strip of shade cast by the short overhang. Speaking through his ɔkyeame, he welcomes us and asks of our mission.

"We have come to speak of good sanitation and the prevention of water-related diseases, and to encourage the formation of a health committee," Agyeman translates for me. Remaining seated, he projects his voice for all to hear.

"Yes, we have received your letter saying that you would come today to speak of these things. We are expecting you and you are welcome."

"Thank you, Nana."

"We want to speak about the loss of our farm land, the lack of employment for our young men, the order to stop all housing construction. WAG should compensate us for all this."

"Nana, we are here to speak on water and sanitation. We are not representatives of West Africa Gold. We receive our funding from the mine, but these men are civil servants and I am a Peace Corpse." I pronounce the word as, "corpse," as do less-educated locals. "We are not employees of WAG." Agyeman's voice does not falter. He loves language as I do. I never worry about the accuracy of his translation, often feeling inspired by what I perceive to be the artfulness of his delivery.

A man speaks from the crowd.

Agyeman leans near my shoulder. "He appeals to one and all to set aside the issue with WAG and work to prevent disease."

There is a long response from Nana, which Agyeman conveys as, "He says we may proceed."

Agyeman stands to describe to the crowd how typhoid and cholera can be transmitted by drinking water from fecal-contaminated streams. I enjoy his solid form and expressive countenance. Takyi follows with a review of sanitation practices that breed mosquitoes and flies. His plodding speech reflects his challenge with words. Takyi's courage to follow Agyeman and his steadfastness in expressing his message inspire my respect.

Thomas describes how using ventilated pit latrines can break the cycle of disease transmission. The only non-Ashanti, Thomas speaks fluent Twi and answers questions without assistance. He never seems at a loss in comprehending the locals.

Osei expounds on the virtues of boreholes and covered wells. Mr. Osei is seconded to the Advocacy from Ghana Water and Sewerage Corporation, where he has served for thirty years. Osei hems and haws while mustering energy to propel his gravelly tirade. He has the greatest mechanical aptitude of anyone on the team and knows all of the pipe-borne water systems in the district. One forgives Osei's coarse delivery owing to his irrepressible passion for his work.

Takyi draws his handkerchief under his armpits. I roll up my shirtsleeves. Agyeman concludes with a pitch for the formation of a health committee.

In short order, a committee of five is formed. The school headmaster, a clean-shaven, smart looking man in his late twenties, is chosen as chairman. Members of the crowd take turns expressing opinions.

"This man says they want relocation and so there is no reason to form a health committee." Agyeman leans close. "The headmaster says they should try to work with us. The old man says he has lost the means to feed himself since WAG's bulldozers destroyed his farm."

Three young men step forward, their faces stamped with anger. No need to speak their language.

Agyeman shakes his head at Thomas. "Do they need to let them speak to us in this way?" Osei and Agyeman exchange words with the men.

"These men have been drinking or smoking weed," whispers Thomas. "They are always troublesome."

With a presence more pragmatic than regal, Nana silences the people. Although it is Akan custom for the chief to speak and be addressed through his ɔkyeame, in many of the villages we encounter no ɔkyeame. In the small small villages sometimes we are met by a man who may be respected by the community, but carries no title. The Bediemhene seems to be a hands-on fellow. He bypasses his ɔkyeame and invites the headmaster to speak. I look forward to a voice of reason. No, he wants me to return to the mine with a report and appeal on their behalf.

"I wrote WAG a letter nine months ago," says Nana, his small palms smoothing his pants across his thighs. "I explained that we cannot farm, so we cannot feed ourselves. WAG must give us work to earn a livelihood. Our children cannot build homes because all of the land has been claimed by WAG. Then WAG must relocate us to new land." With strong hands braced upon his knees, Nana meets my eyes. "I want an answer to this letter."

I hold his gaze before standing to face the largest part of the crowd. "We understand that you have very serious matters to resolve. We understand that you are angry and frustrated. But we are not mine representatives. We have no authority to negotiate these matters with you. You will have to take these issues straight to West Africa Gold. The Advocacy is here to help improve water and sanitation. If you want to work on these things, we can help. Otherwise, we cannot."

Agyeman translates and an elder replies.

"He wants you to speak to WAG for them," says Agyeman.

"I am sorry, I cannot speak for you. WAG will not recognize me."

Nana appeals, "You have been here. You see how we live. In my letter, I invited WAG to bring scientists to live in Bediem and study the impacts of the blasting on our people. It is affecting our hearing and our peace of mind. They do not want to come here. If you care about us, you must speak on our behalf. You must convince WAG to put an end to our suffering."

I roll my sleeves tighter above my shoulders. "Nana, I hear

you. I wish there was something I could do. WAG has stated that
the Advocacy is not to come between the mine and the villages."

"But, you can try . . ." says Nana.

"Please hear me. After the team's last visit to Bediem, I wrote
a letter to the mine describing the situation here. The Safety
Manager called me into his office and told me that WAG has a
long history with Bediem that I know nothing about. He told me
that it's none of my business."

The chief listens with a sardonic smile. He hears very well. I
do not tell him what else Finn Harrigan and Kwasi said—that
when word of a potential relocation got out, people began building homes in Bediem to qualify for resettlement compensation;
that WAG felt too many people were trying to take advantage
of the situation and posted "No Building" signs; that the open
pits would be exhausted in five years and relocating people is a
traumatic thing.

Harrigan had leaned across his ordered desk and said, "What
is a little dust for a few years?" He delivered this rationale from
his office in Manpower Training, walking distance from WAG's
cricket pitch and squash courts, and fine dining at the Obuasi
Gymnasium, while construction crews hammered away at his
new Safety building beside the golf course.

The crowd, at last, relents. The headmaster steps forward and
requests that we follow him on a tour of Bediem. On the main
avenue, for the first time I see the full height of the ridge of the
open pit towering over the village. Bediem lives beneath the toe
of a giant.

The headmaster covers ground to a home on the edge of
town nearest the open pit. Half the durbar audience tags along.
"This home had to be evacuated." The headmaster sweeps a hand
across the room. "When the rains came they deposited silt across
the floor." He scrapes a stick through two inches of mud and

peers at each of us. When he feels we have it, he drops the stick and departs.

We hustle to follow the headmaster's lead between the houses. Everywhere, we pass signs—*No New Building*, and, *No Farming*.

At the far side of town is a water tank, a ten-foot high, concrete box with pipes running to it from the mine. Water streams from the overflow pipe and runs in a scummy trail through this part of the village. When the team last visited, the tank was empty. Water hadn't flowed for two weeks and the town was angry, ready to beat the people coming in the white truck.

My letter to Harrigan had spoken of the water problem and raised the issue of the danger the team was in due to the volatile relations between Bediem and West Africa Gold. Harrigan explained that villagers sometimes interfere with the operation of the pump, turning it on when it's shut down. As a reprimand, the mine kills their water supply for a while. Two weeks might be too long. He would have Dr. Kwarteng-Badu investigate. As for danger to the team, we would have to do the best we could. It was Bediem's loss, if they could not cooperate with our program for their own benefit.

On the side of the water tank someone has painted a life-sized Amadu al-Attar. I recognize the trademark features—a faceless figure dressed in a white jellabiya with a turban-shaped headcloth, whose ends wrap about his neck like a winter scarf. What I have never seen is a suggestion of violence. This Amadu wields a huge cutlass. The tip thrusts into the upper corner of the tank, seeming to stab the open pits rising beyond.

Mr. Agyeman arrives at my side, admiring the mural. "Kofi had to cut his way through the bush," he explains. "The many, many small herbs and mushrooms he used in his pharmacopoeia, many were very rare and grew in remote locations. He was known to disappear for months on his expeditions to harvest these special medicinal plants."

There's no end to the stories about Amadu Kofi al-Attar. I had understood him to be a spice vendor, a miner, and a prophet. Was Kofi an Ashanti beloved by Obuasi's Muslim population? Was Amadu a Muslim beloved by the local Ashanti? Both Muslim and Ashanti hold him in high esteem. Was he an Ashanti Muslim? I reconsider the aggressive image. It is possible that long before this tank was built, the hills beyond were covered with an impenetrable mass of vegetation that only a healer would dare assay. Who is to say what the cutlass represents?

The tour has come full circle. I freeze in my memory the dominating image of the open pit. A flat-topped mountain dropping a fraction lower with each day's blasting. A core of gold buffered by a growing blanket of gold-laden dust and boulders, the chalky remains of the mountain's dynamited innards deemed too low grade to refine. Waste is bulldozed over the edge, a man-made glacial till. Powder chokes the air and muddies the streams.

There is a crowd around our truck. Two men in their early twenties hold out their hands. "Kyɛ me sika," they say, in a blunt adaptation of a children's chant. Two men leaning into each other, red-eyed, reeking of alcohol.

CHAPTER SEVEN

When we arrive in Sansu, the chief is already seated at the top of steep storefront steps. As is often the case, the steps lead nowhere. The project was never completed. Rising ten feet, the thirty-foot long, concrete steps serve as bleachers. We are introduced to Nana and given seats to his right. From this height, the view expands to include the dust-laden forest and the ridge of the open pits.

This Nana also is of modest height, but not so lean as the Bediemhene. With his fuller form comes a more sociable character. He wears an orange baseball cap and has no linguist. While people assemble in the road far below, Nana inquires of me, "Which Ghana foods do you like?"

"Nkontommire with eggs is my favorite food to eat in the villages," I reply.

He stretches one leg, letting his heel rest on the edge of a step. "What else do you like?"

"Red red."

Nana studies the scene in the street. "And fufu? Do you like fufu?"

"I have not developed a taste for it."

"I see you do not care for the fufu. Fufu makes you strong." Nana clenches his fists at his waist and rounds his arms like a fighter boasting. "Wobɛtena ase."

"Thank you." Baseball cap—orange, concrete steps—grey,

women's dresses and men's smocks—multi prints, tropical forest—grit coated green, open pits—chalk, Agyeman's shirt—metallic blue, Takyi's handkerchief—light blue.

It's hard to focus in the heat, delivering the same talks to different villages. I surrender to mental cycling while the team delivers our pitch. Cap orange-coarse grey-multi print-grit green-chalk-metallic blue-light blue.

After the team finishes, a grey-haired woman speaks from the back of the crowd. Elder grey. A driver attempting to pass lays on his horn, drowning her words. Truck red. She begins again, to be interrupted by the driver's return. The woman waits for the rabble-rouser to pass and finishes in a composed voice. Cap orange-coarse grey-multi print-grit green-chalk-metallic blue-light blue-elder grey-recalcitrant red.

Agyeman translates. "She says we have spoken the truth, all right. The woman is a retired nurse. She says to the people it is true that diseases are transmitted as we have said, through the water, and not just a punishment from the gods."

An elderly man speaks next. He worries the lapels of his waistcoat. The crowd answers his earnest voice with laughter. The team members exchange amused glances. Agyeman sways his head from side to side before explaining.

"The man has taken exception to the woman's message. He warns not to be misled into thoughts that God is not just and God will not punish. He appeals to the young people whom he observes straying from the path that is righteous. He says to the woman, let her say with all the people as her witness that she does not fear to be cursed in the river."

A young man speaks.

"The nurse has found support from this fellow," Agyeman tells me. "He is a teacher. He says he read it in a textbook."

A blaring horn announces the driver's return. Nana barks

something in Twi. Soon, an aqua haul truck blocks the offender's access.

"This is one of my trucks," says Nana. "I haul for WAG."

I recognize the bright truck as one of several that first appeared in Obuasi about three weeks ago. They are the newest, nicest trucks on the road. Cap orange-coarse grey-multi print-grit green-chalk-metallic blue-light blue-elder grey-recalcitrant red-Sansuhene aqua.

After the durbar, Nana asks us to visit his new home. It is not a typical village home nor even a typical chief's palace. The floors are polished granite. A worker is installing electrical outlets. Porcelain bath fixtures are due to arrive from Kumasi any day.

"I hope you will help develop my village," says the chief.

In a silent display of disapproval, no one from the team responds. This departure from their high standard of courtesy is the more striking for being directed at a superior, the powerful Sansuhene.

"It is a terrible situation," Nana continues. "But it cannot be otherwise. Do you see those hills? They are full of gold. WAG will mine them all. But WAG is reasonable. You can go to them, express your problems, and they will come up with a solution."

"So, you think the mine has dealt fairly with you?"

"Well . . . no, but we must work with them. Otherwise, we will lose. The government needs money. How can they say this land will be farmed for cassava and plantain, while the gold is there and the rest of the country suffers?"

In the truck, Agyeman offers his supplement. "The people say the Sansu chief got the money to build his house from WAG. The people get nothing and the chief gets a palace. There will be trouble in Sansu."

We approach Obuasi from the southwest, zigzagging across the full width of the road. The tedious sacrifice of speed to potholes reminds me of a joke told at the mine:

A Ghanaian is arrested in England for driving on the wrong side of the road. The magistrate enquires, "You have been charged with driving on the wrong side of the road."

"Yes, sir," the man replies.

"Were you driving on the right side of the road?"

"Yes, sir."

"And which side is the right side?"

"The best side, sir."

"Akua, did you have a steering committee meeting, yesterday?" Thomas asks from the back seat.

"Yes, for once, everyone showed up."

The Advocacy has a six-member steering committee comprised of each team member's boss, as well as one representative of the Adansi West District and one representative of West Africa Gold.

"Was Helen Boateng there?" Takyi enquires of his boss.

"Yes, Helen Boateng was there. She arrived fifteen minutes late and stayed for the whole meeting."

"And Mr. Preko?" asks Agyeman, who is riding shotgun. His boss is a dynamo who finds little time for the Advocacy's affairs.

"Yes, the Department of National Mobilization was present and on time."

Thomas does not inquire after his boss, Mr. Osabutey, who is a regular at the steering committee meetings. Nor does Osei ask about his boss, as he has not had a real boss for many months. The policy of retrenchment has removed most of the managers from the ranks of Ghana Water and Sewerage Corporation. It's been so long since anyone has shown up from Water and Sewerage that no one expects it.

"Four bosses minus one—Boateng, Preko, Osabutey. Plus the District Administration, Abubakar. And, Obeng for WAG."

Abubakar is the Deputy District Administrative Officer. Robert Obeng is Kwasi's assistant at the lab. Except for Abubakar and Obeng, I rarely run into any of the steering committee members outside of our meetings.

"And how was the meeting, Akua?" asks Takyi.

"It was an amazing meeting."

"Oh, really?" Takyi sounds hopeful.

"I do not want to keep you in suspense." I'm talking to all of them. "I did reopen the issue of increasing your out-of-station allowance and the entire steering committee voted against."

It is silent in the truck.

"I am sorry. I raised all of the points you had made to me, but they felt the conviction of their original decision. It is also, perhaps, unfortunate that I had to bring the issue on that particular day. It was a very different kind of meeting."

"What happened?" Agyeman asks.

"Obeng showed up nervous and it soon became clear why. Kwasi had sent him with a list of demands. Obeng said WAG does not want the Advocacy to work in villages that are not impacted by the mine."

"Eh, WAG thinks it owns the District. What did the others say?" Agyeman chuckles.

"They said that West Africa Gold may be funding the Advocacy, but every team member still receives his pay from his parent organization. These organizations have a mission to serve the entire district, not just villages impacted by the mine."

Agyeman scoffs and asks, "What else did WAG want?"

"Obeng said they do not want us to put on health education trainings for villages that are not impacted. He said we should go to impacted villages that are outside the district. We should not waste our resources fundraising for village projects. This is the responsibility of the villages. He said we should not go to mine contractors to raise money for village projects."

"How did the steering committee respond?" asks Thomas.

"They rejected every item. I was shocked. WAG has never made such demands. The steering committee has never demonstrated such unity against the mine. It was an amazing thing to see."

"WAG is responding to your letter. It will get serious, now." Agyeman advises.

For just an instant, I take my eyes from the tiresome road and look at Agyeman. This man with skin so black it shines blue. This man who speaks to me. Because it is his custom to analyze the politics of any situation, because it is his nature to be frank, because he needs me as much as I need him.

"What letter is this?" asks Osei.

"I had to write a letter for Harrigan about the contract," I reply.

"Eh, excuse me, Akua." Osei puzzles. "Excuse me, Akua. Harrigan asked you to write a letter? Have we seen this letter?"

"Agyeman has. Harrigan didn't ask for the letter. He asked for my comments on the contract WAG has drafted and sent to the District for signing."

"What will be the purpose of this contract?" Thomas asks.

"Jim Hansen and I intended to put in writing the amount of funding that WAG had committed to the Advocacy. We agreed a contract was a good idea. But Kwasi must have used a construction contract as a guide and the terms are not at all applicable to our situation."

"But the contract, eh, has already gone to the District. What did Harrigan want from you?" Osei ponders.

"That's a good question, Mr. Osei. What did he want?"

CHAPTER EIGHT

Agyeman says something in Twi and tells me, "I told them they can read a copy of the letter at the office."

I lose myself in the monotonous quest for competent tarmac, letting the events of that weekend replay.

It was a Saturday afternoon when Harrigan had sent word via a taxi driver who I had asked to wait small while I finished my lunch. The mine guards only allow taxis to enter with passengers who are employees. Lynn's legacy won us passage, saving me the trek by foot past the Pay Office and up the hill to Manpower Training. Climbing the stairs to Finn Harrigan's tiny office, I savored the smell of grease rising from the shop floor—a thick, acrid sweetness in which drifted, like prehistoric flora preserved in amber, tastes of men I've known—the meat-and-potatoes diligence of a mechanic who could nurse the most abused equipment, the ebullient cheer of an oiler who never quit.

It was an odd thing that I should be called to a mine manager's office at all, much less on a Saturday. Though I've discussed the incident with Agyeman, it's more detail and more subtlety than feels appropriate to share with the whole team. The men's conversation drops to a lull beneath the memory of Harrigan's voice progressing from paternal to cajoling to angry, and finally threatening.

"Since you're both here. What's going on with this contract?" Harrigan had asked.

I pulled my eyes from his round spectacles and the unflattering line of his bangs to look at Kwasi.

Kwasi chose his words. Speaking in a husky voice, he explained, "Eh, the contract was approved by the General Manager and sent to the District almost three months ago. We have not received the contract back from them." At that moment, he embodied a dreadful blend of Western and Ghanaian mores. Knowing as a professional he had to meet Finn's eyes, Kwasi stared through his heavy black frames with his shoulders hunched and head bowed.

"Why?" asked Harrigan.

Kwasi squeezed words from his parched throat, "I don't know." Disgust welled in me for Kwasi's acquiescence. The ceiling fan creaked from a height that neutralized any benefit. Perched on a folding chair, I let the toe of my sandal grate over the rough, sandy floorboards. I had known where Harrigan would turn his attention next and had no intention of yielding to his intimidation.

From the back seat, Takyi offers, "Akua, we are grateful that you could join us today." I relax in the warmth of his voice. "This is more than we had accomplished at other durbars for Sansu and Bediem."

I assure him, "I'm glad that I came. We cannot have anyone threatening the Advocacy. You are too valuable."

Thomas laughs and exclaims to Takyi, "You are valuable!" Accompanied by much giggling, the men descend into some private joke in Twi, while I recall the events that transformed Harrigan from patronizing to threatening.

At first, Harrigan had let his voice rise with curiosity, as if he delighted in discovering what treasure I might hold. "Louisa, would you know about the contract?"

Had I anticipated the reason for the meeting, I might have taken a moment to prune my hair. That edge sets people back and throws off balance the kind of man who wants to pretend I'm his daughter. "I don't know what the District Administration is doing with the contract," I parried with innocence. "Ankrah and Illiasu gave me a copy to read and we're supposed to discuss it."

"Kwasi says you have some problems with the contract?"

"Yes, there are some places where the language isn't appropriate for our situation."

"Well, why didn't you straighten this out before?"

"I didn't see the contract before."

"You didn't see it! Is that right?" He turned to Kwasi in surprise.

"Yes." Kwasi had flinched.

A giant trotro barrels toward me. The passenger lorry shows no sign of slowing. I check my rear view mirror and glance across Agyeman. Although the lane I should occupy is clear of vehicles, a crater devours any possibility of smooth passage. I opt to hug the left edge of the tarmac to dodge the trotro. The pathetic pavement brings a memory of one of Carol's letters. She responded to my outrage at Ghana's decaying infrastructure with her characteristic insight.

"I know how you feel, Isa." She wrote. "When I try to follow your engineering-speak and legalese, my head hurts. These passages are gaping holes in your letters. I want to comprehend your amazing Peace Corps experience. For years, I've listened to you speak so fondly of Libya. I know what returning to Africa means. I wish I were there with you.

"But that can't be. Your words on the page are all I have. My desire to know what you are going through is dulled by your technical jargon. I try to dodge the potholes and leap to the solid ground of your personal revelations. You question the implications of deteriorated roads—the inferred lack of resources, organization, or perhaps a lack of commitment of resources that may be abundant. In your case we must ask, what causes the holes in your writing? What has decayed? What resources are you failing to commit to your well-intended effort to communicate?"

I pull back onto the road loving Carol's candor—even if it bites, even when she's wrong. She complains I write of too many organizations and acronyms, too many people for her to remember. But this is the reality, my reality. I have to try to hold it all, to perceive the connections, to analyze options and find the best course of action. What if I were to take Carol's attitude and dodge these details? I would never be able to navigate this morass. I would never be able to do anything of value for these villagers. Does anyone want to cross a bridge that was designed by Carol? By someone who just can't remember what all the variables in the equation stand for? Engineers are needed for their steadfastness to hold every small piece.

Faced with the tiresome shadowing of a wending truck, my thoughts prey upon the scene in Harrigan's office. "Well, I want the two of you to get together and work this out," Finn had directed. "There's no reason why this should be a problem. West Africa Gold is trying to help. This is just a friendly agreement. I'm sure we can address your concerns, Louisa. All right? Good. Tomorrow I want the two of you back in my office explaining to me how we're going to fix the contract."

At two p.m., Sunday afternoon, Kwasi and I once again sat before Harrigan in his tiny office.

"Are you both satisfied with the contract now?" Harrigan's tone had been sharper that day. Even at WAG, where operations are continuous seven days per week, senior staff won't be found in their offices on a Sunday afternoon.

I looked away and Harrigan sought an answer from Kwasi. "Did the two of you discuss the contract?"

"Yes, we did," Kwasi responded in a small voice.

"And?"

"Eh, yesterday we reviewed the contract together. We discussed Louisa's concerns. I would agree that while she has some good

73

points, but . . ." Kwasi squeaked. "It's too late. We cannot change the contract after it's been approved by the General Manager."

"Why not?" Harrigan rapped his pen on the desk. "We'll just tell her we made a mistake. That we need to fix these items."

"Eh." Kwasi swallowed an enormous lump. "That would be a deviation from the standard procedure." Prompted by Harrigan's blank look, Kwasi elaborated. "Before the General Manager approves the contract, it must be approved by several other managers—Projects and Accounting—it's a very long process. To revise the contract requires repeating the entire process, getting every manager's approval. It's very time consuming and we'd have to explain why."

"This isn't usually done?" Harrigan played with his wedding ring. "It isn't done."

Harrigan recalculated while lighting a cigarette. "Louisa, you can see the position we're in. I don't know what your concerns are. We can discuss them. But do you think you could find a way to live with the contract as it is?"

"There are a few points that could be overlooked, but the whole tone of the contract is inappropriate. It's written like a hard money construction contract. We're not contractors. We're doing development work," I had pleaded.

As we pass near the borehole of Nyameso, a girl places a full five-gallon bucket on her head and walks into the village.

Harrigan had remained calm. "Let me see your concerns."

I handed him a letter I had finished typing minutes before departing for his office. Based upon the premise of charitable intentions, my letter proposed that the contract be scrapped altogether. It proposed an alternate contract that cast WAG, the Advocacy, and the District as partners. The contract would memorialize their joint venture to improve the water and sanitation conditions in the rural villages of the mining concession and the district.

Harrigan didn't read too far before cutting to the chase. "I don't care for the tone of this. This is a slap in the face to West Africa Gold. All WAG is doing is trying to help the Advocacy do something nice for the villagers. This is just a friendly agreement and you're turning it into a war. I don't know where you Peace Corps volunteers get off coming in here and causing problems between WAG and the District. Lynn never would have done this."

I rolled my eyes at the "Lynn" crap. "I'm not causing problems," I insisted. "The problems are there . . ."

"That's exactly what you're doing, missy. I don't like your attitude. You're going to ruin all of Lynn's hard work. That's a fine thank you to your predecessor."

"You say this is a friendly agreement. If that's what you mean, then why don't you write a friendly agreement? There's nothing friendly about the terms of that contract."

"I'm taking this to my lawyer. That's what I'm going to do," bellowed Harrigan.

By "my lawyer" he had meant Madam Dzodzi Akyineba Tettey, who, in addition to being a lawyer, is WAG's General Manager. I've never met her and hadn't thought to link my letter to the showdown in yesterday's steering committee meeting. The truth of Agyeman's instinct was obvious the moment he spoke. Madam Tettey has us in her sights.

CHAPTER NINE

Given the hostile turn with WAG, the Advocacy might do more harm than good by pressing for a permanent solution to Gyimiso Kakraba's water crisis. As we round the curve at the petrol station, I realize the truck has grown quiet. "Anyhow, I am sorry about your out-of-station allowance," I say to the men. "Everyone wants to be paid well for their work. I am happy to see you receive as much compensation as possible. The steering committee had just rejected all of Obeng's demands and it was nothing for them to deny your request."

As we climb the stairs to our office, the men look dejected. This will die hard and I don't want them to think I've failed them.

"Would you like to meet with the steering committee and make your case?"

Agyeman says, "Yes, Akua. It is good if we meet them."

I drop the truck at the Environmental Lab. With my duffel bag over my shoulder, I pick my way down the steep slope of the golf course, cross a board bridging the stream, and pick my way through the muddy path along the fence. I steal a look over my shoulder at the large cloths spread out to dry near the second and third holes. A vibrant fungus of wax prints mushrooms over the manicured hills. I wait. The old anxiety does not come. More than that, I enjoy the originality of the patterns. It's a far cry from the distress induced by busy patterns that overwhelms me in America. There is something Ghana gives me that my family and my country cannot.

Emerging on the main road beside the Catholic church, I peer through the wrought iron fence hoping for a glimpse of stained glass—another treat I could not endure back home—but the door is shut. I round the curve opposite the petrol station and strain to find the yam chip lady on the far side. She is busy serving customers, but her sister taps her arm.

"Ɛte sɛn, Akua?" Her buoyant voice carries over the traffic.

I raise my hand and yell, "Ɛyɛ. Na wo nso ɛ?"

"Ɛyɛ."

Without slowing my step, I leap over cross gutters, shallow half-pipe conveyances, and up a plank to the entrance of the buroni store. From floor to ceiling are stacked European foodstuffs—jars of salad dressing, tins of corned beef, fruit juice concentrates, canned vegetables, dusty bags of pasta, canned salmon, and stale Cadbury bars. I grab a can of corn. Unlike the yam chip lady, whose clientele is Ghanaian, every expatriate in Obuasi files past the young woman tending the buroni store. When she looks up from the cash register, it is without any intention of seeing me. Though she speaks English and I thank her in kind, we have no rapport.

The seamstresses beside the buroni store have taken to greeting me when I pass, and I return the courtesy. Young women in blue uniforms crowd both sides of the two tables that flank the door of what I presume to be the shop of the head seamstress. These ladies do not speak English. One among them calls, "Ɛte sɛn, Akua?" at which the others echo my name.

Keeping the rhythm of my gait, I toss a cordial response across my shoulder. "Ɛyɛ, medaase. Ɛte sɛn?"

My greeting is met with much giggling and flashing of shy eyes, hands covering mouths. No doubt they are uncertain of my gender, but also it may be the excitement of proximity. No other aborɔfo walk in town. The seamstresses' experience of expats is

77

limited to their driving by and the short transit by foot from a parked four-by-four to the buroni store.

Not all of the shops along the main road have sidewalks. Many front right onto the open gutter, forcing pedestrians into the road along with stray animals, taxis, pickup trucks, and heavy haul trucks. Where sidewalks do exist, one must watch for cross gutters, for moving obstacles in the form of goats, chickens, and other people, and for the waste left behind, both human and animal.

The southern edge of the asphalt matches the grade of the shop fronts, eliminating the hazard of an offset elevation along this portion of the road. I pick my way, stepping on the road-side lip of the gutter, jogging around a small, marching against traffic, and paying no notice to the trucks rattling past at breakneck speed no more than a hand's width away.

An insistent horn pulls my focus to the cab of a passing Land Rover, from which waves an enthusiastic Kwadwo. I respond in kind as he hurtles past. Kwadwo belongs to the drivers' pool, a large group of eligible men in uniform who gather every morning at Transport in hopes of receiving an assignment. As Kwadwo is a good driver, he receives long-term assignments and is rarely out of work.

A small boy runs after me with hand outstretched, chanting, "Kyɛ me penny!"

I cringe inside. It doesn't matter that I've never given money to beggars. The children won't relent.

I do not slow my stride until a mural appears on the side of a row of shops. A faceless Amadu al-Attar stands square to the alley. In one hand he holds a pole, from the end of which flutters the Union Jack. I lose sight of the confusing image as I step up to the wooden doors. The old woman who sells fresh tea bread is absent.

While I ponder whether to step into the darkness behind the half open door, a teenager bounds up. She has hair clipped close and wears what I presume to be a buroni waawu dress. The cost of new Western clothes in Ghana is prohibitive. When in need, I buy from the buroni waawu piles, and presume that Ghanaians of lesser economic fortune do the same. This teenager often helps the old woman and looks at me for confirmation of my usual order.

"Tea bread. Two hundred."

The girl disappears behind the door and returns with a long loaf wrapped in newspaper. I open my duffel bag and she places the bread beside the can of corn. She is efficient and does not smile. We never expand beyond this basic exchange.

"Medaase," I say, handing her a two-hundred-cedi note.

"O ɛnna ase," the girl replies.

I resume my standard pace until it seems I've gone too far. I have missed the old woman. I step back, a little disoriented, panning the shop fronts.

"Kyɛ me penny," the boy insists, standing at my heels.

I return a stern stare. No amount of words will discourage these kids. It is a game to them. Upon seeing the small's outstretched hand, a passing woman turns to me with an expression of endearment.

With some effort, I discover the shrunken body and creased face behind the tables, instead of in front near the gutter. The old woman always wears a headcloth tied in a short knot. She sits on a low, wooden stool, her body crumpled into a tiny ball with her brow against her knees and her arms encircling her crown.

A neighbor pushes her child, who runs to nudge her grandmother. The wrinkled face rises, eyes blinking in the light. As soon as she recognizes me, she gets excited, rattles in Twi at a speed beyond my comprehension, and bows her head in deference. She peeks up and then bows her head again, saying something I cannot understand. She stretches her twig of an arm across the table, scoops three tiny, broken tomatoes, and presses them into my hand. I reach for money and she refuses.

"Mepa wo kyɛw," I say, pulling the coins from my pocket.

"Dabi." With a vigorous shake of her head, she pushes me away. "Me ti yɛ me ya," she grieves, holding her head with both hands. Always, her head pains her.

"I'm sorry, I am not a doctor." I apologize.

Still she holds her head and squeezes her face.

"I'm sorry, Maame. Ntoosi no, medaase. Yɛbɛhyia bio."

She bows her head, extending the back of her right hand against the palm of her left in submission to my farewell.

I step back and into the small, who remains vigilant with palm open.

"Oburoni, kyɛ me penny," he sings.

I hurry away, relieved that he does not follow. The children do not beg from Ghanaians. They beg from other expatriates with great success, which may explain why they never tire of pursuing me. Their dogged chanting feels like harassment. When they follow all the way to my gate, a claustrophobic hysteria takes hold. It's impossible to speak of this. Who wouldn't laugh at my vexation over smalls?

Bessie Head would never take pleasure in my predicament. She suffered far worse. I walk in good company.

Hustling along, I alternate between watching my step and scanning the cabs of passing vehicles. Ned Clyde honks his horn at the same time that I recognize him through his mud-spattered windshield. We both wave as he lurches past. Though our encounters are brief, often nothing more than his driving by, I feel I know him. He is the Old Man found on every construction site.

Antoine was the Old Man on the bridge job in California. "Always walk your site twice a day," he'd say. He had meant there are things you can only know if you see for yourself. I walked the yard where lumber, plate steel, and mammoth anchor bolts were stored. Antoine had meant you know if the project manager is worth his salt by whether the crews care for the site and keep it tidy. I walked the dirt road down past the abutment to where a crew drilled and grouted steel dowels into old piers. He had meant the crews need to see the engineer, hear her ideas, and offer their input to have confidence in where the work is heading. I climbed sixty-foot scaffolding to crawl under girders and inspect the progress of the night crew bolting on beam extensions. The Old Man had meant that so much comes from being there—answers to questions you haven't yet asked, information which you're not aware of, but to which you'll have access when the moment comes.

I walk this road twice a day. It's not clear what's valuable—every detail seems a clue. Seeing Ned reminds me why I'm here.

I dodge a fast-flying vehicle by leaping over the gutter onto a shopkeeper's tiny porch. Under the store awning, a girl thrusts her infant brother at me. The boy screams and bursts into tears. The girl laughs.

At last, the home stretch. I cross the base of a steep slope, at the top of which to my left sits Presby church, and climb ahead to the plateau upon which perch the string of green and red duplexes where I live. A wide, dirt walk along the edge of the plateau separates the government housing from the main thoroughfare of Obuasi town. Reaching the tree in front of my home, I stand at the top of the six-foot retaining wall that doubles as the back face of the gutter in the street below and wave to Idrissu.

"Akua, ɛte sɛn?" he calls from behind his sewing machine.

"Ɛyɛ pa ara. Ɛte sɛn?" I yell over the evening traffic.

"It's good," he answers.

"Akua, maadwo," calls Fathia.

She sits on her wooden stool fanning her charcoal stove. Her frame is huge. The stool is less than twelve inches high. She does not look uncomfortable.

"Good evening, awuraa," I reply.

"Akua," Idrissu now straddles the far gutter, one foot on his low porch, one foot on the road-side lip of the gutter like a hurdler ascending, waving to me. "Bra, bra."

We both mark a feeble Peugeot taxi, after which I scramble across the road.

"Akua, you go to the villages today?"

"Yes, Sansu and Bediem."

"Dat's right. Akua, Kwadwo leave dis for you. I have dis for you." He hands me a paper that I unfold to reveal Kwadwo's truck count. "Dis what you asked for?"

"Yes, Idrissu. Thank you. Please tell him, 'Medaase pa ara.'"

"You fix de road, Akua."

I smile at my supposed infinite capacities. "Inshallah," I say, hearing my mother's voice in mine.

Idrissu hesitates. I'm not sure if he takes offense at an infidel or a buroni or a woman speaking the name of his god. Dropping his eyes and scratching his beard helps him recover. He steps to the curb, a way of letting me know I may go.

Fathia asks, "Worekɔ he?"

If I'm not mistaken, there may be some mischief in her eyes, perhaps amusement at her husband's imbalance. "Menoa aduane."

"Yoo."

CHAPTER TEN

I reach between the piquets of the gate, unlock the tiny Chinese padlock, and slide back the bolt. My neighbor's pigeons scurry home via the half-pipe gutter running under our common wall. I follow their feathered retreat with a resentful eye. I never see my duplex neighbors. Their presence by day is noted in their pigeons' spattering all over my compound. By night, voices drift over our shared kitchen wall, which stops about six inches short of the ceiling for ventilation.

I unlock my front door, toss the duffel bag beside the couch, exchange my sneakers for chale wote and start supper. Propping up one end of the stove sends kerosene flowing to the wick under the opposite burner. Tonight's masterpiece will be sautéed tuna, onions, and corn over a plate of corkscrew pasta.

Blocking under the opposite side of the stove extinguishes the flame. I settle onto the couch, meal and *Newsweek* on the table. The magazine carries the story of the arrest of Ken Saro-Wiwa, a chilling turn that occurred months ago.

> *Ken Saro-Wiwa, an outspoken environmentalist and human rights advocate, has been arrested in connection with the murders of four Ogoni tribal leaders. The murdered men led a conservative faction within MOSOP, the Movement for the Survival of the Ogoni People, of which Saro-Wiwa is the head. The men met a violent end. Those Ogoni who do not care for the confrontational*

stance of MOSOP must ask whether there is a place for them in the aggressive organization.

The talking drum provides much better intel. Within days of the arrest, Agyeman had briefed me: "On the night before the murders, the Nigerian military swarmed Ogoniland. The people awoke not knowing what had triggered the sudden military presence. By afternoon, the four men lay dead. It is clear to all with eyes that the military staged the murders to justify terrorizing the region."

In the following weeks, Agyeman supplemented: "Ken Saro-Wiwa is being tortured in prison. Still he and the others have not been charged. The military is sweeping across Ogoniland burning villages, raping women, torturing and killing the men and boys. They have cut off the head of MOSOP and the people are defenseless. All this for Shell. The Nigerian military is the fetching boy of the foreign corporations."

Mr. Agyeman worked in Nigeria up till the 1983 expulsion. He did a stint in the oil fields, but found it too difficult. He had said, "The normal work in the oil fields will challenge any man. But the Niger Delta must have inspired Dante. It is a lake of boiling pitch into which every politician should be thrown. The Nigerian officials are no more than lackeys for Shell. The rivers boil with the blood of any who would stand against the devastation of the land. It was too much for my heart.

"The flaring of the gas, great plumes of smoke covering the sky, the constriction of my lungs—it was impossible to breathe. The smoke brings toxic chemicals. Like the arsenic and sulphur from WAG's Bediako Treatment Plant, but much worse. My skin and eyes burned without relief the whole time I worked there. Nothing can live in the delta. It's dead, like our Gyimi, except worse. Everything is coated in oil. The people trying to farm their ancestral land are slowly dying from the pollution. Heh, how does a human being treat another human being? This happens before the eyes of the world."

There was a tear in his eye when he spoke. "Ken Saro-Wiwa is a great man. He is not afraid to face Shell and the Nigerian government and ask for justice. He predicted this. When Abacha took power, he said, 'They will arrest us all now and execute us.' It is a matter of time." Although Agyeman is forthcoming in his assessments, he had never before revealed such depth of emotion.

From the Acting Managing Director of Shell Oil, a Nigerian,

The proof is that we are extracting so much oil from this region. We go to these villages and they welcome us. If the people in the villages were unhappy with us, we would not be pumping so much oil out. That is the proof that they are happy with us.

From an environmental advocate working in Ogoniland and the Niger Delta,

We regret that the world puts profit before human rights and democracy, but that is the standard bearer of international relations today.

A rickety table on the porch with two aluminum basins. "The proof is we are extracting so much oil." WAG's goal this year is one million ounces. In the deep basin, I wash the dishes with liquid soap and a dried coil of grass. "The world puts profits before human rights." "What is a little dust?" I see the arrogant curl of Harrigan's lip. "As long as the villagers don't screw it up by asking for too much . . ." Or what, Finn Harrigan? To what lengths will you go? "They will execute us." Ghana is not Nigeria. No one carries a gun. "He is not afraid to stand before the world and ask for justice." A tear disappears in the dishwater. The fibers crunch in my hand. ". . . before the eyes of the world." Before the eyes of this engineer. The shallow basin will hold the drying dishes till morning.

Before the other world manifests as poetry, it is a presence felt. As subtle as a breath, one perceives the presence but, like a breath, one does not remark upon it or respond to it. One's awareness is not even at the level of conscious thought. That perception lives on the level of the autonomic nervous system. The other world enters via this subterranean mechanism.

The visitation may be brief, no more than a single breath. One cannot remember it any more than one can remember the specific exhalation that occurred five minutes ago. It was real. It was experienced. Yet, it cannot belong to the conscious realm.

I open my notebook.

The visitation may repeat. Its persistence may constellate communication between the autonomic nervous system and the conscious mind. This communication may come as a weak signal, something dismissed as part of the white noise of life. That can be the end of it—the visitations stop.

Occasionally, the visitations are robust enough to survive the limitations of the conscious mind. They continue while a differentiation occurs between that particular communication and all other impulses, thoughts, memories, feelings, and fantasies whirling in the maelstrom of the mind.

I hold my pen above the blank page.

Recognition does not occur in a flash. It is a gradual coming into focus of the Visitor. As the form of the Visitor comes into sharper relief, so, too, does one's realization of the existence of the Visitor. If one experiences a flash, it may be the spark when the nexus comes into being, the clarity of the conscious perception of both worlds, each by the other.

The flash is never the moment when the autonomic nervous system sends the first weak signal. Nor is it the inception of the conscious mind's differentiation process. At least not for most of humanity. Maybe the holiest have already mapped the landscape of their psyche so well that they immediately recognize the Visitor. But it is not so for the average being. It is certainly not true for engineers.

In fact, engineers are handicapped. A mind trained to solve problems finds it difficult to endure the teasing out of the resolution of the Visitor's form. The engineer's mind seeks answers. It races to name the unknown in terms of what it already knows—the fundamental principle of algebra.

I close the notebook and cap my pen.

Premature naming is death. The Visitor attempting to be known by the temporal world offers itself in vulnerability. Haste in defining the Visitor's essence is the destruction of that essence, or, at least its withdrawal back to the other world, the end of the visitations.

It is natural, even for those who are not engineers, to forego the delicacy and patience required. How many visitations have been aborted by the mind's compulsion to know? How many breaths in a day? How many of those breaths are remembered?

A man's face. A long, thin, creased face surrounded by the white cotton of a Muslim's gown. The hood of white is crowned by a wide, white agal flecked with red diamonds. Across the bridge of the man's nose rest heavy, black frames. The upper lip supports a narrow, dark moustache, demarcating the base of the pendular nose.

The man uses a walking stick, but does not move as if aged. His shoes are not visible. Only his face and the hand upon the stick emerge from the white folds of the gown.

It is the man's face that I see. Every day. An intense, serious face. Not angry, but possessing urgency. Bold eyes penetrating black rectangles. The black of the glasses, the black of the moustache, the deep brown of his face disappearing in longitudinal seams—all set off by draping, brilliant white and resonating in red diamonds.

This image appears every day, a growing sense that I must make time for him. I press my palms into the grain of the wood and know what I must do. I take the pencil from the cupboard and unroll a large blueline sheet. Over and over, I smooth the sheet, feeling the rough surface of the table beneath.

Starting with the length of the man's face, and according to the proportions of my own body, I lay out the dimensions of the man. I know I am drawing the image of a man I passed in the street. I know that I do not know what I am drawing. If I come with respect, the other world will reveal itself.

Imagine Michelangelo laying out geometry on the ceiling of the Sistine Chapel. Lines radiating outward from a nexus to be bisected, quartered, crossed on skew by lines emanating from other origins, each with a purpose, until the underside of the vaulted dome ensconces asymmetry of triangles, circles, trapezoids with sides both straight and curved—the framework of grand designs. A centerline, rectangles and triangles, take their place on the paper.

Two worlds come together. The fine line of the mechanical pencil provides the necessary underlayment of structure, the foundation from which creativity springs.

The rasp of metal scraping concrete. The hollow bass of an empty bucket. I lay down my pencil and triangle. One never knows how long the water will flow. My neighbor's daughter stands over the pipe located between my home and the adjacent duplex. She fills her own bucket, then that of another woman. A younger daughter carries a full bucket on her head into my neighbor's compound.

"Maadwo," I say, as I set down my buckets.

The girl fills both and I lug them to the kitchen to dump into a fifty-gallon drum. By the time I return, several new buckets and headpans crowd the standpipe. The water bill is paid by the District on behalf of the government employees living here, but many who do not live in the duplexes also draw their water from the standpipe. In the twilight, awaiting their turn, women talk and children play.

I set my empty buckets with the others and return to the man's face, relieved by the necessity of water. The invisible, the imperceptible has grown impatient with me. I may have hoped it would abandon me for a more responsive host. But it demands me. It marches up to me in an Obuasi street.

I am afraid that by attempting to define its form, I will kill it. I do not feel worthy. I never expected to encounter my Muslim heritage in sub-Saharan Africa. I have never said the words, "my Muslim heritage."

My mother's people are Greek Orthodox. They do not refer to a time before the Crusades when I suppose my people were Muslim. Had I not spent my early years in Libya, it might mean nothing to me. It may only be the coincidence of childhood memories and the chance of ancestry.

I have never even formed these thoughts. It is something so old and forgotten. A whisper that reaches the ear long after the words have dissipated. A breath.

I put away the Muslim. From a comfortable position, I let my eyes trace the ceiling. No image emerges, but I recall the dominating form of the open pit.

Bediem and Sansu. Mud filling homes. Drinking water supply shut off. River murky from silt. Tranquility shattered by blasting. How do human beings treat one another? To whom would these villagers voice their grievances, if we did not arrive? Who bears witness? "No one cares about a few subsistence farmers." I can't argue with Finn's words. No one is interested in an engineer's tale.

At the sound of the bolt sliding on my gate, I leap up. It is Idrissu's daughters, Laila and Hasna, each with one of my buckets on her head.

"Medaase." I smile.

They smile and giggle. Their English is not strong.

Hasna and Laila are not tall and not very large. Laila is very much a child, very playful. Hasna is older and silent. She will enter womanhood soon. I know this from the day I was on Idrissu's porch and it was clear that Hasna was beginning to form breasts. She stood bare from the waist up in front of several men and myself, crying, while her mother tried to pull a maggot from an open sore beside her nipple. Peace Corps had cautioned during our training to always iron our clothes dry, as a blow-fly will lay eggs in moist cloth and the larvae will worm under the skin. Idrissu had yelled at Hasna that if she did not stop crying, more maggots would come. That frightened her into hiccupy sobs.

The girls peer into my lit room each time they pass the open door, Laila, wide-eyed and grinning. I reread letters until I feel the girls standing in the doorway.

"Finished?" I ask and rise to check the barrels.

My standard is two hundred cedis for each whole barrel and tonight they kept long because both barrels were low. Four hundred cedis into Hasna's hand. The money will go straight to Idrissu.

No breeze, tonight. Perhaps it will rain, tomorrow. I pull the table away from the couch and lie down. Dirty beige-thread grey-sworl brown-CAPITAL green black red white-Gere grey. Dirty beige . . . I shake my head to stop the cycling. At least here I am able to recognize it. In America, I am lost in the cycling. Sometimes I only know when I hear Carol's laughter.

Turning to the ceiling, my mind travels back to the worn mud block homes in Bediem, the silted floors, the capricious water supply. Is the Sansu chief wise—getting the best for his people? Or is he a sell-out? A haul truck jars the night, ripping me from contemplation. Something primitive in me knows its survival is threatened. Dirty beige-thread grey-sworl brown-CAPITAL green black red white-Gere grey. Dirty beige- . . . The speed of the color strip accelerates my heart.

I shake my head, leap off the sofa, and pull out the engineering pad. My palm presses into the grid. Only rational things are possible. It would have been West Africa Gold that paved the exploration road to the edge of Sansu. The mine does know how to build roads. My mechanical pencil—black, simple, functional, reliable—has been with me since college. Bediem lies closer to the open pit at the end of a muddy path. How can the people of Bediem make do with this road that rains make impassable? I hold the cap down and slide out a remnant of lead. Someone in Sansu was bold enough to disrupt the durbar with his horn three times. Asphalt does not buy loyalty. It takes a few clicks to engage the next lead. The Bediem people had no quarrel with their chief. A sorrowful cry bursts from me at the thought of this village's non-existent road.

I rummage in my duffel bag for the folded paper. My hand passes many times over the note, smoothing it against the rough fibers of the wood table. There are numbers with adjacent notes. My finger traces the flare of Kwadwo's colonial script, distracting me from panic. "13 Recovery"; "5 Waste"; "20 Backhaul." My heart slows. "10 Construction"; "+10 Backhaul." "60"—the ink heavy, several underlines . . . "Day Trips."

Sixty day trips. Kwadwo brings up a good point, the backhaul. Are the trucks empty on the return? I check the tare weight. Does that include tires? Beside TRIPS/DAY, I write, 60. Beneath that, indented, I add, FULL PAYLOAD 28. And, EMPTY 30. Let's say half the backhauls are loaded, changing FULL PAYLOAD to 45; and, EMPTY to 15.

Empty. That's it. Empty trucks fly. In the dead of night without traffic, without people and goats, the drivers wing through town. Without the weight of ore, nothing stabilizes the bed of the truck. Without the roar of Obuasi's day, nothing muffles that smashing of steel that terrorizes me when I'm most vulnerable.

The Obuasi road. The Bediem road. So many roads in this country in need of civil engineers.

It is too early to go to bed. The ceiling holds an image of the old woman, one hand against her head in pain, the other forcing her meager offering of shriveled, broken tomatoes into my hand. I don't know who buys from her. I push the table away from the sofa. She never has a large supply of tomatoes or onions or red peppers like regular market women. I lie with my feet on the sofa, my back flat on the carpet. This old woman's scant produce always consists of tiny, tattered, pitiful specimens.

The way she squeezes her face to show her pain reminds me of my mother. I clench my abs at the top of a situp, hardening my jaw, and distorting my mouth for good measure. As much as Mom wants to control her emotions, she cannot hide her grimaces. Fifty reps. Growing up in a household fraught with Arab volatility, she resolved never to succumb to such outbursts. Even though she plays "emotional" to Dad's "rational," Mom takes a reasoned approach to feelings. One hundred reps.

It was monumental for Mom to express her unhappiness with life in Libya. I lean into the porch wall, my hands aligned with my shoulders. Perhaps that's why Dad ignored her request for so long—she had never before asked that her feelings determine the direction of her family. Fifty reps. I widen the spread of my hands.

Mom did succeed in landing us in California, but Dad never treated her the same. Or maybe nothing had changed. Maybe I just started paying attention. Fifty reps. My own social dislocation may have primed me to recognize the ugliness that had always existed. I began to notice the superiority of my father's rational arguments over my mother's compassionate wishes. I sit against the wall beneath Bessie and Barbara, my knees bent at right angles. In political debates, Dad cited facts. With trepidation, Mom expressed her feeling that the world should be a better place.

It was obvious they were not talking about the same thing and it was obvious who the winner was. This is easy. I can wall-sit forever. Fear of being on the losing end of Dad's intellectual aggression inspired me to study with greater vigor. It was painful to see my mother stare at my father in silent, helpless appeal. My quadriceps strain to push my back into the wall. I suppose Mom's fear of unleashing her ancestral passion overrode her desire to stand up for herself. Thrilled by the litany of his brilliance, Dad ranted on, oblivious to the havoc wreaked by his marauding intellect.

Beyond the ceiling, I see the thick, black frames of the Muslim—very much like Kwasi's. Through which Kwasi projected his servile posture. I come off the wall, rubbing my thighs. There is no limit to the revulsion I feel for such subservence. I shake out my legs and roll my shoulders, feeling strong. I will go toe-to-toe with Harrigan all the way down the line. He has no idea what he's up against.

CHAPTER ELEVEN

Before Jeff Fogerty left Ghana, I purchased his laptop for the Advocacy. Concerned about dust and security, I didn't want to store it at our office. Jim Hansen arranged for me to have a spot in the computer room in the Projects Department. It's quite a hike to Projects, through the main gate, past Stores, Carriage, the Pay Office, over the hill past Manpower Training, to just before the railroad tracks.

I don't know anyone at Projects except the expatriate manager, Larry Wittle. Wittle approves every disbursement to contractors, including Advocacy pay vouchers. I hand-carry the voucher book to him every month or two. He is not a man given to frivolous solicitations. This lack of warmth, combined with his thick black hair and bushy moustache have earned him the moniker, Saddam Hussein.

Today I need to work on last month's budget report. I pull on my long-sleeved shirt before entering the frigid building. The cold and the officiousness of the inhabitants make me feel I'm entering hostile territory. I'm aware of the unsustainability of the arrangement, technology to which I alone have access, not the team and not the steering committee. My work in America convinces me that I need the polished appearance of printed documents to bridge between the realities of a Ghanaian charitable organization and a multinational corporation. There's enough skittishness regarding the Advocacy's legitimacy that I won't risk hand-scrawled correspondence.

The main doors open on a wide hall, the first segment of which is a foyer isolated by a second set of doors. The foyer lighting seems inadequate after the brightness outside. Beyond the foyer to the left is Wittle's enormous office. Further down on the right is the computer room. The polished granite floor of the hall amplifies every footstep, every door closing. It always feels a kind of assault to cross this echo chamber. I open the door to the computer room dreading the arctic blast dedicated to protecting WAG's technological investment.

I take my seat in front of my laptop. Plastic black. Several men in expensive suits work at other stations around the large room. Starched collar white. They are the upper crust of Ghanaian society. Herringbone grey. They received their educations from elite universities in Europe and America, and belong to a social realm beyond my ken. Plastic black-collar white-herringbone grey. Like expatriates—which some of them may be—they will not be found walking the streets of Obuasi. Though of Ghanaian origin, they conduct themselves with the direct, purposeful, efficient demeanor cultivated within corporate America. I have never suffered any specific rudeness here, but my presence often goes unacknowledged—a notable violation of Ghanaian etiquette. Plastic black-collar white-herringbone grey.

Budgets are not my favorite topic. Though I'm at home with engineering calculations, accounting dulls my mind. It takes much inner cajoling to push myself through this kind of work. I'm pleased to find that today I'm able to drop into the numbers and make steady progress. My focus is so strong that I fail to respond to a voice saying my name.

". . . Louisa . . ."

It takes me a moment to realize that someone is speaking to me. I find Larry Wittle at my side. Tie stripe brown. This is irregular. Plastic black-collar white-herringbone grey-tie brown.

Bending toward me, he repeats, "Hello, Louisa."

"Hello." I can't imagine what would inspire Larry Wittle to such a direct and kind approach, but I'm not about to lose the opportunity. "Did you see my letter?" I ask, meaning the letter requesting a list of WAG's contractors.

"Your letter is bouncing all over this place." His voice is soft and admiring. "But I guess you already know that."

". . . Oh, you mean the contract letter. But did you see the letter I left in your office?"

Turning to go, he pauses and gives my forearm a gentle squeeze. "We can't change the whole world overnight."

I bow my head over my keyboard. Wittle is gone. If he is a man like my father, he prides himself on his integrity. This breach of etiquette is the only wobble he will allow himself—both an acknowledgement of the unethical underpinning of his company, and so his livelihood, as well as his vindication—the brief contact with the woman aid worker serving as proof that he takes the broad view. He sees the world's imperfection and charts the practical course.

Whatever else it may or may not be, Wittle's gesture feels an affirmation that my presence here has moved someone. I want to believe that somehow in the invisible world it is my father's heart I have touched. Lifeblood. My fingertips brush the keypad, as a tear rolls down my cheek. Plastic black-collar white-herringbone grey-tie brown–my lifeblood.

ll

ᴓBUASl

You can always get into those places. What is hard is to get out. That is a private fight. Everybody has to find his own way.

—NAIPAUL, *A Bend in the River*

CHAPTER TWELVE

Bahrain, Qatar, China—Dad's letter covers his recent travels. Since I was a little girl, I've felt excited to touch the crisp airmail envelopes and wondered at the bright colors and bold designs of exotic stamps. It has always made me proud that my father is out in the world meeting people from other cultures, sharing his knowledge, and sating his curiosity about peoples and history.

The thin paper crinkles as I smooth it against the fiber of the wood.

> *The Great Wall is really the joining of many smaller walls, some of whose construction began as early as the 7th century B.C. The most famous portion (5,500 miles!) was built in the third century by Emperor Qin Shi Huang, but little of that remains. Most of the wall was rebuilt during the Ming Dynasty (14th–17th century for the historically illiterate). If one takes into account all of the walls of many different types of construction, the length of the wall with all its branches is closer to 13,000 miles! Not too shabby. With a few exceptions, the Wall protected China for 11 centuries. What a closeted society. Thank god for Nixon. Nowadays, the Reds don't mind learning a few tricks from an old capitalist dog.*

I read his words with a mixture of fondness and contempt. I love his voice. It is the voice that taught me about the world.

When I was growing up, we could be standing in any country and Dad could tell us when *it* was built, for what purpose, and by whom. Dad's handwriting slants and loops with the grace of another era, the badge of a schoolboy eager to learn his lesson.

I loved Leptis Magna, which was close enough to Tripoli to serve as the object of a day's outing. I will never forget Dad's tour guide rendition: "Leptis Magna was founded by the Phoenicians in the first millennium BC. It was one of their many trading centers. They called it 'Lp . . . ,' 'Lpg . . . ,' 'Lpgy.' Hm, Leptis Magna was populated by the Garamantes—a Saharan Berber people from ancient southwest Libya, who developed quite an advanced civilization. They are known for their elaborate underground irrigation system. They also hunted Troglodytes to sell as slaves and threw in their lot with the Numidians in raiding Roman coastal settlements. That was their folly. The Romans grew annoyed and began taking their cities, with Septimius Severus overrunning their capital in 202. Let that be a lesson. Don't piss off the lion.

"It was also Severus who built what we see today. This basilica ranks among the foremost examples of a new Roman art that was strongly influenced by African and Eastern traditions. These sculptures were innovative for their linear definition of forms, the crispness of their contours and the angular delineation of their volumes. This comprehensive aesthetic was conceived as a function of the blinding African sun."

I loved that—"conceived as a function of the blinding African sun." Sunlight pours through my open door onto the carpet, splashing across these words of my father.

There was a constancy and reliability in Dad's presentation of history. Now, I hear in that voice a constrained monologue. A man's attempt to order his world by clinging to what he believes he can know. A way to assert his authority upon the vastness of the world. Not unlike an engineer's hegemony.

I feel bitter at the discovery that the narrative I treasured was an attempt to impose his personal will upon life. I feel derision toward a man who, so many years older, remains content with these mechanical recitations that displace a good many other potential conversations. I am interested in the aborted exchanges, in the facts that he chooses not to name.

In this case, Dad's response to my comments about Ken Saro-Wiwa. I had expressed outrage at the sham of the murder charges that had finally been levied against Saro-Wiwa. I asked if Dad had ever consulted for Shell in the Niger Delta.

Do not be so quick to judge, Dear Daughter. The press is liberal and it is impossible to really know the situation on the ground. The rift in MOSOP is, however, well known, and you, having led a sheltered life, cannot begin to imagine the savage acts that an African leader, even your prized Mr. Wiwa, would commit to preserve his position. Yes, he has the alibi of being prevented from entering Ogoni on the day the four were murdered. But a man with such devoted followers need not sully his own hands.

I have not consulted for Shell there. On my only visit to the delta I suffered severe respiratory distress. The flaring of gas pollutes the air and I am more sensitive than most. It is true the environment has been degraded by petroleum operations. But that doesn't mean Wiwa is innocent. It also doesn't mean that Shell is guilty. The natives play a big role in preventing the safe handling of crude. They vandalize the pipelines and terrorize the oil company workers, who are afraid to work in remote areas. The natives have in large measure ensured their own misery.

Reading his words, I hear the voice that cuts down my mother. The voice of authority. The voice armed with facts. I can no longer stomach his pretense of objectivity. Does Dad not see what is happening in Ogoniland? Is his heart incapable of perceiving an honest man with a just cause? Is he incapable of outrage at the sins of his profession?

"They would be worse off without us." This is Dad's defense. "They want our jobs. They want petroleum sales to boost their economy. This is the way the world works." Bright red, yellow, black, and blue give form to powerful dancing Fu lions on the stamps in the corner of the envelope. A missive from a foreign country, from the vast land and ancient culture of China. My father has traveled this earth longer than I have been alive. Who am I to challenge his authority?

When I was young I did not see much difference between a geologist and an engineer. Both apply their expertise to solving technical problems. But Dad made no effort to conceal his disdain. "We hire and fire engineers." His slap of intellectual superiority sparked the fight in me. I would never change my major.

Still I couldn't understand how such a rational man could parse a difference between our professions. Why is engineering demeaned as the dullest, most rigid of practices, even among the technical disciplines? My father echoes the popular sentiment that engineers are expendable. Yet, his company couldn't exist without engineers. Who designs and installs systems for extracting oil from the ground? Who customizes those systems for extreme conditions—on the ocean floor, under the tundra, through desert sands? Who designs and builds the pipelines and ships that transport their black gold? Why are our contributions minimized?

Almost two thousand years later, Dad extols the accomplishment of the Garamantes—their underground irrigation system in the Sahara. How can he fail to recognize that as a legacy of civil engineering?

Why is no one interested in an engineer's tale?

Persevere, Dear Daughter. Your talent for speaking to diverse groups on their level serves you well — a trait you inherited from your mother. Give it your best and see it through. Despite the mess of that place, you may accomplish some good.

Love,
Dad

Pride and love rush to my eyes. I sit straighter. This is who we are, my people. We do things in the world.

Geologists study rock formations to deduce the likelihood that they harbor precious metals or petroleum. Geologists are concerned with extraction. Civil engineers are concerned with sustainability. We study soil to determine the loads it can bear. We collect and treat wastewater, which enables high density living in a clean environment. We monitor water quality to ensure safe drinking water. We study natural processes to adapt for large-scale sustainable practices.

My father was right. Engineers are not equal to geologists. Civil engineers in particular seek to protect the Earth. Did Dad intuit at that early moment that we were on opposite sides? Did he perceive it was me who had thrown down the gauntlet? The truth is I don't want to get there without him. The truth is I want my Dad standing beside me making the Earth whole.

Someone who knows the truth of rocks.

The door to the new Safety building closes on the tomb of a stone hallway, WAG's trademark. I pull on my long-sleeved shirt and wonder behind which door I will find Finn's new office. My footsteps echo on the polished floor. A door opens and Kwasi sticks his head out.

"Ah, there you are. We thought perhaps you were lost."

I follow Kwasi through a secretary's chamber, into Finn's enormous office. Kwasi takes his seat and waits for me to take the only vacant chair, facing the tribunal. Finn Harrigan sits at the center behind his desk, flanked by Obeng and Kwasi, who face me like Fu lions from chairs at left and right in front of Finn's desk.

Kwasi clears his throat and says, "Yes, now that we're all here, we can begin." The grandeur of the office is choked by the oversized desk that spans nearly the full distance across the room. Finn must squeeze his gut to get around. The high-backed executive chair custom made at WAG's carpentry shop accentuates Finn's low height, making him look a child.

Kwasi launches. "West Africa Gold has been funding the Adansi West Rural Water, Sanitation, and Health Advocacy for almost one year, now. And, in this time, several situations have arisen that WAG doesn't want to see continue."

Finn lights a cigarette and gives me a confident stare. Obeng's feet hover above the rug. The thick rubbery folds of his face suggest a creature from a Tolkien novel, one of the hordes of automaton underlings.

"Eh," Kwasi continues, "there's a problem in that the Advocacy sees itself as an advocate of the people. They go to the villages and incite the people against WAG. Then they bring the people here to complain in WAG's truck." He talks with both hands gripping the wide side arms of his chair. A yellow pencil pierces the air from between his knuckles. I brace for the backlash against bringing my small boy to the mine.

"We feel that this is unacceptable. Why should the villagers be angry with WAG? After all, we are funding the Advocacy to go to the villages and help them. Why should the villagers be angry with WAG?" Kwasi flexes his hands, the pencil angling like a bent nail. This man with a doctorate in environmental engineering profanes our profession. Why should Gyimiso Kakraba be angry that you've stopped the flow of their ancestral river? That you did so without notice and with no plan to remedy the situation? You can't even maintain a reliable schedule of water tankers.

"WAG wants to help the villages . . ." Kwasi warms to his script, pouring inflection into his voice. ". . . and our concern is for the villages that have been impacted by WAG's mining operations." And here it is. They have summoned me to try an end run around the steering committee.

"We want the Advocacy to focus its efforts on WAG-impacted villages. This is what we're funding them for. They should stop going to all the other villages in the district." Although I'm facing Kwasi, he directs his words over his shoulder at Finn, tossing an occasional glance toward the ballast on his right, Obeng, who has trouble holding his chair to the floor.

"In a similar manner, the Advocacy is fundraising for villages. Eh, we don't believe this to be essential to the performance of the Advocacy's responsibilities. The villages should raise their own money. Doesn't the Advocacy have enough to do? This fundraising detracts from the effectiveness of their main purpose. The Advocacy must discontinue this fundraising and focus on WAG villages. There's more they could be doing if they weren't distracted by activities beyond the intended scope of the Advocacy."

I can hear Agyeman's assessment, "It will get serious now."

Finn's smug expression hardens as he draws on his cigarette.

Kwasi turns to me and says, "It's your turn."

My turn. You call me in with no warning as to your agenda. My turn. If this were a construction site, I'd rip you six ways from Sunday. I glance from Kwasi to Finn. It's clear that no explanation will satisfy. Truth bears no weight. The Rifleman holds a firm grip on his Winchester, low across his hips.

"We'll have no more of this," Finn says in a quiet voice. "If you want the Advocacy to continue, you'll pull your act together."

I meet his eyes without blinking. There are plenty of assholes in construction. It's all about intimidation. The trick is to display no fear while minimizing provocation. The Rifleman pets the trigger.

"Do you understand?" Finn growls.

I don't blink.

"We're done." Finn dismisses me with annoyance. As I stand, he says, "Be smart, Louisa."

You can count on that. The Rifleman scabbards his gun and mounts his horse. As I step out of Safety, moist warmth envelopes me and I peel off my long-sleeved shirt.

Jim Hansen bursts from the Lab. "Louisa."

"Jim."

He brushes past and pulls open the door to Safety. A low, tense warning cuts through the humidity. "Don't let them take you out of here in a straitjacket." Surprised, I whip around, but the tomb has sealed behind him.

Of course, Jim knows. I drape my shirt through the handle of my duffel bag. Kwasi must have told him of their strategy to intimidate me and command the Advocacy's programme. I duck through the oleanders and trudge down the slope of the fifth hole. Maybe Jim refused to participate.

How does that help me?

What will be Finn's next move? Brooding along the edge of the road's tumult, I remember too late to catch a glimpse of the yam chip lady. . . . *a straitjacket*. Finn's going to make my life hell. I stomp past the empty tables where the seamstresses should sit. Their absence feels an affront. Do not bring villagers to WAG's doorstep. I ignore less familiar voices that herald my passing. Should I have taken them straight to the clinic?

Incapable of expressing the simplest courtesy, I keep my head down. Would WAG dare tell me not to bring sick people to a doctor?

A man dodging an errant vehicle jostles my shoulder. "Excuse me, sah." He apologizes. That's right. I am an angry man. WAG would prefer that I not give the villagers any hint that they ought to be treated like human beings.

A cracked cross gutter signals the unanticipated, a worthy foe. I cut into the alley to confront the madness: Kofi waving the Union Jack. I glare at his eyes, or where his eyes would be if he had a face. Face me.

The proof is that we are extracting so much oil from the region.

A scarf loops two or three times about his neck, transforming the lowest portion of the turban into a winter cowl. Kofi's hypocrisy flutters above. Do you count the British among your friends? Convenient that the cowl covers your mouth. Do you feel sorry for Africa if the white man never come?

The world puts profits before human rights. The standard bearer of international relations.

Isn't that what the university feminists said of me? Why else would I get a degree in engineering? I must desire money and the status quo. Women's history, psychology, pre-law, gender studies—these were acceptable pursuits. Engineering carries no social value. Engineers are not the vanguard of the revolution.

Before the eyes of the world.

I'm struck by how much space Kofi occupies. He must stand seven feet tall. His robe drapes over broad shoulders and flows over a solid, strong form. His turbaned head evokes respect. In contradiction, the flag reduces his noble aura to that of a sports fan waving his colors.

Before the eyes of this engineer.

Union Jack Kofi
Who you appear to be
Who you are
Amadu Kofi al-Attar
"Sah"
Who I appear to be
Who I am
Akua Kwaku Louisa Lehmann

A long conference table takes up half of the Advocacy office. I sit at the end farthest from the door, with Thomas Anyidoho across from me. He is a tall, thin man with a round face and copper skin. Thomas seems more of a city boy than the others. He dresses more refined and has the attitude of a man whose ambitions have not yet been denied by life. Behind Thomas stands an imaginary Carol rolling her eyes as I catalog the room. Beside Thomas sits Agyeman. He has a solid build and wears a vivid blue, starched shirt that sets off his dark skin. Agyeman Isaac Theodore grew up in a village not far from Obuasi. Despite his intelligence, he did not complete senior secondary school. In his forty-four years, Agyeman has worked many jobs, including as a miner for WAG.

"Plodding and impervious as a mule with a plastic pocket protector" is how Carol chides my cataloguing.

Agyeman and Thomas talk together. Takyi rises to switch on the ceiling fan. His eyes are red, as usual, but alert. Charles Yaw Takyi, the shortest of the group, is also low on stamina. Lynn had mentioned that she thought he may have an untreated case of diabetes. I've wondered whether he suffered a childhood illness that would explain the way his waist disappears inside the band of his belt.

Osei stands at the end of the table nearest the door, leafing through papers that he carries in a zippered, leather wallet. About my height, Osei wears a grey, tailored suit of local make, otherwise known as a "political suit." This adaptation of the Western business suit must afford greater comfort in Ghana's heat. Osei's top falls to mid-thigh over matching pants and has four pockets, two at the breast and two at the waist. The fit is looser than a Western business shirt, allowing the top to double as a suit coat with airy sleeves that fall to just above the elbow. Underneath, Osei wears a simple, white T-shirt that is just visible at the base of his turned down lapel.

Our office door is propped open for ventilation. At this early hour, the second floor air hasn't yet grown oppressive. Ewe copper-vivid blue-bloodshot red-political suit grey. This is the whole Advocacy team. I imagine meeting Carol's eyes, which have softened because she loves my color strips.

The men are married. All, except Thomas, have several children. This is almost all that I know about the team. I don't expect to know much more by the end of my two years. I imagine myself a manager of a construction project. These four men are my superintendent and foremen. Our mission is to develop a strong water and sanitation program. My job is to teach them everything I can about organizing and managing this enterprise. As a volunteer, the impact I have will be on these men. They, in turn, will influence the villagers we serve.

I don't ask the team to my house to visit. I don't have drinks or dinner with them. In Ghanaian culture, the nuances of male-female relationships are not subtle. I am not so naïve as to imagine that a marriage bond guarantees fidelity. I will not risk my credibility on any accidental muddling of boundaries. The professional distance from which we regard each other may be what keeps us from the pitfalls that could undermine our endeavor. They are men supervised by a younger woman. They are four blacks supervised by a buroni. We are strangers to each other's cultures projecting our expectations of acceptable conduct. We have so many opportunities to sink our own ship and do not.

Through the open windows drift the sounds of Obuasi starting its day—the coughing of old engines coaxed to give one more performance, the cries of children on their way to school and street hawkers plying their wares, a goat bleating.

For all that I will never know about these four men, I know that the Advocacy represents an opportunity that they will not let pass them by. It is most compelling for Agyeman and Takyi, who have worked for years in the civil service. To be able to come to work every day and have a job to do, to have access to the resources they need, to have a boss who relies upon their judgement—that must be a good feeling, one they have had far too little in their careers.

At thirty-three, Thomas is at his first posting in the Ministry of Health. I doubt he feels any pressure to parlay the Advocacy into the zenith of his career. But, he takes pride in his work. For Thomas, as for all of them, the association with the mine brings some prestige. The eight-thousand-cedi out-of-station allowance is eight thousand cedis more than they would otherwise have. Osei is fifty and nearing the end of his career. The Advocacy serves as an entertaining diversion from his regular duties. Although, more and more, Osei stands in for his missing superiors at Ghana Water and Sewerage Corporation. He may be starting to feel that our programme consumes too much of his time.

I don't need to analyze the team. Thomas, Agyeman, Takyi, and Osei are here beside me every day and they do their jobs well. That is all I need to know.

The harsh stench of bitumen burns as some workers push past the Old Council, the government building in which our office resides.

Through our open door strides Mr. Osabutey, saying, "So this is Advocacy office."

I leap up to greet him and show him the amenities of our space—the bookcase, my desk, and the huge conference table. Osabutey's head bobs a staccato inventorying of our sparse furnishings, after which he gives an enthusiastic shake of the hand to each team member. His rousing energy might inspire, if one forgot that in the more than six months that we've occupied this office, not one of our steering committee members has come to see it.

Osabutey is a tall man with wings of wiry hair fluffing from his temples. He dresses in political suits and carries a leather briefcase. It's always difficult for me to catch his machine gun English, every syllable seems of one breath. I have to wait for the sounds to separate in my mind.

As the district head of the Ministry of Health, Osabutey must have been informed of the situation at Gyimiso Kakraba. He never speaks to me of sensitive matters. Nor do Illiasu and Ankrah, the highest-ranking District officials. I've taken the hint that I'm not to pry into their affairs. Via Thomas, if not by other sources, Osabutey should be aware that twenty days have passed since West Africa Gold last delivered fresh water. I trust that he is a man of compassion doing all within his power—which may not be much—to press the cause of Gyimiso Kakraba.

One by one, the other steering committee members arrive—Preko, a trim man in Western clothes and the prolific district head of National Mobilization; Abubakar, with his petite features and ingratiating smile; and Obeng, looking uncomfortable. He took quite a routing on WAG's behalf at the last meeting. The steering committee doesn't know of my recent meeting with Harrigan. Perhaps if I pretend it did not happen, it will be as if it never did. Helen Boateng, Takyi's boss, sends word via Abubakar that she must preside as queen mother at a wedding in her village. The shifting choreography of the room leaves the team to one side—Ewe copper-vivid blue-bloodshot red-political suit grey—facing their bosses—ingratiating-fluffy machine gun-nauseous-trim dynamo.

"So, we are all here," shoots Osabutey. "Let's get started."

I take a breath and before I can speak, Osabutey launches into the team. "So what is it you want to discuss with us? We are all here, so you can tell us and we can discuss it."

"We thank you all for coming. You are welcome. We want to discuss with you our out-of-station allowance," Thomas responds. Usually, Agyeman is the spokesman. It must have been part of their strategizing that Thomas should respond to his boss.

"You want to discuss your out-of-station allowance. What about it?" Osabutey returns in rapid tempo.

"We would like the steering committee to consider increasing the amount of our allowance. We are spending most of our days out in the villages and very little time in the office. Because of this, we feel you may recognize that our out-of-station allowance should be increased."

"Your allowance is currently . . ." Osabutey glances at the other steering committee members.

"Eight thousand cedis," offers Preko.

Through his peppery speech, Osabutey inhales an exasperated sigh. "You currently receive eight thousand cedis every month. I don't see how this can be increased."

The other steering committee members shake their heads in agreement.

"To what amount do you want it increased? I don't see how it can be increased," fires Osabutey in a single breath.

The team members look at one another.

"Is this even the issue?" Mr. Abubakar waves a cavalier hand. "Perhaps it is really some other matter that is troubling you. You have a pushy woman boss. We all know how a woman can be." He sits to my left and does not look at me.

A stifling heat fills the room. I feel the paralysis of fear. How would Bessie deal with this? By chain smoking? Hammering out a damn fine novel. Is it possible that I don't comprehend how the men feel about me?

Abubakar bunches his hands into fists and starts pumping his forearms, alternating the forward thrust of each shoulder. In his seat, he jams his hips from side to side in imitation of a domineering woman. I look away from the gross display.

"Ehem," Obeng clears his throat. "Yes, please, speak freely. We wish to know your true concern." The small man hopes to stand on my back to reach his place at the table.

Misogynist-fluffy machine gun-yellow belly-trim dynamo. Ewe copper-vivid blue-bloodshot red-political suit grey.

"Women can be so dangerous when they think they are in charge," Abubakar condescends. A memory flares of a foreman who made my life hell. Osei and Takyi, looking confused, turn to Agyeman. I have never detected resentment from the men. Consternation grey-bloodshot confusion-stoic blue-dismissive copper. But I never saw Del coming on the pier job.

Agyeman looks at Thomas, who brushes off the notion with a soft smile, shaking his head as he says, "No, that is not it." Camarade copper. Medaase.

"Are you sure?" Abubakar leans closer to Thomas and repeats his female impersonation. "We all know how a woman can be." Sweat trickles down my forehead. I know how irrational a man can be once he decides that I am dangerous.

Thomas shakes his head. "No."

"We are asking you to consider increasing our out-of-station allowance. That is why we are here." Takyi clarifies the purpose for himself more than anyone. Upon finishing, doubt disappears from his face. He turns a look of serene certainty upon Abubakar, then Osabutey, then Obeng, then Preko. Misogynist—fluffy machine gun—low belly—trim dynamo. The other team members nod and murmur their agreement.

"You see, it is the out-of-station allowance," injects Osabutey. "It is and they have said it is so. I don't see how it can be increased above eight thousand. Is there anything to discuss?"

Preko runs a fingernail under the neat line of his moustache. "It was four thousand. They appealed for an increase to eight thousand and we agreed this was fair. How can we justify a second increase?"

"We can't," says Osabutey, looking around the table.

The other steering committee members agree.

Osabutey looks at Thomas. "So, you have asked us to consider an increase to your out-of-station allowance. We have considered it. We cannot. Is there anything else to discuss?"

Thomas turns to Agyeman.

"No, there is nothing else. You have been very kind to meet with us, today. We thank you for your consideration." Agyeman smiles and offers his hand.

The team members all rise and see out the steering committee. When we are alone, the team stands in silence. Takyi erupts and the room fills with heated remarks. Distressed to see their faces so drawn, I tell them we're finished for the day. I close up the office and walk home. Inhaling the stench of the stagnant gutter, I follow the chute road, and don't pause to enjoy the stained glass through the open church door.

Del was the general foreman on the pier job. He handled the crews well and knew how to think ahead. He often asked questions that helped me resolve discrepancies before they could delay the work. I enjoyed him . . .

"Akua, ɛte sɛn?"

I raise an arm to the yam chip lady and whisper, "Ɛyɛ."

. . .until the end. The project manager and superintendent were transferred and I was left to close out the job. There were still forty crew driving in hundreds of nails to complete the decking. And Del . . .

"Medaase," I say, zipping my duffel bag around a warm loaf.

. . . who could not stomach reporting to a woman. Accustomed as I was to being at ease with Del, I was slow to comprehend the deliberateness of his actions. I tried to respond to all of his concerns, believing them to be as genuine as they had always been. I found myself spinning. He had me coming and going with no time to think . . .

An insistent honk. I'm slow to look up and catch the tail end of a Land Rover.

. . . This man I had trusted, it was as if he felt his survival was threatened by my existence. I could not fathom the amount of energy and forethought he put into undercutting my authority and neutralizing my efforts.

Abubakar himself is trivial, but his opening the door to the insanity of the team harboring such animosity . . .

Idrissu and I exchange waves. The traffic is too dense for our voices to carry. I disappear inside my compound.

. . . the notion fills me with a great sense of helplessness.

I am very grateful for these four men. Agyeman, Thomas, Takyi, and Osei are nothing if not courteous and respectful to each other and to me. It is more than that depth of graciousness inherent in all Ghanaians. The men bring to their work a seriousness and dedication that tells me they, too, are receiving something of value. I can't imagine how many dead ends they have encountered in their careers. I am grateful that, whatever their past disappointments, they are capable of recognizing possibility in the Advocacy and they are not so bitter as to crush it.

I sit on the couch, the table before me like an altar. I press my palms into the grain of the wood. On a fresh page, I write:

Day breaks into a new gallows
The same room entered
by a different door.

Captive once.
Captive always.

Who is the jailer?
Me? You? Them?
We are better than fools,
Better than tomorrow,
Better than this day.

Our eyes never meet,
But you walk beside me.

I lie back on the couch. Dirty beige-thread grey-sworl brown-CAPITAL green black red white-Gere grey. In the contours of ceiling plaster, I locate the tension of being perceived as a woman—the only one—on a construction site. Aware that every pair of eyes sees first a woman and, then, if I'm lucky, they see an engineer. I remember my tricks for blurring the line. The swearing and belching, my stiff man-walk, the loose clothing that swallowed my shape, and always always being Johnny-on-the-spot with engineering. Below my hard hat had draped the sole emblem of my femininity—one thick, luxurious ponytail. It simplified construction to offer that clear demarcation of gender.

I brush my hand against the lay of stiff hair at the back of my head. My femininity and my masculinity do not reside in the length of my hair. This shearing, is it an attempt to get beyond the dichotomy of masculine/feminine?

On the wall, Barbara holds her ear of corn. So much beauty in her approach to her work. An intuitive knowing. A relationship with every plant. What could be more feminine? The value she places on the uniqueness of each plant, which she perceives through the morphological expression of genetic variability.

But her own body—Barbara's unique expression—denied by her armor of men's clothing. She would never shroud an ear of maize. It would block her connection to her life's work. Barbara does not find her own body deserving of the loving attention that she lavishes upon corn.

I suppose I am no better. I betrayed my form that my voice could be heard. A rapid-fire voice that suffered no fools. I came here to escape the coercion to be smart and fast. Barbara wants to forget she has a body. I want what is mine—in body and spirit.

I sit up and slide a palm across the grain, grateful for the solidity of wood.

Ɔbaa anaa ɔbarima?
Static gender
For every culture
I learn that language
Despite knowing
Anatomy is not gender
Femininity is not woman
Masculinity is not man
Honoring form
Is not acquiescence
To assigned gender
Vital container
For Fluid Soul

Cherish the body
Honor the spirit

Dirty beige . . . I brush my hand up the bare nape of my neck . . . *thread grey* . . . A deep, trembling breath slides a tear down my temple . . . *sworl brown* . . . Abubakar discredited me as a woman . . . *CAPITAL* . . . The team did not allow it . . . *green black red* . . . *white* . . . Would the team have stood beside me if I were a Ghanaian woman?

Here, I am not a woman. Here, first and foremost, I am white. My gender is white.

CHAPTER THIRTEEN

You write well." Mr. Illiasu refers to my contract letter. Luc Illiasu is the District Administrative Officer. He is Abubakar's boss and holds the most senior civil service post in the Adansi West District. The only higher authority is that of the District Secretary, a direct appointment by Chairman Rawlings, Ghana's head of state. I don't often meet with Illiasu. No doubt, WAG's maneouvering to control the Advocacy's agenda, not to mention the involvement of WAG's General manager—Madam Tettey, require greater delicacy than the steering committee can provide.

"Thank you." I sit on the edge of a deep box chair before Illiasu's desk. I am in Obuasi at the request of the District, however, I am not included in any District meetings and the only form of accountability is my reporting to the steering committee. I exercise discretion in managing the Advocacy. While I'm leery that recent events may spur the District to tighten the reins, I'd also love to hear insights one better connected might offer.

Mr. Illiasu is a middle-aged man with chocolate skin and a thoughtful demeanor. He has large eyes with heavy lids that give his countenance a tinge of sadness. Despite the frenetic nature of his office, I've never seen him angry or overwhelmed. My boss in Accra has said of Illiasu, "He is in Obuasi for a reason. He's a senior civil service man with a reputation for handling delicate situations." Illiasu sits forward, elbows on either side of the letter, forming a steeple with his hands and letting his fingers intertwine. "Tell me, how did you come to give this to Harrigan?"

"It was a Saturday. Harrigan sent word that I should come to his office. When I arrived, Kwasi—Dr. Kwarteng-Badu—was there. Harrigan was holding the letter I had written about conditions in Bediem."

In response to a loud knock, Illiasu shifts his attention to the door.

A tall, suited gentleman enters with a deferential nod. "Excuse me," he says to Illiasu, while swinging his eyes to me. He carries a folder above his head, extended toward Illiasu.

"Ah." Illiasu waves the man over.

Relieved at his admission, the man crosses the room with ginger steps and much bobbing of his head. I will never appreciate this custom of perpetual prostration to reinforce the message that you do not intend to offend. In fact, "meda wo ase," the Twi equivalent of "thank you" is translated as "I prostrate myself before you." A little extreme for most situations, in my view.

As the man departs, Illiasu picks up my letter and lets out a giggle-sigh. "You seem to have a penchant for writing letters."

"I come from construction. In the U.S., when there's a material issue, one always documents it in writing."

"What did you say about Bediem?"

"Well, the team had visited Bediem without me. They returned in fear for their safety. The people had threatened to beat them, perceiving them as representatives of West Africa Gold. Bediem had been without water for two weeks and the people were angry."

"You put this in your letter?"

"Yes."

Another giggle from Illiasu and an amused query. "Harrigan was angry . . . ?"

"No. He is a fox."

Illiasu takes delight, a spontaneity rooted in intelligence.

"He told me that I just had the best interest of the villagers at heart. That I was just speaking from my heart. He told me that out of my desire to help, I forgot to talk to Kwasi and give him a chance to explain how complex the relationship is between Bediem and WAG. Harrigan told Kwasi and me that this is never to happen again. That we're always to consult with each other and present a united front."

"But the contract?" Illiasu reminds.

"Yes, after Bediem, he asked about the contract."

In response to a rap on the door, Illiasu receives three men. They approach his desk and speak in rapid Twi for some time. Illiasu asks a question and sends them on their way. The receptionist takes advantage of the opening to remind Illiasu of an appointment. The party has been waiting. He thanks her and picks up the letter.

"Louisa, WAG is not happy with your letter." Illiasu lets the document fall to his desk. I could be in the soup if Harrigan has complained to Illiasu. From the perspective of the District Administrative Officer, concessions may be required of the Advocacy. "You have some good comments, but you have exposed the mine's weakness and they are not happy about it. You have to be careful dealing with WAG. If you back them into a corner, they will walk away."

Illiasu doesn't know. Harrigan hasn't brought his case to the District Administration. It stays between us. As long as I don't care, it is as if it never happened.

"WAG may just say, 'Forget it,' and pull their funding and then where will you be? I know, I have worked with WAG for many years."

In all my time in Obuasi, Mr. Illiasu has never strung so many sentences together for my benefit. Balancing on the front edge of my chair, I listen to every word, feeling honored when he digresses.

". . . The U.S. and Europeans love military dictators in Africa. They embrace them. They want uneducated leaders upon whom they can impose their programs."

"Why doesn't Ghana just tell the U.S., tell everyone, to get out?" I ask with frustration. "Why don't they tell them, 'We have our own programme. If you want to give us aid, it must be in this form'?"

"People who are intelligent enough to draw their own program will never become leaders. It is the curse of development. You have no resources and whenever something is given to you, it is given with strings. You go to college and you study it. You realize how it is and that is why we have a brain drain. Everyone leaves for Europe." Illiasu stares at the wall behind me, his visage too subtle to read.

He recovers with a sad smile, looking at me with full, round eyes. He is a person I would trust, if I were allowed to know him.

"No one wants to give aid to Obuasi. They think we are rich, but the local government does not get any of the money. You see it. We are breathing the dust, the arsenic, the sulfur dioxide. West Africa Gold does what it likes and perhaps gives a token compensation or ignores the villagers. This mine is the leading source of foreign exchange for Ghana. We are producing the country's wealth, but we are getting none of the benefits.

"We have to be very careful how we deal with WAG. If we make too many demands, Accra will come down on us. Tell us we are causing too many problems. You see the situation. Sometimes I think I am wasting my time. Why stay here? But where will I go?"

Illiasu's giggle feels incongruous with the gravity of the moment. "I suppose an engineer could confuse our mining activity for construction works . . ." he muses. "You may remember," he clasps his hands in a steeple and gives a faint lift of his chin, "Ghana is not America." Though his tone is gentle, he has never given me such direct advice.

Illiasu lets his eyes fall to the letter. "'The Contractor shall perform all work in a timely manner, to produce workmanlike quality, in accordance with industry standards.' You do not like this clause." He looks at me.

Surprised that he seems now to be taking my letter seriously, I feel my engineer head marshalling to the fore. "That language is the type of language used in a hard money construction contract. We would be fools to sign this contract."

"What is the harm?"

My heart sinks. I detest what I'm about to do. "Is it not apparent?" The Rifleman shouts a warning to his naïve opponent.

"You take exception to these words." Illiasu does not blink.

"That language is the type of language used in a hard money construction contract." The Rifleman works the lever action, getting off shot after shot, always on mark. "It does not apply to development work. 'In a timely manner' suggests that there's some timetable, a schedule, to which the Advocacy must perform. But there isn't a schedule, other than the schedules I make." I hate my droning voice, the mechanical delivery. "WAG has never given us a comprehensive overview of what they want accomplished in two years and they won't—because that would require them to disclose a plan. And if they did, can you say how long it should take a village to learn and develop? How can you put a timetable to this?" Why does Illiasu make me cite these obvious deficiencies? "We go to the villages regularly and they respond, each one differently and at their own pace. They're treating us like hard money contractors. It's meaningless . . ."

"So, it's meaningless . . ."

A chief's party bursts into the room, impressing upon me the privilege of this extended solo audience. Relieved at the diversion from my conduct, I sling my duffel bag over my shoulder, and nod farewell to the man caught in the urgency of his new visitors.

I close the door to Illiasu's office and exit via the waiting room. It is essential in construction. Rights and obligations. Fight for every right that can be squeezed out of the language. Hammer the other party to fulfill their obligations. Though, how else would one respond to Illiasu's question?

"Akua."

I don't recognize the voice and, for a moment, think perhaps it is not me being addressed.

"Akua, you do not have time for me?"

The secretary looks tired as always in her blue uniform. She sits every day at an old wooden desk in a corner of the waiting room that splits the offices of Illiasu and Ankrah. On her desk are a telephone and an electric typewriter.

"Akua, ɛte sɛn?" she asks.

She is not someone whose motives I trust. "Ɛyɛ. Na wo nso ɛ?" I oblige.

"He wants to see you." She points toward Ankrah's door.

"Now?"

"Yes, go."

Mr. Kofi Kwegyir Ankrah is the District Secretary. I don't know his connection to the head of state—whether Ankrah and Jerry John Rawlings were schoolmates or whether Ankrah fell out of the second coup landing on hero's feet. Only someone trusted by the Castle would be given the District Secretary post in Obuasi.

I knock and am buzzed in by Ankrah, who sits behind his desk at the far end of an enormous room. He continues writing while I take a seat in one of the four, high-backed chairs upholstered in red velvet that face his desk, perches for supplicants at the mercy of his whim.

"WAG does not like your letter," he offers, without looking up.

I catch a trace of a fatherly tone. "Yes, I just met with Mr. Illiasu. He explained what's going on, that I shouldn't push WAG too hard. I would have shown you the letter first, but Harrigan was very upset on Saturday and wanted to see something on Sunday. I signed it as a Peace Corps volunteer, rather than as a representative of the District, since no one here had read it. You don't have to endorse it."

Ankrah's skin is milky coffee. Hair sprouts from his round head like the aura of a light bulb. His beady eyes focus on a document in his hands the entire time I'm speaking, but he doesn't hesitate to respond when I'm finished.

"There's nothing wrong with your letter," he says. "I'm going to call a meeting with the mine. Illiasu and I will meet with Dr. Kwarteng-Badu. We'll straighten out the lines of communication, so you're not put in this position in the future."

"Thank you." He's not naming Harrigan. Ankrah also has no clue about WAG's power play. Failing to mention his tactics to the Administration may be a way to signal to Harrigan that I'm not distressed by his ploy.

"They asked me, 'Who is she to be sending us letters about our contract?' I told them, 'She works for the District.'" His wicked pleasure sends a chill. I don't imagine anyone trusts him. Ankrah returns to reading and I suppose I am dismissed.

Just as I'm about to rise, he returns. "WAG doesn't like you going to companies. They called me and said, 'What the hell is she doing going to our contractors?' I said, 'They're private companies. It's no concern of yours.' But you won't be getting a list from them. Every company that works for the mine pays taxes to the District. They know if you get the list, we get the list. You can go around to companies, but don't expect WAG to give you a list."

West Africa Gold is reacting on every front. Who at WAG would have made that call—Finn Harrigan? Larry Wittle? Madam Tettey?

It is getting serious.

CHAPTER FOURTEEN

The District administrative office is a three-story block structure located down a nameless road that *T*s off the main Obuasi road east of Mangoase Junction. Most of the road from the office to the T-junction is taken up by the grounds of a primary school. I usually cut through the schoolyard, which is often swarming with uniformed children. Skinny boys with dust-floured legs will fall into step around me, forcing their squeaky voices into the depths of their bony chests:

"What is your name?

"What is your name?

"Oburoni, what is your name?

"Oburoni, what is your name?

"I am talking to you.

"I am talking to you, oburoni."

Laughter.

I flinch from imagining the familiar scene. Schoolkids wouldn't dare speak to a Ghanaian elder in demanding tones. They put me in my place, remind me that I am white. Yes, Illiasu, "Ghana is not America."

In response to this morning's heavy rains, students and teachers have vacated the grounds. A large group of shirtless men skids in pursuit of a football, the damp air swallowing their ardent cries.

The contract will strip the Advocacy of any protection against WAG. Where was Illiasu heading? "It's meaningless . . ." So . . . sign it?

We would be fools. I feel the litany of rebuttals constellating. It's as if the arguments come right out of the cells of my body. It requires no thought. My engineer-speak, as Carol calls it, materializes in an instant. I'm embarrassed to behave like that in front of Illiasu. If he noticed, he did not react. Of course, he noticed. He dismissed it as what one expects of an engineer. Mechanical. Rational. Narrow.

It is something else. It is my father shooting his righteousness, his rightness, at my mother. I wander over to the schoolhouse and set my notebook on the damp window ledge. I press my palm into the blank page.

> Words spill with ease
> Prohibition provokes
> greater flow
> In the name of Truth
>
> Machiavellian thrill
> of the unassailable
> Words as violation
> Truth as disrespect
>
> Defecated information
> Soils me
> and those I love.
>
> Free speech
> Costs
> Me dearly

The violence committed in my family in the name of truth. The relentless arguing to defend an engineer's hegemony. This is my shame.

I pick my way amid the late afternoon puddles concealing the deep potholes of the main road. "Ghana is not America." What is Illiasu telling me? Don't write letters? Stop barreling headlong into adversaries. How else? Pretense. Not saying what everyone knows.

Is it gracious or obsequious? I don't think Illiasu is obsequious. I could never stomach his job, not under the leadership of as cutthroat a fellow as Ankrah.

A naked child runs into the road, momentarily devoid of traffic. A huge smile plays across the child's face as he hugs his mud-coated football. That ball is as big as the child. A man coming from the opposite direction hurries to the boy and grabs him in his arms. Given the mix of industrial trucks and pedestrian traffic, it's a wonder that one doesn't hear of fatalities daily. A gentle mist falls as the man braces himself against the lip of the crumbling gutter, and leans over to deposit the toddler onto a tiny square of concrete. Spying a door opening onto the small porch, the man calls out for the parents.

A downpour chases all life out of the street. The good Samaritan nudges the child toward the door, hastening on his way.

"Bra!" A shopkeeper waves me to his covered porch. He wears a long Muslim kaftan over matching pants. "Come!" He entreats, opening both hands toward an empty chair.

I wave to acknowledge his invitation, and continue along the row of industrial shops. Dusty bags of cement, rusted bars of reinforcing steel, and shining sheets of corrugated tin are piled on the porches to lure buyers. Many of the shopkeepers extend a kind welcome. These are people with whom I've never interacted, yet I don't doubt the sincerity of their concern. It's impossible to explain to someone who has never been to Ghana. The hospitality for strangers exceeds any social standard, even in relation to the rest of Africa.

"Ghana is not America." Here every child has a place. It may be a poor place, but it's one in which family members take time for the child. One can see it in the subsistence farmer who stands as if addressing the United Nations when speaking on behalf of his village. He possesses a fundamental confidence, a certainty that he belongs on this earth. Not at all like an engineer proving her worth with right answers. Not like a top student cowering behind accolades, certain that the simplicity of her being is neither desired nor valued.

My clothes cling to my body, but are not plastered against me, as on that last night in Philadelphia. Our group of Peace Corps volunteers first met in Philadelphia for a three-day staging. We lost a few. Instead of boarding our plane bound for New York and Accra, they flew back to Minnesota, Kansas, Oregon. Maybe that was the purpose of the staging, to offer a final moment of self-reckoning. I had no doubt that to return to Africa was to claim my life.

My roommate and I went out to dine in style on our last night in the U.S. Amy and I stepped from the hotel, our sandals and pedal pushers bright and new, not yet sodden with the red earth of Ghana. After only a few steps a torrent fell upon us. We goaded each other with the premise that it would rain like this every day in Ghana, better get used to it. Many blocks later, we entered an elegant restaurant drenched. Waiting inside for the rain to stop never occurred to us. Such challenges we pick to prove we are warriors.

Pausing to swing my duffel bag away from my body and unstick my soaked tee shirt from the skin of my back, I recall it was the same with the sun. I spent my childhood under the blaze of desert skies. I came prepared to sweat. Out in the villages, Agyeman, Takyi, Thomas, and Osei were patient enough to call me into the shade of a tree, each time, until I learned that courting heat stroke is not a hero's mission.

I wave in Idrissu's direction as I approach home. He has pulled in his ironing table. Through half-closed doors, a phantom sews.

I think I hear him cry my name, "Akua!" through the wet. My fingers stretch between the piquets of the gate, feeling for the tiny padlock.

Stripping off my wet clothes, I put water on the stove. After a hot bucket bath, I take refuge on the couch with a cup of tea. Shutters and the heavy wooden door hold out the rain. What a blessing for Gyimiso Kakraba. With the Advocacy's guidance, they have established a makeshift rain catchment system off the tin rooves. I feel a tear in the corner of my eye. Here, at least, is one concrete instance in which I know without doubt that my presence here has made a difference. My small drinks good water tonight.

From the familiar geography of plaster I contrive the thick moustache of Larry Wittle. He could have been the one who called Ankrah and protested the Advocacy's fundraising plans. I recall Wittle's touch, the sympathetic press of his hand. "We cannot change the whole world overnight."

Whose voice is that? . . . Whose hand?

My thumb traces the rough lip of the steaming mug. The vague form in the ceiling requires no definition. It is the face of every geologist to whom I've been introduced since childhood. Educated men who travel the world extracting natural resources. It is the face of the first man, my father. "We cannot change." My young heart swollen with tears wants to know: Men who travel the world witnessing the disparities while marveling at your own good fortune, is yours a wise voice that assesses what is possible? Or is yours a fearful voice unwilling to risk?

Some part of me knows the answer. Some part does not want to know, refuses to malign the myth of my origin. Men into whose arms I pitched myself when they returned from months of travel. Men who regaled me with tales of the exotic and incomprehensible. Men who pulled handwrought trinkets out of their pockets and knelt to slide their treasure onto my wrist or hook it around my neck. Men who lofted me on their shoulders as they danced and sang.

The rush of rain pelts the tin roof. I press my hand into my chest sobbing at my ludicrous desire. I want the respect of these men. And I want them to change. In this way, I am my mother, resisting my hysteria. I speak in a controlled voice so that they can hear. And if I cannot control my voice, do my screams pierce their logic? Do the cries erupting from my mouth incite the compulsion to annihilate the lunatic Arab bearing down on horseback, scimitar raised? Is there any possibility that my screeching will be heard as the explosion of history no human can contain? A history that does not ask permission for the change it announces.

The heavens plummet to a mad crescendo of thunderous resonance that my ears cannot reconcile with the cheap tin. If I cannot control my voice, do my sobs melt their fears? Do the wordless groans reverberating in my chest echo the sentimental woman incapable of appreciating the world's realities? Is there any possibility that my moans will be heard as the connection with Source that no human can deny? A connection that does not bow to reason.

The storm dissipates. The quavering chord of tin grows still, the pressure upon my eardrums, now a vacuum.

If I cannot control my voice, do I, like my mother, sit in silence?

I drink tea from a pottery mug, brown and gold glazed. A mug made by a local woman. Bought in passing on a street near the market from a woman I will never see again. A large, sturdy mug of fired earth, whose texture grounds me as the tea soothes. What stops West Africa Gold from relocating Bediem and Sansu? It is not money. The cost to resettle a few hundred subsistence farmers wouldn't shift WAG's balance sheet by a thousandth of a percent. What needs to change? Dirty beige-thread grey-sworl brown-CAPITAL green black red white-Gere grey.

In the photo, Bessie speaks her mind. A freedom her own country did not allow her. But Mandela is free. De Klerk changed the world. Divestment changed South Africa. We rallied for divestment at the university. Change is possible.

My gaze settles on engineering texts. Civil engineering. Something I can do anywhere. That's what I needed, a ticket to the world. I never imagined that the Peace Corps would return me to my father's world.

I see Dad smirking across the dinner table. "They want the profits from the oil under their ground. They need us to develop the fields and produce the crude. They're willing to pay us good money and they're still putting plenty into their own coffers. They profit. We profit. That's how the world works." He swills his wine, intoxicated by the veracity of his argument.

Mom swallows the lump in her throat. Her voice emerges soft and high-pitched. "I'm not saying profit is wrong . . ." Her words shrink as Dad sneers. I abhor my helplessness to prevent the inevitable slaughter. Timid and shaky, Mom perseveres, "I . . . couldn't there be a way . . . it might be possible to also not damage the lives of the people . . . the land . . ."

Dad crashes in. "The government is responsible for the welfare of their people. It's not our job. We comply with the terms of our contracts. Everything we do is legal."

My mother swallows hard and raises her head with a brave smile, nodding in acquiescence. I have fought all my life to not be my mother, to not be that woman unable to reframe the discussion in terms of human dignity.

Steam off the tea caresses my cheeks. As a child, I felt so stimulated living in a foreign culture. The fragrance of cardamom in tea, the deep colors in a handwoven tapestry, the rank scent of fresh leather, the rhythms of an unknown language, the huge stone edifices left behind by an ancient civilization. I placed my hands on carved stones infused with my father's history and dreamed of building grand structures. Here I am, promoting ventilated pit latrines.

Fulfillment comes from building things. To look at lines and dimensions on paper and imagine the final structure. To walk the site with the superintendent planning the work. To order raw materials and fashion them into an intended form. I look to Bessie. She got it. She loved life on a construction site. We are kindred spirits.

One feels part of a continuum, receiving a designer's plan and manifesting her vision in the physical world. That final thing of concrete and steel stands in tribute to the long hours, the bottles of beer at night and Pepto Bismol in the morning, the divorces, the camaraderie, the wiliness and insanity that made it happen.

That final thing stands whole, forever.

I walked away from that straightforward life for the sake of a memory. A memory of my unguarded self, not plagued by this split between the rational and non-rational. When I was a child in Libya, everything fascinated. Every person seemed whole unto themselves, strange and credible at once. If I could hold the pieces . . . if I could discover the interrelationships . . . the fragments would coalesce.

I set the mug on the table and drop my head into my hands.

What is this place to which I have come? Is it the Africa of my parents? Why don't I feel the joy I perceived in my parents—in myself—as a child?

My mother speaks of the world that could be. My father speaks of the world that is. I spend my life trying to bridge that gap.

Medaase. Meda wo ase. I lie down before you. To look some-one in the eye with gratitude. How dire must be the circumstance for the simplest kindness to be met with the nakedness of one's own need?

CHAPTER FIFTEEN

Agyeman, Thomas, Takyi, Osei and I sit under a shelter of dry cocoa palm fronds waiting for the villagers to assemble. The large thatched structure sits in the center of Mamiriwa. This village draws its water from the Fenanana, a stream that originates a few kilometers northwest of Obuasi and feeds a larger river, the Fena, which is tributary to the mighty Ofin. When we first visited this village, the people claimed that recent mining activity had caused a bad scent in their water. They took us to a stagnant pool of reddish-brown water.

"Before WAG worked in the area, this water flowed freely," Agyeman had translated the villagers' story. Mamiriwa is too close to Obuasi for the dam to be the culprit. If their story is true, local exploration activity may have altered the natural course of their stream.

We advised the villagers to put their petition in writing, while cautioning them not to expect much from the mine. In response to our encouragement, today, Mamiriwa will conduct its introductory durbar for a water project.

Surrounding mud-block homes demarcate the edge of the durbar grounds. An old woman takes a seat on the perimeter bench of split bamboo. Her breasts droop over her cloth wrap. Two young boys and a younger girl jostle for position close to the old woman. The boys wear tee shirts that hang to their knees. The girl wears bright red stud earrings and a pair of shorts. She clutches the old woman's leg, struggling to balance bare feet on her grandmother's leather sandal.

A young man leans over the half-height perimeter wall.

"Do you know what 'buroni waawu' means?" asks Agyeman. He speaks into my shoulder and gives a faint jerk of his head toward the young man.

I do, but love to hear Agyeman's stories.

"His clothes we call 'buroni waawu' clothes. This means 'dead white.' The clothes of a dead white. For what living person would give away their clothes?"

The young man wears an unbuttoned short-sleeved shirt. Great heaps of buroni waawu clothes are sold at the markets. By what circuitous route do the old clothes that Americans cull from their closets make their way to local sellers?

I love this sense of the world in the midst of isolation. In a village of subsistence farmers, the peace I feel is not the absence of the modern world. It is the presence of earth, of people connected to the earth who engage the modern world on their own terms. These simple, useful garments do not intrude upon what is essential.

Several other men standing further back from the shelter catch my attention. They are dressed in Western-style clothes that look brand new. On their feet are heavy, black miner's boots.

Agyeman follows the line of my sight and says, "They can afford the finer clothes sold in Obuasi. Due to being so near to Obuasi, Mamiriwa has a greater number of men employed at the mine."

Miners. Men who sweat in the belly of the earth. Who could be more grounded?

Three young women sit together on the perimeter bench. All three have pierced ears and immaculate skin and hair. Two wear bright headcloths. All wear tee shirts tucked into cloth wraps. The local cloth is a lightweight cotton that dries in this humidity.

The patterns range from bold, multi-colored, intricate designs to a simple pale blue or tan with tiny flowers of a darker hue.

The three beautiful women stare at me, whisper to each other, and giggle. I know that they are debating my sex. Though I cannot hear the rest of their conversation, "ɔbaa," and "ɔbarima," ring in my ears. Most Ghanaian girls have their ears pierced, often before their first birthday. My short hair and lack of piercing confuse Ghanaians.

My hips they ignore, perhaps owing to the shorts and pants I wear, garments that Ghanaians associate with men. It makes no sense to go scrambling through the brush to inspect a village's water source in a skirt. I feel I must be prepared for whatever arises, and a skirt would inhibit me.

A well-dressed miner pulls a cigarette from a pack of smokes. One of the young women stands and looks me over. I brace for the insult.

As the time for my departure to Ghana grew closer, the compulsion to cut my hair grew stronger. I felt an intensity akin to a religious conviction to get rid of my thick mane. Sometimes I imagine I will let it grow. I flirt with the notion of ridding myself of the tension induced in every human interaction. But the longer my hair gets, the more distressed I feel. I snip around my skull, feeling the tufts in my fingers. Relief comes in the grating of the blades, the end of each clip like a sexual release on the edge of pain. Shorn locks spider across the back of my arm. I have to take control, banish what oppresses me. Although I peer into my tiny travel mirror, it is not a visual cue that I seek. The cessation of compulsion, the absence of insanity means the scissors may rest.

The standing woman swings into action, sashaying up to me. Her sisters shriek at her daring and leap to her side. Blushing and batting her eyes, the woman asks, "Are you a man or a woman?"

This preoccupation with either/or pervades most cultures.

"If you are a man . . ." She proposes with her sisters pressing against her, giggling. ". . . I will marry you."

This obsession with static gender. "And if I am a woman?"

"I will be your friend."

My friends do not insist that I be of fixed gender. "M'adamfo," I say, giving her hand a soft squeeze.

The woman closes her eyes with a dreamy smile and leans back into the arms of her sisters. Shrieking, the three return to their bench. Agyeman and Thomas smile at each other. I hear no warmth in the women's hysteria and tuck away the offense to focus on our mission.

"Like most of the villages in the Advocacy's program, Mamiriwa is comprised of subsistence farmers." Agyeman loves to educate. It is his nature and I appreciate the private lessons in Ghanaian culture. Just now, the sound of his voice helps me feel human. "Their crops are cassava and plantain, yam, garden eggs, tomato and onion, banana, okra and pepper, and oranges. Obuasi oranges are known for their sweetness. Some say it's due to the high arsenic in the soil." He scuffs the ground with his shoe. "These subsistence farmers spend several hours each day weeding their farms and picking some produce for the evening meal. Our durbar gives many an excuse to skip farming today."

When a crowd of about one hundred people fills the shelter and its surrounds, the chief's ɔkyeame arrives carrying a carved wooden ɔkyeame poma. The chief enters after his ɔkyeame. Both wear fine cloth over their left shoulders. Their right shoulders are bare. The chief wears royal sandals. The ɔkyeame asks of our mission.

"We have received from your health committee a census and a map of your village. As promised, based on this information, we have come to discuss the technical options for your water project," Agyeman translates my English into the local Twi.

"We have received your message saying that you will come. You are welcome. We are ready to meet with you," Nana—the chief, speaks to his ɔkyeame, who stands with his staff planted on the earth before him and addresses the gathering in Twi.

"Before we begin with the project, it is advisable that we do some animation." Agyeman suggests.

Thomas talks about the dangers of cholera and other diarrheal diseases. He moves about the center of the durbar shelter to speak to different portions of the audience. He bows his tall body a bit and floats soft gestures from his long arms. There is laughter as he squats in imitation of someone suffering with diarrhea. Agyeman stands to make the tie to the need for the water project. He projects a stronger voice, a firmer presence. When convinced the crowd is oriented, Agyeman requests the chief's permission and signals that I should begin our long presentation.

"Your census indicates that there are sixteen hundred people living in Mamiriwa. The technology we can offer you is dug wells or boreholes. Dug wells are cheaper, but have a greater risk of contamination. For a population of sixteen hundred, you would need eight dug wells."

Agyeman translates, elaborating on the concept of a dug well.

"The capital cost to build one dug well is one million cedis. You may or may not choose to place a handpump in the well. The cost of one handpump is three hundred thousand cedis." Citing these enormous figures reminds me that since I arrived in the country less than a year ago, the exchange rate for cedis on the dollar has gone from four hundred fifty to seven hundred fifty. "If you use a handpump, it will be faster to fetch water and the well will be sealed, so that the water will not easily be contaminated. But you will have to collect ongoing maintenance tariffs in order to fix the pump when it breaks. Without the pump, you will have no costs after the initial construction of the well."

Agyeman translates. Thomas stands, clarifying with gestures how the well would be sealed with the handpump.

"If you choose eight dug wells without handpumps, including a ten percent contingency for inflation, the total capital cost would be approximately nine million cedis."

This is where Carol would say, "Enough with the numbers." She has pointed out that in the recitation of data, my voice takes on a monotone and my face becomes a mask. She may be right that I lose some of my humanity. But people need facts to make educated decisions. We have to provide this information.

While Agyeman translates, Takyi drags a handkerchief across his face and under his arms. As is typical of the wet season, when not raining, muggy air presses upon us. I feel the dampness of my skin, patches of shirt stick to my back and triceps. I drag my sweaty brow against the rolled cuffs of my sleeves. There is a query from a serious young man in the crowd.

Agyeman replies and turns to me. "He wants to know how they can afford such things. They are subsistence farmers, after all. I told him he has run ahead of his teacher. If he can but wait a moment, Akua will explain the financing of the thing."

"We know that you cannot afford to pay the total project cost, but you can afford to pay something. It is up to you to decide how much you can pay and devise a plan for raising the money. Then, your health committee must come to our office and fill out a funding proposal. This proposal describes your village, explains your water problem and how you have chosen to solve it. In the proposal, you explain what you are willing to give to the project—your labor, the use of your tools, and some amount of money toward the capital cost. The Advocacy will take this proposal to potential donors and ask them to fund the balance of your project."

Agyeman translates and takes a few questions. "Akua, they are unclear on the donors. They want to know who will come to their aid."

"There are development agencies in the world, some of them are formed by private individuals who want to help people who are living under hard conditions, and some are formed by the governments of countries—the U.S., Japan, China, Germany, Sweden, France, the U.K. These development agencies have money that is for helping people to improve their living conditions. There are also church groups around the world that like to help charitable causes and, often, companies will give money to support projects in the areas where they work."

Agyeman translates. Osei dabs perspiration from his forehead. Takyi's head drops, waking him with a start.

"The money is out there. We will do our best to find it for you. But first you must do your part. You must decide on your community contribution to the capital cost. You must open a bank account in Obuasi and start depositing your funds. And you must fill out a funding proposal."

Agyeman translates and turns. "They want to know the cost of the boreholes."

As I review the various project options and their costs, Carol waves and ducks out. Mamiriwa must choose between eight dug wells; adding handpumps to four of the wells; three four-inch boreholes; and substituting one four-inch for a six-inch borehole in anticipation of the possibility of a submersible pump feeding a pipe-borne system if electricity is ever extended here.

While Agyeman translates, Thomas leans over the back of my chair to whisper to Osei.

"Excuse me, Akua. If I may describe for them the pipe-borne water?" enquires Mr. Osei.

"Please."

Nature has created in Osei's body the perfect megaphone. His rough voice, projected from his chest with such force, commands attention, even Takyi's. With the knowledge of an insider, Osei explains in Twi the finer points of a pipe-borne system. Standpipes throughout the village fed water by an electric pump would put Mamiriwa on par with my water service in Obuasi.

When he finishes, Agyeman asks, "Akua, what is the cost of the boreholes, altogether?"

"With a six-inch?"

"Yes, they want everything."

"If you choose two, four-inch boreholes and one, six-inch borehole, the total project cost will be seventeen-and-a-half million cedis."

Agyeman translates and hears the crowd. "They will have the three boreholes."

"You need to recognize that with the boreholes you have maintenance costs. The handpumps may break and so you must collect a pump maintenance tariff to be deposited at the bank to use to repair the pump. We recommend a monthly tariff of two hundred cedis per adult per month."

Agyeman translates while Takyi drags his handkerchief inside the neck of his shirt and under his arms.

Agyeman says, "I think, Akua, we must go now. They have much to think over and they can contact us when they are ready to write the proposal."

We are kept small at the truck while some women and men of the village bring us oranges, avocados, and bunches of bananas, juice trickling down the fresh cut stalks. Agyeman pulls ten oranges from the bed of the truck and hands them back. In no time, cutlasses are in the air, peeling the thin skin and slicing open the tops of the oranges. We suck down the sweet nectar.

My voice feels strained and I ask if I might have one more orange. Of course, one of the young men obliges. He's a tall, broad shouldered man, muscular and healthy in the way exuded by men in their late teens and twenties, as they come to feel the power of their bodies. I stand in front of him and not once does he look up. Beside us are the team and the truck surrounded by a sea of villagers.

All eyes are upon this young man. There is quiet in the air. He concentrates on shaving the skin in one continuous spiral, never losing the bite of his blade, never slicing into the fruit. I am awed by his strong body, awed that he surrenders his beauty to the humble task of preparing my orange.

I once worked a pipe-laying operation with a man named Gary. I had a hand level and Gary had a shovel and together we fine-graded the trenches where the pipe would lay. Gary was tall and wore tee shirts with the sleeves cut off, exposing rippling shoulders that glistened in the sun.

There is beauty in labor, in sweat glistening off muscled arms, in expelled grunts of effort, in sharing fatigue at the day's end. A part of that beauty has always been the cockiness of the young stud—the sureness of his voice, the twinkle in his eye, the slant of his hips. Gary was no youth, but had not lost that air.

The young man peeling the orange is a subsistence farmer who may never have traveled far. How often in life will he stand at center stage? He meets any nervousness by concentrating on the task, prevailing with the flesh whole and unspoiled. I watch him the entire time, anticipating meeting his moment of triumph when he offers me his gift with a bold smile.

But the young man's head remains down. He extends his arms to me, cupping the fruit in his palms.

CHAPTER SIXTEEN

We pull out of Mamiriwa onto a feeder road, to which West Africa Gold's exploration crew is adding aggregate base. The men talk little. Even though we stayed close to Obuasi today, the humidity saps our energies. In the repetition of the same conversation in several villages, I lose my place. The damp air insulates my memory. I hesitate at the sound of my voice, uncertain whether I've already said these words in this village or whether I'm recollecting an exchange from hours before.

Travel is slow back to the office. Someone has decided to repair our haul road from hell. By the Catholic church, travel has been reduced to one lane to accommodate a road crew. Mud from a wheelbarrow is packed into potholes with the flat of a shovel. Beside the road crew works a lone man with a shovel of his own, the gutter mucker.

At regular intervals, the gutter mucker desilts our u-shaped gutters to free the flow of surface runoff. All the dirt, gravel, orange peels, goat droppings, children's potty, kitchen sullage, and stagnant green scum—consolidated into a dense muck by the vibrations of passing haul trucks—is lifted one shovel at a time and deposited approximately ten centimeters away, creating a berm inside the road that parallels the gutter. Pedestrians claim this nebulous margin between speeding traffic and the gutter's edge. Their feet pound the mounded muck into a flatness that sloughs back into the gutter.

The gutter mucker's futile effort always irritates me. It feels maddening today. Why can't the gutter mucker toss his load into the potholes? Does our elite road crew have special pothole mud in their wheelbarrow? I see Carol laughing at me. "How can you get excited about mud?"

"It shouldn't be mud," I fantasize responding.

"But who cares?" She teases.

"You would, if you had to drive this road. Mud has no structural value. It is a pretense of doing something."

Carol steps back at the heat in my tone. She raises her arms above her head, then drops them, bowing and saying, "The Engineer hath spoken. Let no woman oppose Her. There shall be no mud. Death to all who raise a shovel."

Traffic stagnates past the Catholic church and up the chute road. The effort of not advancing defeats me. I wonder if Carol is right. Do I care about the wrong things? But then who would build good roads?

By the time we make it to the office, I'm tired and hungry, and can think of little else as I drive up the road to the lab. Kwasi has not yet moved into the new Safety building. He sees me through the glass in his door and leaps up. I'm not accustomed to such energy from him.

"Yes, Louisa." He meets me as I enter, and pulls the door fully open.

I drop the keys into his palm.

"Thank you, Louisa. Eh, you should know that from this point forward, Finn will be signing your pay vouchers. You will no longer take the vouchers to Jim."

It saddens me to lose an excuse to visit Jim. My stomach growls. Kwasi has done his best to mimic Finn delivering a deflating blow. To rob him of satisfaction, I smile and say, "Thank you, Kwasi. What are WAG's long-term plans for Gyimiso Kakraba?"

"Eh . . ." Caught off guard, Kwasi looks away. When he gathers himself, anger chokes his voice, "That is not your concern."

"All right," I back slowly down the hall. "It would just help when we visit them and they ask, if we could explain all that West Africa Gold is doing to correct the situation." Reaching the exit, I step outside ashamed of my impulsiveness. No good will come of provoking him.

Pulling off my long-sleeved shirt and ducking through the oleanders, I try to ignore the rumbling in my belly. I scramble down the slope of the fifth hole, pick my way through the muddy swath along the fence, and twist around the bent wrought iron picket onto the main road. My head is down, eyes searching for a safe place to plant my next step. A cracked cross gutter marks the moment to steal a glimpse of Kofi waving the Union Jack. Calls from familiar voices elicit a slight nod of my head or flutter of my hand.

A girl approaches with her hand out. I harden my stride and brush past her.

"Kyɛ me penny. Kyɛ me penny. Kyɛ me penny." Her singsong follows me.

She could be eight years old. At her age, I was playing with my friend Deborah. We climbed on limestone blocks in the field above the petrol station. When feeling brave, we trekked to the far corner of the field to visit the Libyan man who worked at the station. Hayyan would kneel and spread his arms. In excited Arabic, he would say what felt like thanks to Allah for the gift of such beauty visiting a common man. We greeted him with, "Sabah'l khair." With rapid nods and proud gestures, Hayyan would encourage our Arabic. Before we left, he would disappear into the station house and return with gifts, an Esso tiger tail and a cardboard tube of Smarties.

"Kyɛ me penny. Kyɛ me penny. Oburoni, kyɛ me penny." The girl laughs as she skips to match my pace.

Debbie and I gave no thought to begging. Libyan children did not beg. This girl beside me does not go to bed hungry. Her begging is not a matter of survival.

At a sharp horn blast, my eyes snap to the road. Ned Clyde raises a hand in my direction. I wave back and watch his truck disappear in a haze of exhaust and dust. His fleeting acknowledgement evokes the solidity and dependability of the quintessential construction man. Recalling the stock from which I come, I look anew at the muck and dust, the pregnant goats and half-naked smalls, haul trucks and taxis, street vendors and shopkeepers . . . and remember that I am walking my site.

"Oburoni! Oburoni! Oburoni! Kyɛ me penny, oburoni." The girl sways her head from side to side, enjoying her song. This is a child's game that I will not play.

Spying me at the tree in front of my house, Idrissu waves me over. I cannot refuse. Holding up a hand, I indicate that I will return. After dropping my duffel bag, splashing water on my face, and grabbing a *Newsweek*, I head over. Idrissu greets me, takes the magazine, and motions for me to sit.

Kwadwo halts his iron. "Akua, ɛte sɛn?"

"Ɛyɛ, Kwadwo, ɛte sɛn?" I reply.

"Ɛyɛ." He smiles and presses on. A large bolt of dark fabric covers the table beside Idrissu's door. It seems an endless job to which Kwadwo attends.

Another man sits on the bench beside me. Idrissu squeezes his bulk behind the sewing machine. "Akua, what did you do today?" Idrissu asks.

Owing to fatigue, I'd like to keep it brief. "We visited villages around Obuasi to check their sanitation practices and encourage the formation of health committees. Kokoteasua, Bogobiri, Nkamprom—they are too busy for us. Only a few people gathered. Then we had a long durbar at Mamiriwa to discuss their water project."

"Mhm." Idrissu scratches his beard. "That is good, Akua. You will help Mamiriwa get good water." He nods to the man on the bench.

The man unfolds the *Daily Graphic* from his lap and reads:

Another good man lost at mysterious well in Mpraeso District. Powerful spirits live in the well and draw men to their death. Dear Reader, you will recall that at last accounting two men had already lost their lives, the second in the valiant attempt to rescue his brother.

"You remember, Akua?" Idrissu interjects.
"Oh, yes."
The reader continues.

The fire department did not arrive on the scene until four days after....

The article disintegrates into a rant about the fire department's slow response and revisits last year's salary increase to firemen, as well as the diversion of general funds to the coffers of the fire department. Vehicles fly past, a couple of feet from our bench. I avoid local papers due to the rampant hyperbole. I'd like to eat a good meal.

Idrissu says something and the man skips down in the article.

The people appealed to the local fetish priest who poured all around the well the blood of two sheep. The people held an all-night vigil. The church of St. Matthew Our Brother in Christ has posted members at the mouth of the well reading scripture to the demon or demons therein.

Despite these proper actions taken by the good people of Mpraeso District, more harm befell this devout populace. The

153

fire department's highly trained, brave men using the best quality ropes and sophisticated lifting devices proved no match for the evil within. The first man lowered in let out a cry and was never heard from again. The powerful drum on the fire truck jammed and could not retrieve the fireman. The fire department had to enlist the aid of the villagers to pull on the rope.

As before, a mighty force responded from the well, pulling from below. In fear, the villagers let go of the rope. The FD's Captain Tijani has ordered that no one else shall enter the well while the FD contemplates its next move. If he can pull off a rescue of the bodies — tragically too late to save lives — he may restore the reputation of the FD and help us feel less cheated by the padding of FD coffers. To be continued.

The man closes the paper and looks at Idrissu.

Idrissu cannot contain himself. He stands up. "Akua, do you get it?"

I nod, thinking he refers to juju.

He steps in front of the sewing machine and searches my eyes. "Do you see how we cannot rescue dese peoples? Do you see? Would dis happen in America? Even de FD is helpless. I feel sorry for Africa if de white man never come." Idrissu shakes his head. "Akua, you come to help de African. You leave your family to come here and help de African. Nkamprom, Bogobiri, dey no have time for you! I feel sorry for Africa if de white man never come."

Yes, yes, I feel sorry too. Now may I go? I let my gaze hang low. When I raise my eyes to his, Idrissu waves me to the curb.

"Akyire yi." I take leave of Kwadwo and the reader.

When Idrissu finds a safe traffic break, he steps aside and extends a protective hand toward the road. "Nante yie."

"Yoo."

In the time it takes to cross the road, hunger displaces Idrissu's agenda. Clothes and shoes drop on the concrete floor. A cold bucket bath gets my blood flowing. After a feast of tea bread topped with groundnut paste and banana, and washed down with a cup of hot, sweet tea, I find myself more alert than I'd like to be. I cannot write another letter. I cannot bear the thought of reading.

The very black glasses, the pendular nose, the cropped, dark moustache I can see. I press my hands to the paper, smoothing it against the fiber of the wood. A discipline of arcs, triangles, and rectangles announces a readiness to receive. Holding the fat art pencil between thumb and middle finger breaks my rigid control. Letting it float under my palm allows something else.

The tip of the pencil looks shiny and rounded. I think if I just draw, I can find an edge. I prefer this to the facility of the knife. The lead drags against the heavy paper until it catches the coarseness. A nose establishes a faint presence in the narrow rectangle.

The nose cannot take its form before the glasses. The heavy line of the glasses benchmarks the rest of the Muslim. The triangular notch lets the nose pass beneath the frame. The man's eyes are alive, penetrating, staring at me. I hesitate to darken the body of the frames. I am afraid it will obscure the detail of the eyes. It seems a betrayal, though, to not remain true to the blackness of the glasses. Imagine how the eyes and face will be altered by the heavy line of the frames. There will be no undoing it. I roll the paper and place it back in the cupboard.

My eyes wander the ceiling where they discover two thick fingers of plaster crossing in an "X." My mind conjures the missing cross of the Union Jack. Why the Union Jack? Why would the revered, the sacred, the holy Amadu al-Attar raise this symbol of the colonial master? Why would no one obliterate this travesty? Is he Ashanti? Muslim? Ashanti Muslim? Who the hell is Union Jack Kofi?

"Who the hell is she?" WAG's challenge mocked by Ankrah rings in my memory. I feel the Rifleman stir within. He rapid fires five shots, each bullet trimming a tail feather of the tin rooster at seventy yards atop the poultry barn, swing cocks the Winchester, hangs it across his hips in both hands, and turns a wary eye to his opponents.

Who am I? Really? Is one young woman enough to turn WAG on its ear? Finn imagines I will fret over his scrutinizing of my pay vouchers. The Rifleman won't back down.

I stretch out on the couch and tug at my hair. My fingers slide through the cropped tufts behind my ear, above the soft spot at the base of my skull, pulling my scalp taut then releasing in a slow traverse.

In that moment when my fingers clench and skin sucks off bone, Ankrah's taunt hits home. "Who the hell is she?" Who am I? Ɔbaa. Ɔbarima. Oburoni. What am I doing tangling with this corporation? My fingers release and that sensation of the separateness of skin and bone is lost.

I am a civil engineer. Structural, geotechnical, environmental, sanitation, water, transportation, construction, surveying. At root, it was a simple distinction; civil engineers were not military engineers. We were everything else. Non-military. Why do I feel I'm always at war?

A horn booms above the din of the road, answered by the screech of brakes.

This isn't what I came for. I came to be that typical volunteer. I came to slow down, to have time for myself. If I could choose, would I not be here? Would I leave the Advocacy defenseless in the face of WAG? My eyes rest on the simple black frames and the two formidable women they hold on my wall. One look at Obuasi and I knew this place was mine. There is no escaping one's self.

Bessie could not escape her skin. Mixed race. Forever conscious of South Africa's caste system. To the Masarwa, she gave the last word.

Barbara does not escape gender. Despite masking her body, her professional opportunities have been determined by her sex. If she allows herself a morphological expression of her femininity, could the cost be any greater? Would the moments of gender "falling away" be compromised? Or would they rise in stature by virtue of carrying their full depth?

I stare into the tiny travel mirror. Ɔbaa. Ɔbarima. I would never have risked such confusion on a construction site, but as an expatriate I have license. I am a country of one. Who in Ghana is to say how an American woman, civil engineer, manager of a watsan organization should wear her hair? By virtue of my skin color I am granted wide latitude. Oburoni. No matter how artificial or temporary, I cherish the circumstance that places me beyond the construct of woman/man.

My gaze returns to the mason's "X." Is that the secret of Union Jack Kofi? Indigene/Colonizer. Loyalist/Rebel. Muslim/Ashanti. Does he step beyond categories? Is the appearance of these contradictory constructs Amadu's assertion that he is none of them? Kofi cannot be seen through the lens of the temporal.

Union Jack Amadu would never survive in Bediem. I peel a fresh blueline sheet from the roll of construction drawings, a luxury well worth the sacrifice of limited luggage space. With the unprinted side up, I smooth the sheet against the grain of the wood and summon the image of Water Tank Amadu. The pencil yields form. A cutlass fills six square feet. The blade reminiscent of scimitars wielded by Arabs. A blade in the hands of a master can cleave the cosmos. Lay everything bare.

I brush graphite inside the edge of the handle and smudge it with my thumb. Who painted Water Tank Amadu? I love the way

the blue lines of a forgotten project ghost through the paper con-
founding free form and structure. Does the cutlass hack the jungle
to clear a path to healing herbs? Does it challenge the audacity of
West Africa Gold? Does it rise to heaven serving divine intention?

CHAPTER SEVENTEEN

I s West Africa Gold improving the road?" I ask, thinking that
the bulldozers on either side may be improving access for
exploration in the vicinity of Gyimiso Kakraba.

"No," says Thomas, "they are raising the road. It has flooded."

He's right. Our wheels crunch on freshly compacted gravel.
The trees to either side stand in water, while dozers work to
regrade. The village rests on higher ground. We park on a bare
mound where the road dies into the durbar area.

Thomas locates the Chairman of the Committee for the
Defense of the Revolution and enquires as to a treatment for
the skin rash.

Feathering his lapel, the CDR Chairman reports, "The District
health team came yesterday. They offered a cream to cure the rash.
The people refused to pay and were given nothing."

Thomas and I exchange a glance. We had hoped the ointment
would bring some relief.

"What is happening at the road?" I ask. The Chairman looks
at me without speaking. With my eyes, I appeal to Thomas, who
conveys my question in Twi.

Inhaling, the Chairman elongates his stature. He stares at
me. "It is WAG's dam." He flutters his hand in the air, dismissing the mine's arrogance. He then speaks to Thomas in
restrained Twi. He turns to point beyond the vibrant growth
of the tropical forest.

159

"Akua, apparently the mine engineers are not good at predicting the effect of the dam," Thomas explains, falling silent when the Chairman places a wrinkled hand on his shoulder.

The Chairman turns away. Thomas nods that we should follow. We measure our steps behind and to either side of the old man. The Chairman leads us across the expanse of the durbar ground, then along a well-worn path through dense forest. We emerge into a great opening, the village proper. Osei and Takyi wander off to inspect sanitation practices while we take what must be the main street down to a broad stretch of the Gyimi's bank.

The Chairman brushes a fleck from the pocket flap of his suit coat and begins his address. "For as long as anyone can remember, women's feet have pounded this earth, passing into the shallows to launder and fetch water. For as long as anyone can remember, children have raced this bank, clambering into the depths to swim and bathe.

"We brought the engineers to this place." He presses his feet into the earth to emphasize the impossibility of a person standing here without comprehending. "We showed them, 'This is the height of the big water.'" He looks at the flooded basin, which has swallowed that old reference. "We told the engineers, 'The dam will raise the water above our bridge. That is our only way to our farms.'

"'No,' they said. 'The water will not rise so high.'" The Chairman stands with his arms folded. He says something to Thomas and shakes his head.

I feel my face flush for my profession. It's a simple thing to project a hydraulic grade line. It could have been a survey bust.

"The Chairman says now there are four dozers spreading earth and rock on either side of the road." Thomas translates. "Although they must use this basin, they do not trust the stagnant water. They want their old river back, the flowing water."

I look from the Chairman's thick coat to the reddish-brown water.

"Akua," Thomas interjects, "we have seen enough. We must proceed to the scheduled villages."

"When did they last see a tanker?"

"It has been thirty days," Thomas translates.

How long would Kwasi let his family go without water? "Thank you." I bow to the CDR Chairman, while extending a hand. "We will inform WAG of your plight."

As Thomas and I head back to the truck, a small races toward us, arms pumping over his head, a great smile on his face. He clasps his thin arms around me and buries his face in my hip. I place a hand on the head of my small and he peers up, smiling, his chin pressing into my bone.

Osei appears and sees the sores still covering the boy. He interrogates the child in Twi about whether he received medical treatment.

Fear clouds the boy's face. "No, we are strangers here and have no money."

"Because you are strangers did you not have money to chop today?" Osei's booming voice a military onslaught. Osei is also a preacher. It is not difficult to imagine him hurling fire and brimstone.

The boy stands apart from me. As if receiving punishment from a schoolteacher, the boy holds his head up and chest out, arms at his sides, while casting his eyes down.

Osei repeats his condemning query.

The child does not respond. I place my hand on his head as we depart, and receive his bright smile.

In the truck, Osei shares what he learned. "The medicine is an ointment that cost three hundred cedis."

"The people say WAG should pay," adds Takyi. "WAG has

spoiled the water which is causing the skin disease. WAG should provide the medicine free. That is what the people are saying."

Osei, Thomas, and Takyi continue to discuss the matter amongst themselves. I hear their anger and impatience with the villagers for refusing to purchase the medicine. Three hundred cedis is forty cents. Are the people so ignorant? The team seems to think so.

I see my small exposing himself. More devastating than the marring of his masculinity is the absolute trust with which he offers himself. He can know nothing of multinational gold mines. Dr. Kwarteng-Badu, Jim Hansen, Finn Harrigan, Madam Tettey—it is up to them to redress Gyimiso Kakraba's water problem. How long would they fumble around with water tankers if their families did not have water? How many times would the calculations have been reviewed if an error would flood their homes? Did Dr. Kwarteng-Badu think to offer to have WAG pay for the medicine?

Turning onto the main road at Tutuka, I see the bicycle of the Fanyogo boy and recall my attempt to cheer the smalls. Useless. Medicine exists and my small does not have it.

My small can know nothing of district government. Ankrah, Illiasu, Abubakar, and Osabutey—how high does Gyimiso Kakraba rank on their list of crises? Does stagnant, muddy water and a skin rash rank above Bediem's silted homes and daily blasting? Did they bother to ask WAG to pay for the medicine? Never mind the gross imbalance of power that requires the government to ask for rather than demand the protection of its people.

In whom does this boy place his trust? In a powerless Peace Corpse? In his mother? Is there a mother who does not know the value of a cedi . . . or the value of her child?

Forty cents. Absurd. It is not about money.

I round the Miner's Circle and pull in behind the Old Council. Forty cents. A mother will let her child suffer before she will pay one cent to remedy the damage caused by a multinational gold mine. This whole village of subsistence farmers knows what Larry Wittle and Finn Harrigan and Madam Tettey know. It is not about money.

How does a human being treat another human being?

What does it take to move the human heart?

What is broken?

CHAPTER EIGHTEEN

Agyeman awaits our return. Gathering that he wishes to speak to me, while the others finish for the evening, I occupy myself organizing stacks of village files. A file cabinet would go a long way to improve the orderliness of our office.

When we are alone, Agyeman stands in front of my desk. "Akua, there is something I wish to discuss with you."

A vague thought of money flutters, but I don't feel cynical.

"Akua." Agyeman lets his voice ramp up from a gravelly breath to his smooth speaking voice. "As the out-of-station allowance was not increased, I am forced to ask whether it may be possible for you to grant me a loan. Only for some weeks. I will repay you."

"Of course," I reply without hesitation, refusing to entertain cliché. I've never found myself in a position to need to make such a request and don't want to prolong his discomfort.

Agyeman accompanies me to Standard Chartered Bank. As we head down the stairs of the Old Council, he offers the scuttlebutt he learned today. "There is trouble in Sansu. The chief's new trucks were vandalized. The damage will be expensive to repair."

I catch his eye. Reading my mind, he says, "It will get worse."

Our conversation falls off as we enter the bank on the adjacent lot. I always appreciate Agyeman's insights. I can't help feeling this latest was offered in exchange for the loan. Something has changed between us. I do not wish to buy now what was once given.

Agyeman waits near the entrance as I approach a teller. The suited gentleman eyes me after reading the amount. It is half my monthly salary. Washington pays ample to support the beer and cigarette habits of most volunteers. Few make it through their two years without cultivating dependence.

I've never found solace in such indulgence. My addiction was always Libya. No matter the odds, like the Rifleman, I will not hesitate to aid my friend.

It is never wise to flash large amounts of money. Agyeman and I return to the office to make the exchange. I'm willing to be a fool once.

"Thank you, Akua." Agyeman bows his head and offers his hand.

"You are most welcome, Agyeman." I give his hand a good squeeze. "Nante yie."

He laughs. "Nante yie, Akua."

"Agoo," Idrissu calls.

"Amee," I reply, coming to the window.

"Akua, ɛte sɛn?" Idrissu asks through the screen.

"Ɛyɛ. Idrissu, ɛte sɛn?" It is hard to see him through the tight mesh at dusk.

"Ɛyɛ. Akua, the tap is open. Are you needing water?"

"No, medaase."

"The tap is open. My girls can take water for you."

"Medaase, Idrissu. My barrels are full."

"Akua, you are writing?" Idrissu sounds pleased.

"Aane."

"Dat's right." Passion bursts through the screen. "You write everything. You write. When you go back to America, you tell dem everything, Akua. Tell dem everything you see here."

"Aane. Medaase."

"Dat's right."

165

What does Idrissu know? I scan the ceiling for clues. He seems certain I will take a message to the world. He doesn't even know if he would like my writing. He has no idea whether he'd agree with my point of view. Worst of all, Idrissu cannot know the prejudiced ear the world turns away from an engineer's tale.

"You write." His words constitute a contract. His inability to reach beyond his porch compels his trust in my capacity to hold a pen. All else is moot. There is no choice but to strive for the highest integrity.

From the base of my spine comes the knowledge that Idrissu is working his Ghanaian mojo of obligation. Why don't I resent that? He has tapped my cowboy construction sense of honor. I will not fail him.

I send a prayer to Bessie to guide my pen.

III

ACCRA

The built environment of roads, railways, and buildings as well as the bureaucratic apparatus that brings all these elements together instigates social relationships that are in turn progressively redefined as people interact with their built environment.

—ATO QUAYSON, *Oxford Street Accra—City Life and the Itineraries of Transnationalism*

CHAPTER NINETEEN

I used to work for Mr. Richard Edmonton," says Kwabena. "The engineer."

I remain ignorant.

"Mr. Richard Edmonton is an engineer. He is the engineer who built this road." Kwabena points down the hill to Ring Road, the six-lane thoroughfare encircling Accra. "Mr. Richard Edmonton is the engineer who built this road. There was nothing before he came and I was his cook."

Kwabena might be in his sixties. He is short and wiry with a sparse covering of grey on his scalp. He squirts a puddle of oil into the center of a frying pan. My egg sandwich must wait for the water to boil on Kwabena's single-burner charcoal stove.

Kwabena continues in his perfect British English. "I know how to cook for white people. I know the spices and the foods that taste good to white people. Mr. Richard Edmonton built the road and then independence came and all the British left. Now it is very difficult to find work."

Kwabena speaks with that certainty and directness that is the birthright of Ghanaians. What holds my attention is the lack of bombast, the nakedness of his eyes conveying without apology that he is a man who found his place in this world, and when the world changed, Kwabena did not. He knows his place and he watched it evaporate in the sun of Nkrumah's independence.

Kwabena's table displays the tools of his trade: tins of Milo, tea bread loaves in a basket, tomatoes, onions, lettuce, sugar, a large slicing knife, and a crate of eggs. The table sits in the dust below the low wall bordering a petrol station. Kwabena occupies a prime location on this residential street leading from Ring Road into the neighborhood of Kokomlemle. At the road's edge, a placard proclaims, *Kwabena's Tea Bar The Original and The Best.* The hand-painted sign leans against an abandoned stub of pipe poking out of the ground.

Kwabena removes the pot of boiling water from the stove and replaces it with the frying pan. He fans the coals to put sizzle into the pool of yellow. His motions are adroit from years of repetition. Kwabena uses a long knife with a broad curve reminiscent of Amadu's blade. Unlike any egg lady—or man—I have ever seen, Kwabena adds chopped lettuce and green onion to the tomatoes already in the cup of beaten eggs. Thank you, Mr. Richard Edmonton.

Commuters motor past, lacing the morning with the sour scent of petrol. Well-dressed pedestrians step down to Ring Road, the best place to hail a taxi. An ample woman dressed for work takes a seat beside me. Kwabena dips a mug into the boiled water. A cup of instant coffee and a large slice of sweet bread smeared with margarine seem too meager to carry this large woman through the morning.

Kwabena serves my egg sandwich on a plastic plate. He has toasted the tea bread, another rare touch. I want to move the bench closer to the table, but notice it's balanced on tiny remnants of concrete, mesas eroding in the dust.

"I have tried to get hired at the Bus Stop," Kwabena continues.

The Bus Stop café serves fried chicken and ice cream on the opposite side of Ring Road. I've eaten there and know it's owned by Lebanese.

"They will not hire me. I have worked for them, already. They call me when their cook is sick. I can operate those gas stoves. I know how to operate the gas stove. It is so much better than charcoal." Kwabena clicks his tongue at the charcoal stove, a reminder of the low station to which life has reduced him. "I worked for Mr. Richard Edmonton. Mr. Richard Edmonton is the engineer who built this road and I was his cook."

As if its existence proves his story, Kwabena points to Ring Road, where taxis and lorries blare their horns and hustle people to work. Decades after Independence, it remains a fine road, incomparable to the misery Obuasi calls a road.

It is hard to imagine a scarcity of white households in Accra in need of a cook. Accra is loaded with expatriates, a large portion of them white. Perhaps the modern breed is not as reliable as its colonial forebears. The expatriates of the 1990s have made development a family affair. No more lone men in the bush. The spouse is on hand to shop and cook. If the spouse cannot brave the stench of the abattoir, familiar foods can be purchased at the commissary. Or perhaps the jobs are there. Perhaps Kwabena is outmarketed by younger, smoother cooks who have grown up catering to Accra's international clientele and have adapted a new script.

The 1990s breed finds no appeal in a cook who knows his place. But a cook who can manifest energy, who projects the sense of preparing for bigger things, for whom being a cook is one step in a chain of progress, this cook is to be nurtured. This cook epitomizes the ostensible mission of the expatriate. Just as the expat has come to develop Ghana—and each extols the merits of their own peculiar brand of aid—the expat will develop the cook, a personal mini-project to serve as metaphor for the greater works pursued by their agency.

One day, when the 1990s breed finds itself in the 2010s on a veranda in the tropical heat of some other country, the expat will recount in detail the fate of the cook. Despite all the expat's efforts and unwavering loyalty, the cook lapsed into old habits and self-defeating beliefs. "This," the expatriate will confide to veranda companions, "this is the real proof that you cannot change people, that some people are trapped by history or culture or race and you can give and give and give, nothing will come of it." Veranda companions will rattle their glasses and murmur their accord.

Or perhaps the expat's recollection is of the cook who made it, not to extravagant success, but to a better life. The expat lets on that the cook still sends a card every year and the expat still tries to help when the occasion arises. Despite the arguable contribution of the expat's agency, this personal success remains proof that the expat's career is not in vain. Veranda companions tip their glasses and swallow.

Or the expat may ponder the cook in silence. The expat still has not unraveled her personal relationship with the cook, a man who came daily into her home, who learned the right quantities of the right spices to please her, who shared stories of relatives in villages making demands upon the cook, stories of obligations plunging the cook's life into chaos. The expat recalls a part of herself that surfaced in relation to the cook, an inexplicable part, an ugly part, a painful part, and the expat's hand tightens around the glass until with resolve she addresses veranda companions, "Another drink?"

CHAPTER TWENTY

Accra is not an accessible place on a Peace Corps volunteer's budget. I know this because I tried all of yesterday to find a place where I could just be. I had in mind a quiet spot, clean, not extravagant, where I could read and write, or just sit. I started out at the American House. This club with a swimming pool a few blocks from the Peace Corps office offers American expatriates an island America. Ghanaian waiters decked in stiff white coats with gold buttons proffer menus that tantalize the home-starved imagination with entrees like "avocado burger," "pizza," "club sandwich," and "milk shake."

I sat with a few other volunteers on the thick cushions of a deep bench seat below wood paneling. My toes brushed polished parquet flooring. I watched the *Voice of America* broadcast on satellite TV while waiting for my dollar pancakes with syrup, bacon, toast, jam, and orange juice.

At the American House, an irresolvable tension plagues interactions between waiters and Peace Corps volunteers. Volunteers are riff raff. We study the menu for the cheapest, most filling entree, glad when a fellow volunteer appears to split the bill. We aren't dressed in business suits, are given to taking off our shoes, and tend to lounge around as long as possible in this air-conditioned haven. Yesterday, our waiter stiffened when collecting his tip. He refused to refresh our drinks, leaving no doubt that we five volunteers were a far less lucrative proposition than the lone embassy employee upon whom he doted.

Our grumblings at this hostile treatment fell silent when the bartender interrupted the *Voice of America* to play the video, *Little Lord Fauntleroy*. We settled ourselves to drink in images of that home for which we longed. I was glad for a story that I didn't know, but soon felt otherwise. The little lord was walking his horse through town past roadside pits of green scum and asking his stately father, "Why don't you help the townspeople?" when I left in search of a different kind of place.

Inspired by beach tales circulating at the American House, I fashioned an image of myself seated on a sand dune, no people about, waves crashing into the surf. After a stifling trotro ride to the eastern end of Ring Road, and a gritty, sweaty hike in the full sun along Labadi Road, I discovered beach dunes serving as a public toilet.

Exhausted and hungry, I set my sights on Osu. From the reports of other volunteers, it stood in my mind as a purveyor of gastronomical extravagance. Osu, in particular, Cantonments Road, is the part of Accra where the Lebanese have established their shops. Incredible goods are to be had: yogurt, cheese, deli meats, green peppers, cauliflower. Ned Clyde once said to me, "The Lebanese are the world's merchants. Watch them. When they set up shop in a country, you know it's safe for business."

Ghana is safe for business. Since his second coup in 1981, Chairman Jerry John Rawlings has retained leadership of the country and toed the line on International Monetary Fund austerity measures, making Ghana a darling of the World Bank. World Bank and USAID money flow into Ghana. Last year, the Ghana Stock Exchange opened. This year, USAID allocated one hundred twenty million dollars for the diversification of Ghanaian exports. Next year, the government, which owns fifty-one percent of the stock of West Africa Gold, plans to float twenty percent of the mine's total shares on both the London and Ghanaian stock exchanges. This December, Ghana will conduct its first presidential election in over a decade.

In stores, shelves are well-stocked. Soap, tinned fish, toilet paper, and cheap Chinese goods ranging from batteries to paraffin lanterns to bicycles are there for the buying. In cities, every type of appliance can be found. Calculators, microwaves, stereos, and computers are priced to match the going rate in the U.S. What is unclear is how people, other than Ghana's elite and the expatriates "developing" Ghana, are able to purchase these goods. The average annual income in this country, seventy percent of whose population is rural, is three hundred dollars. Inflation has averaged thirty percent per year for the last five years.

A large *KFC* sign offered the first indication that I had hit the southern end of the fabled realm. Grateful for this enterprising Ghanaian, I seized the opportunity to rest, and fortified myself with mouth-watering fried chicken, mashed potatoes, and rolls. Heartened by the tasty repast, I sought Cantonments Road full of optimism. The further north I pushed my weary feet, the more spectacular were the restaurants defying my parochial experience of Ghana. Dee's Spot features spring rolls, samosas, and hamburgers. Opposite Dee's is Chez Suzie, a French restaurant said to be delicious and beyond my means. Past Chez Suzie is the Regal Chinese. I had studied their menu and decided that if the reimbursement money came through at Peace Corps, I'd have dinner there tonight.

I've come to Accra to get a gamma globulin shot, which must be done every three months to boost the immune system. Also, in the past few days, a burning itching in my vulva has grown more frequent and more pronounced. I'm grateful for the timing—coinciding with my routine visit saves me a trip. Another bonus, the medical necessity of the gamma globulin shot entitles me to per diem pay.

However, there's trouble in the accounting department. For the past ten years, Donald has been in charge of disbursing cash to volunteers. It seems that, while carrying out his duties, Donald has also been disbursing funds to Donald. He no longer works for Peace Corps and the inflow of cash from Washington has been delayed. This leaves a lot of volunteers stranded in the capital weighing the merit of staying another day in hopes of recouping all of their out-of-pocket expenses, against the possibility of funds not arriving before they exhaust their cash reserves.

My pilgrimage ended at the doors of Afridom, one of the popular Lebanese establishments. I had bought a bottle of water and spent over an hour wandering the aisles. Every shelf held an orgy of flavors. Barbecue sauce, spicy mango chutney, lima beans, tinned peas, pickled beets. I tried hard to find a single item that I needed enough to justify the price of thousands of cedis. The things I would've been willing to buy, cheese and yogurt, could not be kept cold on the journey home.

I clasped a bottle of Worcestershire sauce and read the ingredients—white vinegar, molasses, garlic, tamarind extract—rolling my tongue around the texture of the blend which, unlike ever before, epitomized home. Steak fresh off the grill dashed with the spicy sauce, exuding a succulent aroma. I tried to imagine this bottle was what I needed, what I could not deny myself. I never buy raw meat in Obuasi. I stared at the price: nine thousand cedis. Ten percent of my monthly income. Most of the meat I consume comes in the form of tinned fish. Worcestershire sauce would not improve the taste of fried yam. I had placed the bottle back upon the shelf and stepped outside laden with the disappointment that none of this was mine.

CHAPTER TWENTY-ONE

This morning, Kwabena's egg sandwich tastes like a gift from the gods. If nothing else, at least I'm starting today on a strong note. In addition to the medical visit, I'm hoping to turn up a few leads for the Advocacy. My biggest concern is finding funding for village water projects. We've promised the villagers that if they raise their part, we'll find the balance of the money.

My first stop is Tao Bronson of the World Bank. Lynn, my predecessor in Obuasi, met Tao when searching for donors to support the Advocacy. Although direct funding of a small organization was not an option for the World Bank, Tao did endorse Lynn's proposal. From the day Lynn introduced us, I remember Tao's generous smile, his direct speech and quick wit, and his enthusiasm for the Advocacy.

Lynn, a health education volunteer, had pointed out that Tao and I are both engineers. Tao had responded, "Then you may rest easy. While you pursue your graduate degree in international health, you may trust that Louisa has the problem-solving skills necessary to get the job done." I admire Tao's charisma. He's one engineer in whose story the world might delight. I'm hoping that he'll provide a letter of recommendation that I can show to prospective donors for village projects.

The World Bank office is located in a converted home in North Ridge, a nice residential area south of Ring Road, between

Circle—the vernacular reference to Kwame Nkrumah Circle, and Sankara Circle.

When I arrive, Tao steps back. "Why, Louisa, we'd given up on you! You made it after all." He squeezes my hand and pumps my arm, while walking me down the hall. "Wonderful, Louisa." He opens a door and waves across a large room to a man presenting to a small audience. "Don, Louisa made it after all."

I recognize the gnattish form of Don Welsch. He heads WaterCore, a British charitable organization that supports several local organizations working in the water sector. Don returns a sardonic smile.

"Please, Louisa, find a seat," Tao says. "We're glad you could make it." He exits the room.

I take the nearest empty seat at a gleaming table that could serve as a negotiating forum for decisions with global ramifications. The massive table has ample space on all sides. The vaulted ceiling and walls are crisp white. Our small group is dwarfed by the space.

"Well, well, Ms. Lehmann," Don whines in his nasal voice. "How nice of you to join us all the way from . . . Obuasi. Shall we reintroduce ourselves for Ms. Lehmann's benefit?" Don looks to the others, five men and two women, all Ghanaian.

Ignoring Don's amused arrogance, one of the men says, "Yes, let us introduce ourselves." He looks about to do just that, when Don cuts him off.

"I am Don Welsch. As you all know, I am not Welsh. I am English. I am the Country Director for WaterCore. World Bank has hired WaterCore to conduct this introductory workshop for potential Watsan Collaborators in the pilot implementation programme of the Capital Investment Programme or 'C-I-P.'" Don projects from the far side of the room, his attempt to compensate for his stature frustrated by his election to stand distant from his audience.

"Potential Collaborators, introduce yourselves, please." Don nods at the gentleman who had volunteered.

The man looks to be in his fifties. He wears a long, woven shirt. Brown with white thread. "I am Wilberforce Wiafe. I am the coordinator of Water Vision, a charitable organization in Dromakese. Formerly, I worked for Catholic Relief Services building homes and watsan facilities. I am happy to be here." Wilberforce nods and smiles to each of us.

"Water Vision of Dromakese, that would be in Brong-Ahafo Region," Don interjects. "Though north of the Ashanti Region, somehow, Mr. Wiafe was able to arrive on time."

I'm familiar with Don's stinging remarks. WaterCore conducted a handpump maintenance training for our team some months ago. We had the pleasure of a solid week of his acerbic wit. Despite his lack of charm, he's knowledgeable and well-connected in the water sector. WaterCore seems to be everyone's go-to resource for training.

As the introductions round the table, it becomes clear that there are three charitable organizations represented by two to three people each. There's Water Vision of Brong-Ahafo, WomenCare of Ashanti, and Hope Together In Love of Western Region. The Advocacy makes a fourth. Don injects his rudeness in equal parts to all.

"Now, let's carry on. Shall we?" Don enjoys a rhetorical style. "Miz Lehmann," Don drawls my name in annoyance.

I lower my hand. "Excuse me. 'CIP,' could you explain what that is?"

"As already stated, CIP: Capital Investment Programme. The new policy for rural water in Ghana. Surely, Louisa, you couldn't have found your way here without knowing that."

That's exactly what I've done. Insults always seem more pejorative when delivered in a British accent.

"If you'll hold your questions, I believe all will be made clear."

"Thank you."

"Very well. Now, where were we before Louisa made her grand entrance?"

"The C-O-M," ventures Mr. Wiafe.

"Community ownership and management. Who can tell Miz Lehmann what that means?" Don raises his brows at one of the women.

"Please," Elizabeth says with folded hands. "The C-O-M philosophy is the belief fundamental that development will fail if not carried out by fostering ownership of the beneficiary community. Without a sense of ownership, the community will not feel responsibility for operation and maintenance. Although a community may be willing to be responsible for its development, the people may be lacking skills. It is vital that technical, administrative, and managerial capacities required to operate and maintain the proposed facility are developed within the beneficiary community." Elizabeth's impeccable costume of vivid orange sets off the rich tone of her skin. Her hair is groomed in a short afro. Her politeness belies the eternal patience that most Ghanaians seem to possess.

"Very good, Elizabeth." The intended compliment suffers from the condescension that laces all of Don's utterances. Elizabeth, however, accepts his patronizing acknowledgement. Vivid orange.

Community ownership and management is not a new concept. It's consistent with the philosophy espoused by the Peace Corps and central to the operating strategy conceived by Lynn. "Give a man a fish and he will eat for a day. Teach a man to fish and he will eat for a lifetime." Uncle Ryan, one of our Ghanaian instructors, must have repeated this adage ten times daily during our pre-service training.

Part of our training consisted of visiting villages that had been the prior recipients of development aid. A clinic less than a year old stood unused. There was no money to pay for a qualified health attendant. The clinic had been constructed over a huge cistern so that it would be self-sufficient in water. The cistern was almost dry. The elaborate water collection system was separated at the roof-line where it joined the downspout. No one had tried to repair it.

"Can we think of examples of development projects that did not adhere to the principle of community ownership and management?" Don peruses his prey and settles on the gentleman to my left. "Fortunato."

The gentleman raises his head. He wears a Western suit, tight about his girth and appropriate for this chilly room. Sleek grey. "Yes." He nods his head repeatedly, but does not elaborate.

Don clears his throat. The rest of us wince in sympathy for Fortunato.

"Yes . . . ?" Don unfurls a hand as if to lead to something.

Fortunato sits a little more erect and with a wide smile, restates, "Yes."

Don advances to the edge of the world table and leans in the direction of Fortunato. "Yes . . . what?"

Fortunato glances down. He does not appear perturbed. He raises his eyes with confidence. "Yes, I can think of an example of a project that does not adhere to the principle of C-O-M."

We squirm in our seats on Fortunato's behalf. I'm also trying to ease the burning discomfort in my delicate region. Brown with white thread-vivid orange-sleek grey. Don pulls himself as vertical as possible. From the grandest height of which he is capable, Don hurls his contempt. "What . . . Fortunato . . . pray tell . . . what is your example?"

"My example is a water project for the school children in Adwumadiem. Gutters were installed on the roofs of the class-rooms to bring rainwater to a storage tank. It is very nice that the children should have good water to drink. But the system has broken only six months after it was constructed. There is no water in the tank."

"The system has broken," Don replies.

"Yes."

"And why hasn't the system been fixed?" Don's tone softens in anticipation of receiving the desired explication.

"There is no one to repair it."

"There is no one to repair the water collection system? What if the roof is damaged? Who repairs that?"

"Well, I cannot say who repairs the roof. I can say the agency that constructed the rainwater system did not educate the people on the operation and maintenance of it."

"No education on operation and maintenance?" Don asks.

"That is correct."

"How is it possible that this unnamed agency gained access to the school to construct this system, but did not educate the beneficiaries as to its operation and maintenance?"

"I was not present at that time." Fortunato delivers a solemn tone through his joyful smile. "I have been given the understanding this agency had funding to provide water for schools. They undertook at the highest levels to obtain authorization to install the system in one hundred schools in the Western Region. The Regional Administration granted each district permission to select a number of schools."

"If I am hearing you correctly," Don resumes his tedious tone. "The project chose the school. The school did not choose the project."

"Ah?" Fortunato furrows his brow, still smiling.

"The school did not determine its primary need to be a water collection system, then seek a solution. The solution to a problem identified by a third party was given to the school."

"Aha, I see. Yes, of course. That is it."

"What has Hope Together In Love done to correct the situation?"

"We are a new organization and are just formulating our programme. We are learning from the past."

"Good. Another example?" For a moment, I think Don has chosen me as his next victim. I find him a bore, though a powerful one. I shift my gaze to Candace Issahaku's green headcloth. It doesn't serve the Advocacy to alienate WaterCore, but I make no secret that Don's game doesn't interest me.

"Candace?" Don inquires. She looks at Don. In contrast with Fortunato's perpetual smile, her calm seems impertinent. Green twist. "Candace can you give us another example?"

"Yes. I have an example of a Kumasi ventilated improved pit latrine, built at Afromso School in Ashanti Region that the children will not use."

"If the children do not use the new latrine, where do they go to toilet?"

"The problem of the children relieving themselves on the school grounds has not been eliminated by construction of the latrine."

"Why don't the children use it? Can they not see it is preferable to the practice to which they are accustomed?"

"In fact, they cannot see it is preferable. The facility is more elaborate than that to which the children are accustomed, the bush or a bucket. No one educated them or their families about the benefits of using a Kumasi ventilated pit latrine. Also, the smalls are afraid of falling into the drop hole."

"No education," Don bellows. "No education of the people intended to benefit from the project. How was the project built, if no one values it? The people contributed their labor?"

"Yes, the people value the latrine. They were willing to build it. The village is very happy to have completed the project for their school."

"The people are happy, but the children don't use it. Candace, can you explain?"

"As a sign of development, the people see that the Kumasi ventilated pit latrine enhances the status of their village. For this, they are proud."

"Did the people request the latrine?"

"No. An organization that was building sanitation facilities approached the school to enquire of their desire to have the Kumasi ventilated improved pit latrine. The people accepted the offer."

"Another case in which the beneficiaries did not identify what they felt to be their primary need. Another case in which the donor has not taken the time to know the beneficiaries. The beneficiaries don't maintain the project because they don't own it. Here we see the waste of development resources when projects are undertaken without adhering to the principle of community ownership and management."

At our training, Uncle Ryan had told us, "Take your time in the village. Get to know the people. Eat with them. Drink with them. Learn about the different groups within the community. Don't assume that one person speaks for all. You must learn the felt needs of the people and then you must build the capacity of the people to address their own felt needs. You cannot impose your good will upon the people. If you try to do this, you have seen the sad result."

"For the past four years," Don pontificates, "a major effort has been underway to reevaluate Ghana's strategy for providing water and sanitation to rural communities. The World Bank/ United Nations Water and Sanitation Programme in Ghana has funded studies of the economic viability of changing from the centralized management of rural water systems to C-O-M. World Bank hired WaterCore to host a series of conferences to promote a national discourse on this subject. On behalf of World Bank, WaterCore has brought together a diverse inter-section of entities—public, private, and voluntary; governmental and charitable; grass-roots educators, well-drilling companies, university professors, international development agencies . . ." Don drones on. Brown with white thread-vivid orange-sleek grey-green twist.

Community ownership and management. Echoes of Freire and Schumacher. I never imagined how radical such ideas still could be, thirty years into the development game. I never understood before that there is a distinction between organizations working at the grass roots level, and multilateral agencies charting plans on national, regional, and global scales. World Bank seems to be discovering what the small outfits have always known—people need to determine their own destiny.

". . . All of this has culminated in the Capital Investment Programme, for which some of you will have the privilege of participating in the pilot programme." Don plays on the perception that our fate lies in his hands. "We will now break for twenty minutes. When we return, we will discuss implementation, in particular, the pilot role of the Watsan Collaborator."

CHAPTER TWENTY-TWO

Don Welsch leaves the world room and I excuse myself. While it's auspicious for the Advocacy to be included in this gathering, I need to get to Peace Corps. As I head for the personnel offices, Tao rounds a corner. Although wearing a woven tunic that falls to his knees with trousers of matching fabric, his ease suggests an American casualness.

Seeing me, Tao gestures toward a door. "Come, have a seat."

It's a small, modern office, bright with the newness of its finishes and furnishings. Even sitting behind his desk, Tao looks energetic. His moustache is thick and trimmed, perhaps intended to dispel a hint of boyishness. "Louisa, I'm sorry I haven't been down to see you. I've been meaning to come see you. In fact, just last week I was at a meeting in Kumasi and I planned to stop by Obuasi and see you and your District Secretary, but I didn't. I'm sorry."

I can't imagine why Tao should be apologizing to me.

"We're focusing on finalizing the Capital Investment Programme. The new constitution will be taking effect with the Fourth Republic, and we're hoping that the Parliament will be able to turn the policy into law. You've read it?"

"No."

"It's our new approach to rural water in Ghana." Tao hands me a thick, bound report. "You can have this copy. I was going to give it to your District Secretary last week in Kumasi. I sent Ankrah an invitation, but he didn't come and he didn't reply."

"Hm, he didn't mention it to me."

"I'm still hoping to meet with him."

"I'll let him know."

"We're thinking the Advocacy might be an appropriate Watsan Collaborator. Under the new plan we have Watsan Collaborators that work with the villages. There are certain steps the villages have to be taken through: health education, the formation of a committee, identifying a problem, writing a proposal, making a commitment to the capital cost, opening a bank account and collecting tariffs."

I try to keep a straight face. That is exactly how our operation is set up. When he finishes I want to show him what we're doing. Another man walks in, whom Tao introduces as Jim Kelly from Washington, D.C. Jim's an inch or two taller than me and slim as a middle-aged man whose self-esteem rides on his body. His once-black hair has a sheen of premature grey.

"Jim, this is Louisa Lehmann of the Adansi West Rural Water, Sanitation, and Health Advocacy in Obuasi. She was able to make the introductory workshop after all."

Jim shakes my hand too loose and too fast. "The Advocacy . . . that's the nongovernmental organization you mentioned that has a programme in line with our strategy."

"Possibly," Tao clarifies. "I haven't had the opportunity to review their progress." Tao queues it up for me.

This moment screams for a map showing the villages in the Advocacy's programme. I wish it was finished. However, in Ghana there is no expectation that I would have access to such a resource. Instead, I produce a list of all the villages with health committees, show them a sample village map—hand drawn by a villager, a census taken by the village health committee, and a project proposal. I explain our health education program and our efforts to raise funds.

Jim says, "It looks like you're in good shape to work as a Watsan Collaborator."

Tao bursts with approbation. "Every time I see you, you're moving in leaps and bounds. Lynn had the vision, but it took a civil engineer to fulfill that vision."

I love Tao's pride in our profession. "It's a start." I admit. "But nothing's built yet."

"World Bank could help with that via the Capital Investment Programme," Tao responds, "if the Advocacy joins the pilot."

While flattered to have World Bank's attention, I cannot fathom why they should be courting me. Testing that impression, I enquire, "This pilot project, how soon will it start? If Parliament must act first . . . You know, we're looking for commitments now for our village projects."

"You'll learn all about the pilot programme in the workshop," Tao offers. "Don will go over everything."

"If you're ready for funding now, some allocation could be made." Jim adds. "We can talk further after the workshop."

"Thank you for your flexibility," I say to Jim. Turning to Tao, I take a deep breath. "I very much appreciate your consideration of the Advocacy. We're doing good work and it would really give us a boost to have your support. I . . . I'm sorry to admit I didn't come here today for the workshop. I knew nothing about it." I offer the confession in hopes of gaining leverage in dealing with Ankrah.

Tao looks at Jim. "We need to connect with her District Secretary." To me, Tao says, "All's well that ends well. Come back after the workshop and we'll go over things."

"I'm afraid I'm in Accra on Peace Corps business. I need to get to an appointment there."

"Could you come back this evening?" asks Jim.

"Absolutely."

"Four p.m.?"

"I'll be here."

Tao asks, "Louisa, what brought you here?"

"I was hoping you'd provide a letter of endorsement I could show to prospective donors."

With his gorgeous smile, he says, "Of course. We'll talk more."

CHAPTER TWENTY-THREE

Wow, I think when I'm outside, World Bank money. That could be endless.

Pressing into a taxi at Ring Road, a stinging scent assaults my sinuses. The pungent odor of unwashed body saturates the confined space. I breathe it in, recognizing this smell—acrid, sweet, human—that announces the lack of access to water daily in taxis and trotros, in tiny, unventilated offices. I try to roll down the window but find it can go no lower.

At the traffic circle known as, "37," I escape. The Peace Corps office is nearby in a residential neighborhood. From amid the morning's commerce taking place along the perimeter of the circle, a man thrusts a gold watch at me. It's a nice looking watch. I've gone without one since my battery died. I've no confidence in local batteries because too many Ghanaians wear watches that don't run.

If you ask a Ghanaian the time, he will study his watch and then pronounce the time to the exact minute. However, the Ghanaian sense of time is very loose. A seven-thirty work start may be any time between seven and nine. You may see someone at seven-fifty, knowing you have a meeting on the hour, but by eight, he will have disappeared. I needed once to meet a well digger at seven-fifteen in front of my house. Idrissu yelled at him in Twi and I heard mention of six-thirty. "No, not so early," I said. "African time," Idrissu had replied.

It is therefore comical to me to observe such effort in the accurate reading of a watch. I asked the team about this and Mr. Osei explained, "You are a white man, a white lady. I know that you use every minute. When you ask me the time, I give you the exact minute. If you are a black man, then I will say, 'Well, it is getting to twelve.' The African time has six a.m., twelve noon, and six p.m., that is all we think of. You see, when we are farming, before the white man come and we get watch, we look at the sun. The sun rises, it reach the top, and it sets."

"Then you can meet with three people in a day and I can meet with twenty-four," I had quipped.

I hold up the shiny gold watch to get a better look. "How much?" I try to sound cynical.

"Fifteen thousand." He is not the best-dressed fellow, but not the worst.

"O, is too much." I put all my emotion into the *o*.

"How much?" He pushes a long, plaid, buroni waawu sleeve up his arm. "You pay ten."

"Is too much." I hold the watch out for him to take.

But he draws his hands away and won't touch it. "How much?"

"Two thousand."

He shrinks back, shocked at such an offense.

A memory of my mother haggling with Libyan shopkeepers bolsters my confidence. She knew the rhythm of their language. I move to leave.

"All right," he says. "You pay five thousand."

I am descended from Phoenicians. "Fifteen hundred." I counter.

He clasps his head in both hands. "O, you are cheating me."

I set the watch at his feet and turn away.

"Yes, it is a good price. Two thousand. I will take it."

I am feeling very happy now. The World Bank looks promising and I know what time it is.

"Hello, Lionel," I greet the guard at the gatehouse of the Peace Corps compound.

"Hello, Madam," he replies, turning the registry toward me.

"How are things?" I ask, while signing in.

"Things are good," he says, in a pronounced manner.

"They are treating you well?" I ask, as if I am onto something.

"Yes . . . somehow."

A Ghanaian will never speak ill of their employer. The lack of a compliment is the only indication. The word, "somehow," is, in my book, the fatal determinant. It can be weighted with feeling and tone, but it is always open-ended and nothing ever follows.

"Saa," I say, and shake Lionel's hand.

There's enough time to see if McKenna is in. I cut across the parking lot to the two-story office building. One step inside and I greet Ozwald, the young man who occupies the mailroom. He distributes packages to volunteers through a window in the lobby.

Ozwald is stooped over to read the recipient's name on a box. He stands to his full height, all of six-four, to respond. "Louisa, how is Obuasi?"

"Good, somehow."

Ozwald shakes his head.

I furrow my brow.

"I'm sorry, Louisa, there is no mail for you."

"No mail?" I hadn't allowed myself to acknowledge how much I was hoping to see my name scrawled across an envelope in Carol's handwriting.

"Genevieve has gone on trek. She will pass through Obuasi and has taken your mail with her. I'm sorry."

"Genevieve?"

"Genevieve Garnier, the new associate director for the secondary schoolteachers. Genevieve has replaced Connie and she is on trek visiting her volunteers. Genevieve has your mail. I'm sorry."

The loss of someone known and the introduction of someone new sends through me a familiar wave of despair. It's a discouraging aspect of being in Ghana, the endless turnover of people. It's not just the unsettling effect of change, it's the way the pull of someone leaving highlights that I'm still here. "Oh, that's all right. There is mail for me, then?"

"Your mail is with Genevieve. I'm sorry I have no mail for you."

"Thank you, Ozwald. Next time."

I bound upstairs to the second floor, relieved to encounter no more staff on my way to Matt McKenna's door. Even his secretary is absent. I cannot remember the names of all the staff who occupy the downstairs and with whom I rarely have business.

When we first arrived in-country, the second-year volunteers impressed upon us how critical it is to greet every Ghanaian we know every time we see them. This acknowledgement of another human being is essential in Ghanaian etiquette. One of the Peace Corps office staff had felt snubbed by a second-year volunteer. Tension had spread throughout the office, infecting everyone's interactions. It required several months of diligent efforts on the part of the second-years to heal the rift.

"Come in," Matt calls in response to my knock.

I enter to find Bai standing beside Matt's desk with his pack over his shoulder. He's a forestry volunteer posted in the North. As I approach, Matt pulls money out of his wallet.

"Am I interrupting something?" I ask.

Matt rolls his eyes. He plays deadpan well. "I suppose you want some of this, too." Matt accuses like a martyr.

"Sure, as long as it's being handed out."

"How long have you been in Accra?"

"Since yesterday."

"On official business?"

"GG shot."

"When are you leaving?"

"Maybe tomorrow. I don't know. It depends on this World Bank thing. That's what I want to talk to you about."

Matt hands Bai several thousand cedis.

"Thank you so much, Matt. I'll pay you back the next time I'm in Accra," Bai vows.

"You bet you will," Matt growls.

Bai is ex-army. He stands straight as an arrow and speaks as if at the mercy of a higher power. "Yes, sir, I will."

"Don't make me have to come looking for you."

"No, sir."

"All right." McKenna watches Bai exit, his wallet almost in his pocket, whipping it open as I advance. "Do you want any of this?" His tone is impatient like I'm a chump wasting his time.

I give him no quarter.

Matt relaxes. I think he likes the severity of my appearance. He knows I'm tough. I get the job done. "A gamma globulin shot is good for two nights and one day," he says, pulling out several thousand-cedi notes.

I don't move.

"Come on, this isn't a candy store."

Our eyes meet and we smile.

"I know you're good for it," he says.

"Thanks." I put the money away and take a seat.

"Poor Bai." Matt stows his wallet. "It took him a day and a half to travel down here from Walewale. He had his gamma globulin shot on Friday. He's been stuck in Accra five days waiting for his per diem so he can afford to go home. Bai's doing a great job setting up a nursery. He had some tough politics to overcome." McKenna chuckles. "An inheritance from the volunteer who preceded him.

"Bai's really doing a great job. And I'm sitting in Accra filling out reports. All I do is paperwork. I don't get out to the sites like

I used to. Can't. They want so damn much paperwork. I sit here and fill out forms and play banker when we can't even cover our people for medical visits."

McKenna is a stocky, barrel-chested fellow, with a soft outer layer attributable to his penchant for fufu. He served in Vietnam. It's not clear how he ended up in the Peace Corps, but I know he's been in Ghana for years. He started as a volunteer. Then Peace Corps hired him to live in Tamale and provide field support for rural development volunteers in the North. That was back in the days when Ghana's shelves were empty and supplies had to be driven in or air-dropped to volunteers. Now Matt's the associate director responsible for the rural development program.

"All right, what's this World Bank thing? Spill it," shoots Matt.

"Well, I don't know exactly, but they sound very interested in working with the Advocacy."

Matt looks skeptical.

"It's part of the Capital Investment Programme—the new national rural water strategy. You know about that."

"I don't know much more than that. They involve us last. We're small potatoes to the World Bank."

"Well, they want the Advocacy to be a Watsan Collaborator. That's an organization that works with villages to implement water and sanitation projects—like the Advocacy is already doing. At least, that's the impression I get. I haven't had a chance to read their programme, yet."

"If the Advocacy's already doing it, what's in it for you?"

"Money for village projects."

"How much?"

"I don't know. I'm going to find out more this afternoon. They want to meet at four p.m. Say, you wouldn't like to come with me, would you?"

McKenna hangs his head and stares at his desk. He rubs his

eyes and looks up with a stone face. "I can't. We've got a staff meeting. I have to finish these reports. Let me know how it goes."

"I will. Do you want a copy of this?" I hold up the new rural water plan.

"Where'd you get this?" McKenna takes the document.

"Tao Bronson at World Bank. You know him?"

McKenna shakes his head while skimming the table of contents. "This looks interesting. Yeah, I want this. Have Samantha make a copy for me."

"She wasn't out there when I came in."

"Are you here tomorrow?"

"Well, I don't know. I'm not sure how it will go with World Bank. If it's quick, I might try to make Obuasi tonight. I could come by first thing tomorrow morning. In fact, I'd sure love to bounce off of you what's going down in Obuasi these days."

"No good. I've got a meeting first thing with Tombe. He just returned from a trek to the North and we need to review what he found. Then Genevieve and I are meeting with the Japanese Volunteer Corps . . ."

"I thought she was on trek."

Matt looks surprised. "No, I believe she's here. We have a meeting tomorrow at the Japanese Volunteer Corps office."

"Ozwald told me my mail is with Genevieve on trek."

Matt takes in what must be the hundredth unforeseen turn of the day. "Excuse me. *I* will be meeting with the Japanese Volunteer Corps tomorrow."

"Japanese volunteers?"

"Mhm."

"What for? Would Peace Corps do joint projects with Japanese volunteers? That could be cool."

"That's the idea. This kind of stuff gets bandied about year after year. Nothing ever comes of it. The Japanese Corps has a new director who thinks they're the first to think of it. Look, just mail me a copy and . . ." He shrugs. "Now's as good a time as any to talk."

"Great."

Matt listens to my recounting of the steering committee's rejection of WAG's agenda, at which, he observes, "They are learning from you. Your letter has emboldened them." He affirms Harrigan's claim. "The mining agreements signed by the government disregard the people already living on these lands. They are at the mercy of the multinationals."

"The road through Obuasi town is a disgrace. It's more potholes than pavement. And there're no sidewalks. It's a wonder pedestrians aren't flattened daily by haul trucks. I'm trying to estimate the loads to calculate an appropriate asphalt depth. Don't get me started on the open sewers."

"You're not there to build roads."

"But . . . we're supposed to determine the felt need of the people. We're supposed to adapt, regardless of our original assignment, to the reality of the community."

"Obuasi is a district capital with an administration that looks after its needs. That is not where Peace Corps works best."

"That road affects everyone in that town."

"Is there not a real need in the outlying villages for water and sanitation?" Matt's voice quiets in the certainty of his position.

"There is." I concede.

"You're in Ghana. Need is everywhere. Focus on doing one thing well."

McKenna sounds like the Old Man. Knowing when I'm bettered, I attempt to recover his good graces by venting my outrage at the situation in Bediem and Sansu.

Matt apologizes. "Peace Corps volunteers aren't meant to deal with such politics. Louisa, I'm sorry. After all Lynn's hard work to find funding for the Advocacy, we felt obligated to provide a volunteer to manage the new organization."

It's time for my medical appointment. But now that Matt's opening up, I'm willing to share. "There were sores on his . . ." with both hands, I form a *V* pointing toward my crotch. I meet his eyes with helplessness. "The whole village must be the same. How is it even possible that West Africa Gold could design and construct a dam, and they can't anticipate the impact of forcing a village to use stagnant water? Do you know how long it's been since Gyimiso Kakraba had good drinking water?"

Without emotion, Matt says, "Corporations tend to fall short when it comes to the human factor."

"The District should hold WAG to accounts," I declare.

"The District isn't going to risk offending the Castle for one village."

Frustrated by the lack of options, I say, "I'll bet you I could find a contractor willing to sink a borehole for Gyimiso Kakraba."

"Don't interfere with WAG's affairs," Matt orders. "Do not ask their contractors to get involved." For a brief moment he meets my eyes with a hint of admiration. "We both know you're going to do what you're going to do. When they come to me, I'll tell them I told you to stay out of it."

"I don't want to keep Gladys waiting."

"No, I wouldn't."

I pause at the door. "Thanks for the per diem."

He stares at me and says nothing.

CHAPTER TWENTY-FOUR

I hurry downstairs, calling to Ozwald as I pass. The medical unit and medical offices are housed in trailers to the right of the office building. I bound into the trailer and into the arms of Amy. We cry each other's names in unison.

"How are you? I haven't seen you since we left Koforidua!" Amy squeals at the memory, as if we've been dear friends for life.

"I know!" I say, returning the feeling. "How are you? You look great!"

"I do?" she speaks with an innocent glow. "I feel great." With rosy cheeks, a pixie haircut, and wearing a long, loose sundress of local cloth, she could be the volunteer in the brochure.

"So, you like your site?"

"I love my site. Everyone is so good to me! I love my students."

"That's great."

"How about you? How's . . . where did you go?"

"Obuasi."

"Right, there's a gold mine there."

"West Africa Gold."

"My headmaster's son left Chereponi to work in the mine. How do you like Obuasi?"

"I don't know if 'like' is the right word. I live on the haul road of an open pit mine. The place is filthy, dust everywhere. I'm meeting good people and we're doing good work, but I don't know if I could say I like it."

"Oh." Amy considers this. "Don't you have any close friends?"

"Well . . ."

"People who care about you?"

"Uh . . ."

"Isn't there someone you eat with everyday and talk to everyday? In my village, the headmaster is very concerned that I am happy. He doesn't want me to be lonely or sad and think of leaving. Clara's the most wonderful woman. She lives in the adjacent compound house. I have two rooms in the compound house of my family. They're very kind to me. Clara comes to my room every evening and we have tea together and talk and laugh. Don't you have anyone like that?"

"No."

Amy looks perplexed, then confides, "They're with Lorne. They've been with him a long time."

Lorne is a second-year volunteer due to finish his tour. "You don't know about the accident?" asks Amy. "Two weeks ago he was in a wreck. Three others, including the taxi driver, were killed. People bled on Lorne, but he wasn't injured. The scuttlebutt at the American House is that Doc Macey told Lorne there's no way to know if he contracted AIDS. He will have to get tested every six months. I overheard Lorne saying, 'If you ask me if the two years was worth it? No.'"

Public transport in Ghana is a life-threatening prospect due to poor roads, ailing vehicles, and reckless drivers. I think of Grandma's Bible open every morning and night. At prayer time laminated Mary, Jesus, and John the Baptist beckon from the ends of twisted, red cords that overhang the binding. Grandma's Greek Orthodox crucifixes on every wall and prayer cards on every table have always seemed an ancient custom to be respected, but in which I've found little of relevance.

I remember Grandma's protection for travelers. She is no longer a feeble old woman, frightened by a world moving too fast. I realize now she has lived days in Lebanon and perhaps in America when any traveler was uncertain of reaching their destination.

"Amy.." the nurse calls from an open door. Amy disappears as a distressed Lorne leaves the trailer. I read the *Capital Investment Programme* until another volunteer arrives.

"Hey!" Steve Simmons holds out his arms to give me a hug.

"Steve! How are you?"

"Not so good."

"You're looking pale."

"Yeah, they can't figure out what's wrong. I've been in the med unit for a week. I was urinating blood, but I'm not anymore. And there's a fungus growing on my tongue . . ."

I don't get to see the fungus before Gladys calls me in. Gladys is the Peace Corps Medical Officer for Ghana. She's a strong woman and a good nurse with a reputation of having zero tolerance for volunteers who try to abuse the system.

"Welcome, Louisa," she says when we're seated in her office. "You are in luck today. Doc Macey is visiting from Lome, so he will examine you." Gladys is not a tall woman and not thin. There is an orderliness about her. While many volunteers find her intimidating, I draw comfort from the vitality of her smile and the steel in her eyes.

"Examine me? I thought this was just a gamma globulin shot."

"Hah?" Gladys flips through my file. "Yes, you are just in for the gamma globulin, but the doctor will question you to be sure there's nothing else that needs to be taken care of."

Gladys and I go into the treatment room, where I drop my shorts for the shot. When we return to her office, Doc Macey is there reading my file.

"I see you've had giardia twice already." Doc Macey squeezes his watery eyes to peer at my chart through steel-rimmed glasses.

"Yes."

"How is it now?" He lowers my file and offers a thin smile from beneath a pinched nose.

"No problem."

"Bowel movements are normal? Any fever? Sulphur smell?" The doc runs a hand over stringy, grey hair that flips up at his neck.

"Normal" is a relative term. I've grown accustomed to loose stools and diarrhea. As long as there are no other symptoms, I try to avoid antibiotics.

"Normal," I reply. I'm not trusting of Doc Macey. He has a flimsy air. Everyone knows he'll retire in another year and he's using his position as the Peace Corps Doctor for the West Africa Region as a means to travel.

"Good. Any other complaints? Cuts that won't heal? Infections?"

"I need cream for a yeast infection."

"Ah, well, Gladys will examine you and if the results are positive, we'll get you the proper medication."

"I don't need to be examined. I just need the cream."

"Yes, Gladys will examine you and we'll see what you need."

"I know I have a yeast infection. I don't need to be examined. This is over-the-counter in the U.S." But Doc will have none of it.

I return to the exam room, where Gladys confirms my diagnosis. "You were right!"

"You don't get yeast infections, do you?" I ask. She shakes her head. "Well, if you did, you would recognize the symptoms. It's not difficult to know when you have a yeast infection." This seems to strike her as wondrous.

We return to Doc who prescribes the yeast cream. "Three," I say, holding up fingers.

"What's this?" Doc looks confused.

"I want three."

"Why?"

"So, if I get another yeast infection, I'll have it."

"Well, if you get a yeast infection, you can come to Accra and Gladys will examine you . . ."

"But that's another trip to Accra!"

"Yes," he agrees. "That's another trip to Accra."

"But I don't want to have to come to Accra every time I get a yeast infection."

"Why are you so sure you're going to get a yeast infection?"

"I get them all the time. I've had two already."

"They're not in your file." He glances at Gladys.

"That's because I brought yeast cream with me. Now I'm out and I'd like to have more on hand because I get yeast infections easily."

Doc points at my medical history. "It doesn't say that." He turns the file toward me.

"I don't care what it says. I wrote this. I'm telling you I get yeast infections. What do you anticipate as the problem? Do you think yeast cream is addictive? Do you think it's fun to take?"

"Peace Corps needs to keep records. We cannot dispense medications prior to identifying the cause of symptoms."

"Oh, but you can let me self-treat for malaria?"

He glances at Gladys to ask, "True?" She nods. I am disgusted. Of course, he knows that every volunteer is sent to their site with a medical kit.

Doc Macey sits back. "Well, one is above the waist and . . ." he bowls his hands at his lap, ". . . one is below."

CHAPTER TWENTY-FIVE

A simple condition appropriate for self-diagnosis. Doc's arbitrariness or stupidity or prudishness or need to control others lets him withhold from me a cream that requires no prescription in the U.S. He will make me spend a minimum of two days traveling in the heat risking my life via public transport, for what?

"One is above the waist, one is below." His words. I shift in the taxi seat, searching for a position to ease the itching burning. "One is below." My small. Displaying his privacy before medical professionals who do nothing for him.

I arrive early to find that Tao and Jim are not around. Doc's gesture. Both hands needed to invoke the sacred place. Wasn't that my reaction? I felt distress and compassion for suffering sores on limbs and torso. But the boy's sex . . . scratching the sensitive skin till it bleeds . . . Isn't that what I was saying to McKenna? Crossing the waist—transgressing a natural law, an unforgiveable inhumanity.

I wander down the vacant hall to Tao's office. Maybe Doc isn't an asshole. Of course, he is. If he wanted to honor my sanctity, he would help me care for myself. But his reaction comes from instinct. The same instinct I suppress when I force myself to look at the boy's indignity.

I pull out the *Capital Investment Programme* and set up shop at Tao's desk. I am grateful for a profession that lets me set aside emotion. Grateful for the chance to escape myself.

Air conditioning keeps the World Bank comfortable, but not icy like the offices at WAG. I like working in a country where I'm allowed to sweat. I love this place that lets me meet with an exceptional person like Tao Bronson and his World Bank colleague wearing shorts and slinging a duffel bag. I settle down to read more about their rural water plan, struggling to retain the proliferation of unfamiliar acronyms, the hallmark of development. Almost an hour later, Tao and Jim shuffle in.

Tao stops short upon seeing me in his chair.

"The light was better on this side." I stand and gather my things.

"It suits you, Louisa."

Jim Kelly licks his thin lips and opens, "We were planning to start our pilot programme in the Brong-Ahafo Region, extending later into Ashanti and Western. But since you're so far along, it might make sense to work with you. We're going to be based in Kumasi, so that would be convenient. We have a half million dollars available right now, of which fifty thousand could be allocated for your program. How many water points do you expect to put in by next July?"

"Perhaps twenty. But it's difficult to know. You seem to be more interested in funding wells. Some of the villages we've been working with are large enough to qualify for boreholes. We've touched forty of about one hundred and fifty villages in the district. Most of those remaining would be of a size appropriate for hand-dug wells."

Kelly places a hand on each hip, as if aligning his form. "Size has nothing to do with it. If you have more people, you put in more wells."

Now I'm confused. "We've been using the criteria that villages under five hundred people should be served by wells, one well per two hundred people. Then for every five hundred you install one borehole."

"That old . . ." he says, looking at Tao. "That's old Water and Sewerage criteria written ten years ago, probably by Tao."

Tao mumbles something about an American consultant. His lower lip brushes the bottom of his moustache.

"Boreholes are expensive," says Kelly. "Twelve thousand dollars . . ."

"Fifteen thousand," I interrupt.

Tao looks at me surprised. "It's six million cedis for a four-inch . . ."

". . . and seven point seven million for a six-inch. That's our quote from Ghana Water and Sewerage Corporation."

He looks at Kelly and shakes his head. "That's too high."

"They are the only ones who returned our request for a quotation and they're already doing work in the area for WAG."

"You can serve two hundred people from a well, three hundred from a borehole. For the price of one borehole you can put in four wells. Wells make sense," says Kelly.

I feel a bit stupid. If you seal a well and put a handpump on it, the quality of the water will be as good as from a borehole. Why was I so quick to jump for a high tech, high cost solution?

The topic changes. We are not a nongovernmental organization, as Tao and Kelly keep asserting.

"In fact, we're in a very complex situation with WAG." I caution.

"Well, you've got till January to straighten that out," says Kelly.

I don't think he gets it.

"We met with Don Welsch this afternoon. That's going to be WaterCore's mission, to get you independent." Tao adds, "I've been meaning to get in touch with Ankrah."

While Tao takes my papers to the copy machine, Jim and I chat. He's from Martinez, California. He went to Berkeley where he majored in chemical engineering. "That was to make money." Jim confesses.

I don't think there's anything wrong with making money, but

don't offer my opinion. Jim wants to know if Peace Corps can provide more people to help with regional organization of the new water policy.

"Sure, but the request has to come from the community. I can't make the request."

"Make a request form. I'll make the regions sign it," says Kelly. Appreciation for the virtues of C-O-M must not have trickled up to his level.

Tao returns and I give him information to use in crafting his endorsement of the Advocacy's programme.

Jim says, "Sure, we'll give her a recommendation, as long as she endorses our programme." I wonder who the hell he thinks I am that my endorsement matters.

They seem finished. I ask, "So . . . what's the next step?"

"You just go do it," says Jim. Brilliant.

Tao is going to drop me at the Regal Chinese, but first he takes Jim to his hotel. I contemplate asking Jim to join me for dinner. Even though the prospect doesn't excite, any social opportunity beats the null that is my status quo. However, I take my cue from his own reticence.

By the time we leave Jim's hotel, it's dark out. On our way to Danquah Circle, Tao talks. "I work too much. Long hours, all days. I'm forcing myself to go dancing every Friday night. I've done this twice. It's a good thing. I'm going to leave World Bank. I want to retire when I'm forty, start my own organization. Work at home, sleep when I want on the living room floor." At a stop-light, Tao cracks his window.

"People told me to get my masters. It was a good thing. I was working for Ghana Water and Sewerage. Every vacation I came back to Ghana to work. My professors were so frustrated. They didn't know what I was doing. I only showed up to take exams. I spent my time driving around Europe.

"I've lived. I have a wife and kids. I know what it means to have a family. My wife works. She has to, to cope with my stress. We take turns picking up our daughter at two-thirty. I forget. That's why she calls to be sure I'm going to get her." He downshifts for an unexpected pedestrian.

"I'm supposed to move to Côte d'Ivoire with World Bank. I'm going to retire in five years. Right now, I'm managing Côte d'Ivoire, Ghana, Togo, and Nigeria. Of course, nothing's happening in Lagos because of the situation. Jim's good. He keeps you on your toes. So many guys come in. They spend two weeks in the country and start talking lines.

"When I was at Water and Sewerage, I worked for Bagley. You know, I had his basket cleaned out by nine a.m. Then I was gone, on the road, helping people with field problems. The Kumasi Project, I really loved it." Tao's palm bounces on the stick.

"Oh, I'm happy with what I'm doing. I make good pay and I own a house. I work on it a little, fix it up. And I've got a family. I've done things in life."

Tao is the golden boy. He's very likeable. I could invite him to dinner, but he has a family waiting and my interest is less than noble.

CHAPTER TWENTY-SIX

I'm seated at a small table in a large room of elegant décor. From the interior, one could imagine the Regal Chinese on Sunset Boulevard . . . but for the accents of the employees and the patrons' attire—khaki amongst the expatriate gentlemen, and amongst the Ghanaian professionals the full spectrum—Western business suits, political suits, and local costume.

Before plunging in, I luxuriate in the aromas wafting from my plate and applaud the chef's artistic presentation. A thank you to Matt McKenna comes from my heart for subsidizing the best meal I've had since coming to Ghana. I do love to eat.

While I'm savoring that first delicious, spicy forkful, an expat, English by his accent, steps up to my table. "Excuse me, are you Louisa Lehmann?"

I swallow.

"My apologies. Didn't mean to catch you mid-bite." The man chuckles revealing crow's feet and a gap-toothed grin. "Peter Clayton, at your service," he says, extending a hand.

I set down my fork to extend mine.

"You are Louisa Lehmann?"

"Oh, yes."

"I knew it! Lovely. I've been meaning to introduce myself." He spreads his arms in grand presentation. I like this lanky fellow with a potbelly, balding, in khaki shorts and shirt, Guinness in hand. He has the feel of what in construction we call, "people."

"Lou . . . May I call you 'Lou'? May I join you for supper? I've just returned from leave. Just stepped off the plane."

"By all means." I gesture toward the empty chair.

He sits and scrutinizes my face as if verifying my authenticity. Satisfied, Peter says with a flourish, "Allow me to introduce myself properly." He leans over his drink. Perhaps he already consumed a few in flight. A thin beard runs along his jowls. A graying moustache trims his lips, which flex with the liquidity of his drink. "I knew your father in Libya . . . and you are his spittin' image!"

"Did I know you?" I ask, wishing I could place this comical character. Obuasi's failure to supply my band of mates has impugned the gold standard of expat life in Libya. But this character who lacks only a pith helmet to have walked out of a Kipling novel could redeem my cherished memories . . . and the vision of the life I have always wanted for myself.

"No. You wouldn't remember me. I lived in Benghazi. I'm a metallurgist. I ran lab tests for the oil companies."

I try to temper my eagerness while grasping for connection. "But you knew my father?"

"I hit Tripoli to socialize. I met your parents a couple times. When I learned the Peace Corps volunteer had lived in Libya and when I heard your name, I knew you had to be Lou's daughter. That was just as I was heading out on leave. Didn't get a chance to say hello."

Was Peter among my parents' camarades raising their glasses to the moon? I indicate my plate. "I hope you don't mind."

"Not at all. Don't let it get cold. I ordered before spotting you. Mine'll arrive in no time."

"So, Peter, are you working for an oil company in Ghana?"

"Didn't I say?" Peter looks shocked. He seems to take mental stock of his recent conversation. Amused by his own buffoonery, Peter swallows and says, "Well, well. I work at WAG. This is my thirteenth year."

"Impressive," I reply. "Most expats don't last one."

Peter shrugs. "It's all in here." He taps his temple while raising thin brows. "And here." He rests his palm over his heart. Peter bows his head, revealing thin strands of brown hair combed across his scalp. His lips tremble as he recalls something or someone dear.

I want both to cry at his unreserved display of emotion and to laugh at this eccentric figure's flair for the dramatic.

Sniffling, Peter raises loving, tearful eyes. "Evelyn is the light of my life." Peter nods with respect, pursing his lips, acknowledging the depth of his passion.

I want to kiss the ground of Ghana for finally bringing me a remnant of the wondrous world of my parents. It wasn't all a child's illusion. "Evelyn?" I ask.

"Yes. I just set her up at college in London. That's why I took such an extended leave. I'll tell you all about that another time, Lou. Tell me what you're up to."

A waiter wearing a black bow tie delivers Peter's dinner. We enjoy fine food and rambling conversation. Peter knew Lynn and her fiancé, Jeff Fogerty.

"All of WAG's environmental programme, hell, the safety programme for that matter—it's all because of the loan." Peter sucks his tongue at a speck caught in the gap in his upper teeth.

"The loan?"

"The International Finance Corporation loan to expand into surface mining. You see, Lou, historically West Africa Gold has been all deep shaft mining. The ore from the shafts is extremely high-yield. But improvements in technology have made it profitable to mine the lower grade ore at the surface.

"Except it's not profitable if you're inefficient as hell, which WAG could afford to be with the high grade ore. So WAG secured the loan to upgrade refining methods and bring in experts to train our people, mostly South Africans and Aussies."

"All the consultants who are here today and gone in a month."

"Three months, typically. But you're right, Lou. That accounts for ninety percent of the idiocy and arrogance in Obuasi. They're not here long enough to learn anything about the place or the people and they don't care to. They're paid top dollar to work nonstop. All they think about is how they're going to spend that fat check."

"I thought you said the loan was responsible for the environmental programme?"

"Absolutely. 'World environmental standards.' That's what the International Finance Corporation requires."

"So that . . ."

"That led to hiring Jim Hansen, building the Environmental Department, and the Water Policy, and, I presume, funding the Advocacy."

"Well, I know Jim asked Lynn to research the mine's impact on water supplies in the villages."

"He did and she did. In fact, if I'm not mistaken, I believe it was Lynn who drafted the Water Policy for WAG."

"That would explain why it's such an enlightened document. It's right in line with the current rage—community ownership and management. Except, WAG doesn't actually follow its policy."

"Doesn't surprise me." Peter pops a forkful into his mouth.

"I'm not sure why, though. Before I came, all the Obuasi suburbs and many villages already had boreholes from WAG. The Advocacy wasn't given the opportunity to mobilize the villagers and build support for C-O-M. It's very difficult now to go back and ask the villagers to take responsibility for something they didn't ask for and that was given to them without consultation.

"Why was it so urgent to get boreholes in around Obuasi? I guess that's where you'll find most of WAG's employees, but I don't see what was wrong with their water. They're not downstream

216

of Bediako Treatment Plant, so they're not on the contaminated river system."

"Metals, Lou." His cryptic speech doesn't register. "Heavy metals. Except for the mine proper, which receives treated water, Obuasi used to rely on local rivers. The rivers receive runoff that has passed through the tailings dams. It's chock full of cyanide and heavy metals. Metals in high concentrations are bad news. Of course, it had been bad news forever. Probably WAG needed to show that it was making progress and couldn't wait for the Advocacy to get off the ground."

"And is it right that the problem for the Gyimi River system downstream of Bediako is the arsenic trioxide? Is that what's killing the river?"

"Arsenic trioxide and tailings runoff. No killing about it. It's dead."

I try to hold Peter's gaze, but he's chasing rice with his chopsticks. I suppose I can't expect him to react to things he's known for years.

Feeling my stare, Peter looks up. "That's right, Lou. Mining gold kills rivers. It's worth it. This country needs the revenue. West Africa Gold is the largest single producer of GNP in Ghana. Nearly a third of the GNP comes from WAG—not from all the mines in Ghana." He holds up a long finger. "Just this one mine. A third." He jerks his finger up for emphasis.

Peter's perfunctory manner would offend if he held a position from which he could influence the outcome. Or, if I were not so interested to gain this window on WAG.

What is the worth of a river? Is it impossible to mine gold and protect the river? I don't ask these things. "Hey, Peter, can you explain something to me?"

"I'll sure try." He gives me a camarade's upturned lips.

"There are lots of small villages far from Obuasi that are slated to receive dug wells. Jim and Kwasi say it's due to exploration. But when the team goes there, it doesn't seem like there's any impact. Why does exploration hurt the water supply?"

"Trenches, Lou. We dig trenches parallel to the slopes of the hills. When it rains, the runoff blasts down the hill taking a lot of soil into the river. Makes the water very muddy." Peter throws back the last of his drink, catches our waiter and orders another. "What brings you to Accra, Lou?"

I tell Peter of my visit to World Bank and the exciting prospect of being a Collaborator.

When I finish, Peter gives me that gap-toothed grin. "I see you've got the fire in you." He laughs and I wonder if twenty years ago I fell asleep to his throaty rumble and whistling delight. "There's no chance you'll be quitting. You've already made it longer than the others."

"Lynn . . ."

"Not Lynn. The two that came after."

"Who?"

"Your Peace Corps sent a fellow to take over from Lynn about a year before you showed up. Max. Max didn't last a month. So they sent another one. Never learned his name. He quit, too. Obuasi's hard. They couldn't take it. But you're gonna make it, all right. And Lynn lived at the mine. You're down in the village. That's rough."

"I don't see it that way."

"That's why you'll last." Peter leans over his drink to punctuate his affirmation with a soupy grin. The farcical quality of his appearance makes it impossible to trust his endorsement. On the other hand, he's lasted thirteen years. And there's no doubting his sincerity.

Peter picks up the tab and offers me a lift to Kokomlemle.

"No, thank you. It's out of your way. Besides, I like the night. I'm fine."

"I believe you are." Peter gives me a warm handshake and says, "Cheers, Lou."

"Cheers."

I stroll toward Danquah Circle, musing over this character's unpretentious nature. Peter speaks to me like an equal. Unlike the professional Ghanaians, he has no need to impose an artificial distance. Unlike most expats at the mine, he doesn't veil condescension in pity. He treats me as if my existence is valid.

CHAPTER TWENTY-SEVEN

Nights in Ghana soften everything—the temperature, the noise of the city, the color of skin. Enjoying a rare veil of anonymity, I pass a wide array of locals. Well-dressed gentlemen and women clutch briefcases and board their busses. Women sell street chop, their faces illuminated by the stoking of the embers of their charcoal stoves. College students debate at an outdoor café. Such a gift to be in a country where one does not fear to walk the streets at night.

At Danquah, I squeeze into a taxi and recollect Tao's response to my asking why people had gotten into boreholes in the first place. "Because they're easy," he'd said. "You just go slap them in and leave. You don't have to involve the community."

"What should I do with the borehole projects . . . should I change them to wells?"

"No, don't change them. Don't worry, if you don't get funding by January we'll find the money to cover them. Jim was just being cautious. He doesn't want to promise more than we can deliver."

The taxi drops me at Circle and I hike uphill into Kokomlemle. Kwabena has long since closed for the day. Roadside vendors, women who form the core of Ghanaian commerce, offer discounts to loyal customers who collect essentials from tables laden with goods for the night's enterprise. Lanterns cast a soft glow on my staples: roasted groundnuts, bananas, a thirty-cedi bag of gari, a toilet roll, and a bottle of drinking water.

Around the corner, I stop at the manager's desk at the Kokomlemle Guest House. Along with my key, I'm given a candle and matches. A large bucket of water in the bathing stall signals that the water is also off tonight. Such courtesies as the bucket fuel my loyalty to this establishment. That and the fine price of four thousand four hundred cedis, for which the beds are clean and nothing ever "goes missing."

I bathe wearing chale wote to protect my feet from the scum of the bathing stall. By torchlight, I wet down, one cupful at a time. The toilet has no seat. I crouch above the porcelain, taking care to not press my leg against either the toilet or the scaly wall enclosing the shower stall. Just before bed, I insert the soothing cream, grateful for relief from what has become a constant burning. Things will get better now.

I lie awake, watching the thin curtain billow and fall above my head, wondering what World Bank is offering. They want to claim early success. They will attach the new rural water programme to the Advocacy, which is already implementing, without any assistance from World Bank, the type of development they want to advocate. We need money. They need a poster child.

I recall my small boy's smile and the way he threw his arms around my waist. I should have asked whether he liked the Fanyogo. Was it sweet enough to distract him? How miserable he must feel. What will happen when World Bank sees the plight of Gyimiso Kakraba, Sansu, and Bediem? That could really blow things wide open.

In the morning, I pour water over a plate of gari and top it with sliced banana and groundnuts. The simplicity of the food soothes my belly and my soul. I leave three hundred cedis on the table, a thank you for a bed without fleas, for keeping the water bucket full, and for not disturbing my things. I'm looking for

Mankessim Station, a place I've never been, to experiment with returning to Obuasi via Cape Coast rather than Kumasi. I put my faith in Ghanaian hospitality, asking strangers to be my guides.

At Ring Road, I hail a taxi and inquire whether it's possible for me to walk to Mankessim Station.

The driver furrows his brow, then says, "Yes," pointing west on Ring Road.

I navigate the morning bustle to discover a large station not far beyond Circle, where I ask a man to direct me to the right location to catch a Mankessim car. It turns out that this is Neoplan Station, and the man points further west along Ring Road. I strike out in that direction, but before I take many steps, the man yells and motions for me to go around. Looking up, I realize that I'm headed for an enormous drainage canal, a grander version of *Little Lord Fauntleroy*. I hold up a hand of thanks and head for a narrow pedestrian bridge.

Slogging along Ring Road quite a distance, I feel small in this urban landscape. The width of Ring Road is vast. Street hawkers cry from both sides, as well as from the generous median. Unlike in Obuasi, sidewalks provide safety for pedestrians. All that can be seen of adjacent properties are high walls and treetops. The sun is already heating things up. There's no station in sight. I get the attention of a street hawker and ask again.

"Take this bus," he says, pointing to a large vehicle barreling toward us, two lanes away.

The bus stops in the far lane to let me on, as if the driver could hear our exchange. I am so taken by this courtesy that I step off the curb. The hawker grabs my shoulder and pulls me out of the path of a speeding taxi. Our eyes meet. I mouth a heartfelt thanks, check for oncoming vehicles, and bound over to the bus.

Taking an empty seat behind the driver, I observe the rest of the bus is packed. When we reach our destination, Kaneshie

Market, the driver refuses my money and twirls his hand down the street to indicate my course. All I see are throngs of people bustling about one of the busiest markets in Ghana.

"I'll take her," offers a woman getting off the bus.

She takes me to the foot of the stairs leading to a pedestrian bridge above this busy thoroughfare. Once again, I'm on my way. I cross the bridge, which is every bit as congested as the street below. On the opposite side, I ask a newspaper seller where to go. An elderly man from the next stall leaps up to show me the way. It is perhaps a half-mile around a crowded city block. He takes my money, buys my ticket, and leaves me in the care of the driver. I should get on last, the driver says, as this is a Cape Coast car and I'll be the first one dropping.

The large trotro fills over the course of an hour. I'm glad to board last, to not be sticking to the hard plastic seat covers in the cramped rear seats. Our ride begins in typical fashion, with a suited hawker standing behind the driver's seat extolling the value of the small pamphlets he is selling. They teach the ABCs and provide a wealth of facts about every aspect of life. Atypically, this man speaks in clear English and does not yell above our heads. He reads in a pleasant voice, "'. . . B is for boy, C is for cat . . .'" Then he engages the audience with questions from his pamphleted encyclopedia: "What is the longest river in the world?" "Can women lactate when they are menstruating?" "What are the functions of a bank?" The crowd responds and each correct answer is rewarded with a blessing and a free religious pamphlet. After we hit the petrol station, also a first order necessity at the outset of a journey, the man praises his audience and bows out.

As the thinning city drifts past, my mind wanders to Gyimiso Kakraba. How long will it be before they have good water? The WAG engineers and workers who wrought this mess, do they consider each night, as they bathe and eat, the wretchedness of washing with water that infects the skin, of cooking with water that carries disease?

Who gets good water? Who does not? Who decides?

The city gives way to palm trees, sometimes merely lining the road, other times fronting on vast groves. Something simple and certain about the solidity of a tree. Nothing at all like the vagaries of life in Obuasi. What will Harrigan have dreamed up in my absence? Will Illiasu and Ankrah have arranged a meeting with Kwasi? Even though Kwasi is not top dog, WAG's desire to maintain pretense with the Administration could work to my favor.

Why am I game for this? When people asked why I signed on for Peace Corps, I said, "I want to change the world." I wanted to be cast into the world with nothing. To discover what is possible by virtue of one's wit and character. In the truest sense, to know the depth of my own resources and the limits of my capacity. I don't subscribe to the delusion that I am rescuing the world's poor. I am no Amy skipping through a fairy tale. If my presence makes a difference, I don't expect to have the luxury of knowing how or to whom.

Low dunes bring us into Mankessim, where I board a mid-sized trotro. I'm given the seat beside the driver because I'm a buroni. I share the bench seat with a talkative businessman. The distance we must travel is not so great, but there are frequent stops and night falls upon us.

Most passengers sleep or the best approximation possible when traveling over tattered asphalt. A young man in the front seat cradles a transistor radio in the crook of his shoulder. "Eei!" he cries, blurting Twi at his groggy neighbors. My riding companion cocks an ear.

When he turns to me, the businessman has a look of smug knowing. "They have confessed. Two witnesses for the prosecution have recanted. They say they were bribed by the State."

Of course, he refers to the case against Ken Saro-Wiwa. Agyeman has apprised me of fears that the prosecution will go to any length to obtain a conviction.

"There is no doubt," the businessman insists. "They have signed affidavits attesting to the bribery." As if realizing that I am a buroni, he says, "Do you know?"

"Yes."

"It is a travesty."

"Yes."

He stares at the dark through the spattered windshield. "They cannot kill him." He peers at me, determined that his words be true, terrified if they are not. "We are all watching. They must not kill Ken Saro-Wiwa. His death would be the death of Obuasi. West Africa Gold knows we are all watching. A victory for the State is a victory for WAG."

I feel overwhelmed, once again, by the intimation of the depth of life all around me, of which I have not the least perception. Ghana is not Nigeria. Ghanaians are not a violent people. Is there outrage at how WAG treats its workers, the nearby communities? The bus stops near a tree that serves as the boarding place of a village hidden by the brooding tangle of bush. Is there organized resistance? They are not marching in the streets. They are not calling on Parliament. There is so much I do not understand. A passenger gets off and the driver digs his bag out of the boot. Who in Obuasi fills the shoes of Ken Saro-Wiwa?

The engine roars to life, delivering pungent diesel fumes to our lungs. The businessman says, "A half hour more," and returns his imploring gaze to the night. I shift my weight on the seat to ease the itching burning from which I was granted a reprieve for most of the day.

Not long after we achieve our cruising speed, there is the

sound of something—like a piece of steel—bouncing between what sounds like asphalt and the bottom of the bus.

I glance at the driver and say to my companion, "He has no brakes."

But my friend explains, "The drive shaft has dropped. If he hits the brakes, the bus will roll. He is a good driver."

Grandma's prayer leaps to my lips:

> Be mindful, oh, Lord,
> Of all those who travel
> By land and by sea and by air
> The sick and the sorrowful
> The suffering and the afflicted
> The widows and the orphans
> The Gentiles and the Jews. . . .

We coast to a stop. The driver's mate and several young men comb the road with a junky Chinese flashlight. The driver breaks out tools. I grab my heavy, steel flashlight and follow the men down the road to assist in the vain search. No bolts announce themselves to our beams playing over the tarmac and flirting with the dense bush encroaching upon the road.

We head back and I scramble under the bus to hold my light for the driver, who has a wrench and two bolts on the ground beside his head. There are eight boltholes at the connection for the drive shaft. I conclude that six or maybe four would do, but not two. The driver proceeds to bolt up. A vibration spreads from the asphalt through my hip and shoulder. The driver's alarm confirms my suspicion. We hug our knees to our chests, as vehicles roar past.

Just as the driver finishes installing the two bolts, the driver's mate produces a bolt from the box through which he is rummaging. The third bolt is tightened into place. The mate applies himself with greater vigor. The contents of the box mouse against the cardboard, frantic to escape. One more bolt appears. It is tightened into place and the driver calls to his mate. But the box is silent. The young men grab the box and ply the weak beam of their Chinese flashlight. I stare at the drive shaft connection. An empty hole alternates with each bolt. For his balancing of the load I concede what a good driver he is.

I repeat Grandma's prayer while scrambling out from under the bus, "Be mindful, oh, Lord, of all those who travel . . ." As I climb into the front seat, the businessman gives me an approving look. When we reach town I drop first at a lone streetlamp just beyond the Miner's Circle.

The driver passes down my bag and the businessman calls, "Nante yie."

IV

THE SAFETY

DEPARTMENT

They sang so that everyone should know that they were
the *Bamelima*, . . . girls who had been blessed with the blood
and were now women. . . . Finally the door opened. . . .
Then came Akidinimba and Kidaya . . . , resplendent and
magnificent, . . . covered with elaborate patterns skillfully
drawn with fingers and thin sticks. . . . They began singing
then, together with the women, . . . songs whose words had
no particular significance, but which in themselves were of
the greatest significance, being songs sung only by adult
women. . . . [Kidaya] put the pot between her knees, and
sang quietly into the mouth of it, getting a deep reverberating
effect. This sounded so much like the molimo [exclusive to
men] that the men started, and one of the women turned
and said something sharply to Kidaya. Kidaya herself was a
little startled and put the pot away from her. She . . . slowly
and deliberately . . . [rubbed] off all the beautiful decorations
so laboriously painted on her body . . . When the singing
ended . . . Kidaya was just a mass of streaked and dirty gray.
And there were tears in her eyes.

—TURNBULL, *The Forest People—A Study of the Pygmies
of the Congo*

CHAPTER TWENTY-EIGHT

Dirty beige-thread grey-sworl brown-CAPITAL green black red white-Gere grey.

"The drive shaft has dropped."

What life cultivates an ear for steel striking asphalt?

"If he hits the brakes, the bus will roll."

What tragedies spur knowledge of rolling hazards?

"He is a good driver."

How many injured? How many dead? Honing recognition of the good.

"It is a travesty."

Clear. Certain. The heart does not quibble.

". . . the death of Obuasi."

". . . a victory for WAG."

Dark curtains cover the windows down the long sides of Ankrah's office.

"Tao Bronson said he hopes to meet with you." I make a final attempt to coax a response from the District Secretary. News that the World Bank has five hundred thousand dollars to put into play has made not the least dent in his dispassionate countenance.

Through the gloomy light, Ankrah's voice cuts. "I will contact Tao Bronson and try to set up a meeting with him. Here, I think.

I'll invite him here. It's difficult to match everyone's schedules. We may have to meet him in Accra."

"Okay," I say, shifting my weight on the high-backed chair. "Have you set up a meeting with Dr. Kwarteng-Badu?"

"No, we haven't done that yet." Mr. Ankrah beams at me like a proud father, his common fallback position. The tell of his impassive eyes disturbs me.

"Thank you," I say, taking my cue to leave.

"You're doing good work for the District."

"Thank you."

In the reception room, the secretary sits hunched over her typewriter. With effort, she lifts her head, giving me plenty of time to recognize her lack of industry. With the conviction of one who suffers, she says, "No electricity. You see? What am I to do?"

I head out the door.

"He wants to see you," she says, poisoning my escape.

Illiasu's door is locked. I knock and he buzzes me in. He's finishing with two well-dressed gentlemen carrying oiled, tailored briefcases. Illiasu waves me to a seat beside his desk. I sink in. These local box chairs are deep.

Illiasu sees the men out and sticks his head back in the office. "If you don't mind, I'd like to ask Mr. Abubakar to join us to discuss the contract."

Left on my own, I move to one of the chairs facing the desk. This office must be less than half the size of Ankrah's. An intermittent breeze dances in the thin curtains behind Illiasu's desk.

Mr. Abubakar is a small-boned man with petite features set off by a discreet moustache and beard. He could be an attractive man were it not for his cloying personality. Today he greets me in his typical fashion, with excessive graciousness. Quite a stretch after his attempt to provoke the team into condemning me as a pushy woman. Does he know any other kind?

"Oh, Akua, how?" Abubakar takes my hand, offering a saccharine smile.

"Normal," I say, withdrawing my hand. If I do not pull my hand away, he will hold it forever.

Taking the chair beside me, Abubakar asks, "You are recently from Accra, isn't it?"

"Yes."

"I've heard you've met with great success there." He swells with elation.

"Nothing is certain."

"I'd like to review your comments regarding WAG's contract," interjects Illiasu. I hope he's had time to reconsider the implications of signing the contract.

Mr. Illiasu reads aloud from my letter: "'The payment terms specified in the contract do not reflect current payment practices. The contract terms should be modified to indicate that funds will be disbursed monthly based upon a projection of the coming month's expenses and actual costs shall be documented in a monthly budget report.'" Without pausing, Illiasu comments in a predetermined vein, "The contract states that the Adansi West Rural Water, Sanitation, and Health Advocacy will be reimbursed for its expenses within thirty days of submitting documentation of its costs for that month. You are concerned that the Advocacy would not be able to finance its operations in this manner."

"That's right."

"Presently, the Advocacy is paid in advance for each month?" Illiasu speaks in an even tone.

"That's right. Presently, we get steering committee approval in advance for unusual or high cost expenditures. Then we fill out a pay voucher. WAG managers review the voucher and sign it. Then we get the cash."

"Has there been any problem with this system?"

"No, it works well."

"There is no need to worry," says Illiasu. "This contract will not change anything. You will continue as you are."

"That's right." Abubakar drips with sweetness. "There is no problem. This is a formality."

Illiasu dismisses West Africa Gold with a wave of his hand. "WAG imagines it is wielding power over the Advocacy, but if the Advocacy has no money, it cannot function, and then where will WAG be in its dealings with the villagers?

"West Africa Gold is afraid of the villagers. I wish you could have seen them the day their equipment was stopped by Bediem. The people stood in front of WAG's dozers with guns in their hands. The equipment stopped. WAG came running to the District, begging us, 'Please help us.'"

Abubakar and Illiasu giggle.

Illiasu reads the next item out loud. It becomes clear that he intends to read through every point in my letter, dismissing each, one by one. I no longer care what's in that letter. There are reasons why Illiasu may have to sign the contract. Why doesn't he just do it? He doesn't need my complicity.

Both Abubakar and Illiasu are looking at me. I stare back, reaching for the question that has passed.

"You do see it?" Abubakar cries. "The Advocacy is here to serve the district. Anyone who likes can give money. Whether it is WAG, World Bank or WaterCore, the Advocacy can take contributions from any of them. The Advocacy is here for the district."

"Without WAG's money, the Advocacy doesn't exist," I reply. Illiasu and Abubakar laugh. The phone rings. Illiasu picks up the receiver.

Abubakar leans near and whispers, "Confrontation is a bully's trick." If he held any real power, his despicable attacks would concern me. As Agyeman would say, if I choose, I can crush the flea on the ass of the steer, and the steer will thank me.

"Why did you write that letter? The contract would be signed by now. You think you can bully Dr. Kwarteng–Badu, a senior staff at WAG? Who are you?"

Who is the bully, Mr. Abubakar? "Have you read the contract?" I ask. His cruel face turns blank.

The receiver returns to its cradle and Illiasu to his humor. "Of course the Advocacy exists without WAG." He cajoles. "The Advocacy exists to serve the district. Anyone can come and give money." Illiasu floats on delirium. I'm shocked at his behavior.

"Then why didn't the Advocacy exist before WAG funded it?" I let each word hang in the air. "How could the research ever have been done to create the Advocacy, if Jeff Fogerty hadn't loaned his car and driver to Lynn?"

"Akua." Abubakar glows. "We are trying to help. You shouldn't worry so. Everything will work out. If we don't like how WAG treats us, we can go to World Bank or to anyone else." Abubakar places his hand on mine.

I'm out of my seat, saying, "I have to go."

"What?" Illiasu looks surprised.

"I have to go."

"But . . . when will we finish this?"

"It's finished," I say, dropping my eyes to soften my rudeness.

"What? We must finish this. WAG is asking why we haven't returned the contract. When can you return? This afternoon?"

"Oh, I'm afraid I'll be away from the office this afternoon." Abubakar apologizes.

"What time?" I ask.

CHAPTER TWENTY-NINE

I don't want to participate in this charade. A small follows on my heels as I cut across the schoolyard. "Gift me my money," the boy says, in a mock man's voice. "Gift me my money."

Raising my hand, I spin around and shout, "Mɛbo wo!"

He shrinks back in alarm. As soon as I turn around, he laughs. He continues to follow, chanting, "Gift me my money. Gift me my money, buroni."

I pick my way home without acknowledging anyone, cheating Idrissu of a proper greeting before disappearing behind the gate. The duffel bag careens into the farthest corner. Sneakers and socks fall to the floor. My back hits the sofa and my eyes bore holes into the ceiling. If I return, I'll rip Illiasu apart.

I don't know what to do with anger. I only know that I'm good at it. I learned at the family table, at my father's knee. My skills were honed in college and lauded at work. There is so much opportunity for confrontation on a construction site. I reveled in applying my brilliance to deliver scathing arguments to defend my position and win the day. Be right. Be smart. Be fast.

I deplore the sham of reviewing my letter. I've never known Illiasu to succumb to giddy delusions. "Anyone can come and give us money." "If we don't like WAG, we can go to anyone else." Where are the people lining up to give us money? One conversation with a Peace Corps volunteer and Illiasu thinks the World Bank money is in the bag? He can't be that facile. Nothing is real till it's in writing. As WAG's contract shows, what goes on paper can be very different from one's expectations.

I root around in the kitchen to make lunch. Peeling an orange takes me back to Mamiriwa and the strapping young man wielding a machete two feet long. How could anything so coarse produce something so exquisite? The flesh of the orange intact, not one nick marring its integrity. A blade in the hands of a master . . . I see his head bowed, the perfect fruit in his open palms. What man is this? Strong, solid, and humble. Not seeking personal glory. A man who recognizes something larger and his own place in it. I am not worthy of his offering.

After lunch, I head up to the office to do paperwork and meet the team when they return from the villages. Two smalls follow me as far as the buroni store, laughing and chanting.

"Kyɛ me penny. Kyɛ me penny. Kyɛ me penny. Oburoni, kyɛ me penny."

The ceaseless singsong enrages me. On the busy main road, I will lose face if I react.

"Kyɛ me penny! Oburoni, kyɛ me penny! Oburoni, kyɛ me penny!" They skip along at my heels. In defense, I hurry my stride. "Kyɛ me penny! Oburoni! Oburoni! Kyɛ me penny!"

I never encourage beggars. But, what penny would I give you? My salary is in arrears due to the Peace Corps accounting palaver. Agyeman has a good chunk of my savings. I hope he meets his promise date for repayment. Kyɛ me penny, Agyeman.

Past the Catholic church, I cut through the golf course and up to the lab. Under a grey sky refusing to rain, WAG workers move furniture into the newly constructed Safety Department. The Environmental Lab and Safety Department are the only WAG offices bordering the golf course. They sit just outside the fence of the main mine, accessible by a public road that spokes off the Miner's Circle, fronts the bank and the Old Council, and terminates at the golf course clubhouse. Cutting through the golf course saves me the treacherous walk up the chute road and doubling back from the Miner's Circle.

I find Kwasi in his old office. While I pull on my long-sleeved shirt, Kwasi opens a folding chair for me.

"Yes, Louisa." Kwasi sits forward with a solemn face. He's afraid to give anything away. Worried he'll say the wrong thing and face the consequences of his unforgiving employer.

"Good morning." I try to sound like his colleague.

"Good morning, Louisa. What brings you here?"

"Gyimiso Kakraba . . ." I hesitate, recalling my last mention of the village had incited Kwasi's anger. I drop my eyes.

"Eh, Jim and I have given some thought to Gyimiso Kakraba." The calm tone of his voice brings relief. He will spare me further retaliation. "Jim and I are thinking it may be best to provide a water source for the village. That way I will not have to always be arranging water tankers for them. . . . And, of course, it would be more reliable for the villagers."

When he finishes, I raise my eyes, trying to acknowledge without provoking.

Kwasi rubs the palms of his large, thick hands together. "Eh, we are wondering whether dug wells will be adequate or whether a borehole is necessary. Doesn't the Advocacy conduct surveys of the villages? Do you know the population of Gyimiso Kakraba?"

"Yes, each village health committee conducts a census. I can check the exact number, but I'm sure they're close to a thousand."

"Yes, I thought they were larger than the tiny villages. I didn't want to request such a large expenditure without checking with you first."

That's odd, as I have no standing at West Africa Gold. Kwasi should verify such information himself. I don't mind being helpful, but am suspicious of the phrasing. "I'll get you a copy of the census. As you know, the villagers sometimes distort their number in anticipation of increased services or decreased tariffs. I've no reason to doubt Gyimiso's census, but you should beware of the possibility."

"Of course, 'Akua'? Is that what the team calls you? I am Ashanti. I know the mind of the villagers."

Ignoring his terseness, I ask, "How soon would this happen?"

"We are contacting the driller now. We hope to move quickly, as the situation requires . . . They are participating in the Advocacy's programme?"

"Yes, Gyimiso is cooperative. But they were happy with their original water source. It may be hard to persuade them to take responsibility for the boreholes, given the circumstance."

"I see." Kwasi chews his lip. "Well, the Advocacy will have to do its best to convince the people. We cannot delay the boreholes."

"You've decided not to take World Bank's advice, then?"

"Jim and I gave some thought to the dug wells. We wonder about their reliability," Kwasi rasps. "Do you think they'll provide water year-round? I pulled some of the water company's drilling records. The wells they've drilled for us in the villages go down fifty meters. Can you dig a well to that depth?"

"Fifty meters, are you sure?"

"Yes, I'll show you. You can see for yourself."

I peruse the records of three boreholes, indicating one drilled to a depth of forty-eight meters and two to a depth of fifty. "Something is wrong, Kwasi. This record is for the borehole at Nyameso. When WaterCore trained the team in handpump maintenance, we pulled that pump for repairs. It was set at fifty feet. I can't believe they drill another one hundred feet past the pump setting."

"Well, here's the record."

"Yeah. I'm going to find Mr. Moses," I say.

"He should be at Yeboah Estates," offers Kwasi. "Ghana Water and Sewerage is drilling for the new senior staff homes at Yeboah. The audit results should be in any day now."

I meet Kwasi's eyes, but say nothing. It's clear he's pleased with himself for catching me off guard.

Kwasi smooths a paper on his desk, an excuse to break eye contact. Still looking down, he says, "While you were in Accra, Finn ordered an audit of the Advocacy's accounts. The final report is due." At the last, he looks up with a vindictiveness I have never seen before. Kwasi's daily diet of Finn Harrigan is having its effect.

"There is nothing the Advocacy does that cannot stand the light of day. We welcome the report. Is there anything else?"

CHAPTER THIRTY

I've plowed through every stack of village files in hopes of finding notes from our field training in handpump maintenance. The obvious candidate, the Nyameso file, is nowhere to be found. It drives me crazy spending so much time locating information. I study the bookcase, wishing it could transform into a file cabinet.

While waiting for the team to return, I shift to a more productive pursuit, updating accounts. From my pocket notebook, I shake out folded receipts and remember . . . the photos dropping out of an envelope years ago . . .

All of my advances to the men, their pay-ins and expenses are recorded in my notebook. . . . The inspector had pounced on photos he perceived to be incriminating. Shrinkage cracks in concrete piles . . .

I flip through every page, scanning my notes for accounting entries. . . . The strength of the piles was questioned, because they were already installed, scandal implied.

I can still feel the Old Man's solid grasp upon my shoulder, as he reassured me. "There is nothing we do that cannot stand the light of day." It was true on the pier job and it is true of the Advocacy. I stand shoulder to shoulder with an army of tough construction men. We do not back down. We are getting the job done. Finn's attempt to intimidate is child's play.

On a clean sheet of paper, I log recent activity. I hate accounting. I should get a real accounting ledger. In a short while my attention drifts to the conference table where the map is unrolled and weighted by folders.

I've taped the narrow strip to the bottom of the main map. It was confusing to me that WAG would not have made a map that encompassed the entire district. It is the mining concession that occupies the center. The narrow strip does not contain any concession land, but is needed to complete the district. Bless Jim for requesting the entire area for me.

Referring to a report turned up by Osei that shows the outline of Adansi West, I've been sketching the district boundary onto the blueprint. I love to draw. There's a thrill in creating a map that no one's seen before, at the prospect of visualizing the whole. The scarcity of such basic information . . . the engineer in me feels helpless at the magnitude of what is lost.

Upon hearing the truck pull in behind the Old Council, I head for the balcony. "Maadwo," I call down to the men. "Please tell the driver I have business and he should leave the truck."

Takyi is the first to arrive upstairs. He leans over the map.

"This is the main road through Obuasi and this is the Old Council." I point at the unlabeled landmarks.

Takyi places a finger at the site of our office. Aside from Osei, it's unclear whether any of the men understand how to read a map. The details of Obuasi town are tiny. I don't imagine Takyi can see the representation.

When everyone has gathered, they enquire about my meeting with Ankrah. I describe every detail, including his demeanor.

After a moment's reflection, Agyeman says, "The District Secretary holds his hand close to his chest. His peacock chest."

Takyi chimes, "World Bank will come and we can say goodbye to WAG."

I catch his eye and say nothing. I had tried to downplay to the team my meeting with World Bank. We have nothing concrete and I didn't want to get their hopes up, but who cannot be excited at the mention of five hundred thousand dollars?

"WAG has conducted an audit of the Advocacy's accounts. Kwasi says the report is due any day."

Agyeman raises his chin. "The lioness, Madame Tettey, cats with the Advocacy mouse." He reminds me how narrow my view is. I had only thought of Finn's malice. I failed to consider WAG's general manager, a woman I've never met.

Takyi speaks in Twi with agitation. Thomas explains. "While you were in Accra, two WAG accountants came to the office. They wanted to understand the Advocacy's mission and accompanied us to the villages. They spent two days with us. They wanted to know how often we go to the villages and what we do when we are there. They observed our animation of the villagers. They questioned the villagers about how often we visit them and how long we stay, and the taxi drivers about the rate to charter a taxi for the day. They talked with the drivers about how long it takes to go to the villages and the charges to take us to different villages. When we returned, the accountants stayed in the lorry park questioning other drivers."

I surmise. "They are trying to evaluate the validity of the amounts we are reporting for chartering taxis."

Takyi again shoots a stream of Twi. Osei injects his gravelly concern. "They wrote down the cash amounts we have in our pockets. Should we return our cash to you?"

"No. It is accounted for." The men look distressed. "Do not worry. There is nothing we do that cannot stand the light of day." Agyeman meets my eyes with respect. It feels normal, the camarade who stands beside me; until I remember that he doesn't acknowledge me. He seems to realize the course of my thoughts and pulls his eyes away. Grabbing the back of a chair to steady my balance, I say, "I need to go to Yeboah to find Mr. Moses. Does anyone want to go with me?"

"I'll go, Akua," says Takyi. "On the way coming, you can drop me at home as it will be late."

Traffic is heavy. We pick our way past a taxi. As is the custom, the vehicle is being repaired in the road in the spot where it broke down. Takyi tells me of the team's day. He pulls his notebook from his pocket and reads with agonizing effort. Literacy is not his strong suit, but he possesses the fortitude to study a single page for an eternity. I have learned to respect his effort. Once he has read a document, it is locked in his mind, where he gives the contents careful consideration.

We pass the turnoff for the District administrative office. I keep my eyes on the road to Yeboah.

"Wamase was very happy to see us-ooo." Relates Takyi. "Ve-ry happy. The people were ready to receive you and we had to explain to the people that you are just from Accra and have business in Obuasi town. When they understood, they were disappointed. They are missing Abena Lynn. Abena was very good to Wamase. She spent all her time in that village helping the mothers' cooperative to make weanimix. Now the people realize that they have lost Abena and they are curious to know what Akua brings."

"I am sorry. I will try to be sure to join you the next time we go to Wamase."

"Oh, do not worry, Akua. We made them happy. We explained to them about the Advocacy and they became ve-ry happy. They formed a health committee and have identified the need for a ventilated pit latrine for the village."

Once we hit Yeboah Estates, it's easy to spot the top of the drill rig. A man in dirty dungarees, one suspender flopping at his waist, steps toward us in knee-high, black rubber boots. "Mr. Moses's not here," the driller tells us. "He has just left for Kumasi."

Takyi's curiosity lures him to the rig where he cranes his neck in awe of its height.

"Will he be here tomorrow?" I ask.

"I cannot say. Mr. Moses may be here tomorrow and he may not come. But we shall relay the message that you're looking for him."

"Medaase." I wait for Takyi, now engaged in earnest conversation with the crew. Like a proud student, I expect Takyi to deliver a lesson in drilling on our ride home. The somber expression he wears as he climbs into the cab of our truck reflects his concentration upon the facts of drill rigs. I know he will begin when he is ready.

Yeboah Estates is a new tract of senior staff housing. We drive through portions of the development that are already occupied. The lack of mature vegetation and its close proximity to the noise and dust of the open pit prevent Yeboah from evoking the charm of the senior staff housing at the main mine. Yet, this tract represents luxury living. An attempt by West Africa Gold to reach parity with amenities afforded by other Ghanaian mines, such as Tarkwa.

WAG is capable of creating comfort for those who have choice regarding their employment. WAG has no pennies to build a village for subsistence farmers, whose homes would look like garden shacks beside the stateliness of Yeboah.

Takyi clears his throat and says, "It is not good, Akua." Such consternation over a drilling method? "Akua, one of the drillers is just from Nigeria. One of the drillers told us what he learned, as he has just come from there." The talking drum. I glance toward Takyi, catching the depth of his feeling. My eyes return to the road and I await the terrible news. "Akua, do you know that Ken Saro-Wiwa has a brother? Do you know of his brother? Owens Wiwa?"

"No, I didn't know there was a brother." We pass the school and the specter of meeting Illiasu.

"Ken Saro-Wiwa's brother, Owens Wiwa, has gone to the company of Shell Oil to appeal for Shell's assistance in the case of his brother. You know that Ken . . .

"Yes."

"Owens Wiwa has gone to Shell Oil and spoken to the head man. This man . . . Do you know of this Michael Vaughn?"

"No."

"Just here, Akua," Takyi says. "You may turn here past the shops. This Michael Vaughn is the director of Shell Oil. He met with Owens Wiwa."

Takyi's home is uphill from the main road. I balance the tires on the ridges that define the shifting gullies cut into the narrow lanes of red earth. Years of heavy rains have eroded the lowest tiers of mud blocks in the walls of the dwellings that stand inches from both sides of the vehicle. "And what happened?"

"He said that he can only help free his brother if Owens can help Shell. He will only help if Owens will also help. Left here, Akua." Takyi points.

"How can Owens help Shell Oil?"

"He would like that Owens has MOSOP tell to the newspaper that Shell's operations in Ogoniland are not damaging. If MOSOP can tell the newspaper that Shell is not hurting the land, Owens could help Mr. Michael Vaughn. Here, Akua."

I stop the truck. Several families live in divided portions of Takyi's two-story house. As government employees, they pay a discounted rent. Takyi's four children run to the courtyard wall to greet him. His oldest daughter climbs into the back of the truck to collect Takyi's share of plantain.

"What did Mr. Owens Wiwa say to that?"

"He said, how can he come to the aid of a man who speaks truth, by telling a lie? He said, how can he say that Ken Saro-Wiwa has been lying to the world for all these years?"

Takyi's wife, dressed in a simple wrap and headcloth, waves to me from the doorway.

I wave back. "You are right, Takyi. It is not good."

"I don't understand why we are supposed to do capitalism," Takyi's heated voice reminds me of the day the steering committee rejected the team's out-of-station allowance. When he is passionate, his halting, tentative voice gives way to moral authority. "I don't understand, Akua. Where is the honor in the capitalism? Why does everyone say we are backward? How are they better?"

His words strike home. I am forever sitting at my parents' table.

"They cannot kill him." Takyi says, his voice riding between threat and despair. It pulls me low to hear anguish from such a gentle soul.

At a loss, I borrow an expression of my mother's. "Inshallah."

Takyi looks surprised at what he perceives to be my attempt at local expression. "Yes, Akua, inshallah."

CHAPTER THIRTY-ONE

After dropping the truck at the lab for Kwasi, I walk home through the golf course and around the Catholic church. Illiasu doesn't need me to sign that contract. Why doesn't he just do what he has to do? Leave me out of it?

I cross the street to pick up dinner. The yam chip lady greets me with a warm smile set in the texture of her softness. Not delicate or weak, a gentleness imbues the radiance of her greeting.

I imagine the yam chip lady is about my age. She stands a good head shorter than me, with shoulder length hair that is stiff, but not kinky. I focus to catch her queries in Twi. Unlike most Ghanaians who are familiar with my limited repertoire, the yam chip lady makes no effort to simplify her language. I enjoy the chance to attempt new meanings.

Two new customers arrive and the yam chip lady gets down to business. "Wope ahe?" Although I know our routine, I try to hear her words, which slows my response.

To prod me, she asks, "Wope bayerɛ a yɛakye?" Her tongs hover above the basket of chips.

"Aane, two hundred."

She picks amongst the thick wedges, placing the best pieces in the banana leaf spread in her palm. Although her attention is focused on the table of food, a hidden smile glancing off the smooth complexion of her cheek warms me, making me feel like a man who has captured a woman's heart.

"Wope nkyenam?"

I hesitate before responding and she fires back, "Nkyenam?" Without looking up, tongs poised above the fried fish.

I catch her words this time. "Dabi."

"Pepe?"

"Aane."

This is the drill through which she puts every customer. I am entitled to no leniency and I love her for this.

In one quick, fluid motion, as if completing a natural process, the banana leaf is folded over the yam chips and pepe sauce, then wrapped in a sheet of newspaper that is proffered to me by the yam chip lady, who meets my eyes once again with the concluding statement of her art, "Two hundred cedis."

We exchange yam chips and bank note, at the same time exchanging medaases.

"Yɛbɛhyia bio."

"Yoo," she responds, while positioning the next banana leaf in her palm. Gliding on that deep, low, comforting sound, her softness follows me down the road.

I don't usually travel along the downhill edge of the road, which doesn't offer much protection for pedestrians. There's a considerable elevation drop from the road to the shop fronts, making it difficult to make an agile escape from errant vehicles. I cross back to the uphill side and assess the immediate obstacles—a goat tied to a post on my left, a stream of kitchen sullage in a stagnant cross gutter, a shopkeeper's infant crawling on a crumbling porch slab. I chart a staggering course avoiding the goat and cutting within inches of the infant. Glancing up at the right moment, I catch a glimpse of Union Jack Kofi. I'd trade him for Water Tank Kofi, right now.

Springing to the road-side lip of the gutter, I leap into the thoroughfare at the heels of two men. To pass these unhurried travelers, I venture beyond the strip claimed by pedestrians at the road's edge. But an oncoming Zion train forces a hasty retreat into the protection of their trail.

The Zion train is WAG's major means of moving labor to feed the three shifts mining around the clock. Not a train at all, Zion "trains" are made of two steel shipping containers welded together, end-to-end, and fixed to a tractor, creating a forty-by-eight-foot steel box on wheels. There are no seats in the train. Steel pipes hang parallel to the ceiling for taller men to grab. Shorter men fill the voids.

What is the value of human life? Does anyone care? What is the value of Ken Saro-Wiwa's life? Is it worth a lie? Why does there have to be a lie? Why can't Michael Vaughn own what he has done? How can my father speak in defense of such a man? I stomp past the two men. How necessary is this charade of Illiasu's? Sign the damn contract. Leave me out of it.

A thoughtful engineer did provide ventilation for the Zion trains. A six-inch strip of steel has been cut out of the top of each sidewall. A great relief, I am sure, to the press of human bodies inside. The only entrance to the box is a narrow, steel door at the back. The floor slopes up toward the front, forcing passengers to climb to their fate and balance their weight on an angle. The men are either packed in the windowless box like sardines or pitched askew by the vehicle crashing down our abominable road. The Zion trains are painted bright, safety yellow.

"*Safety First!*" had been the slogan printed on triangles of bright, safety yellow. *Safety First!* stickers were everywhere on our construction site—on every piece of equipment, on bulletin boards and hard hats. My first safety meeting was on the pipe-laying job with Gary. Bob Drucker was our superintendent. Bob held safety meetings at the tailgate of his pickup. He wore a safety yellow hard hat with his name printed in tiny, block letters above the rim. A huge *Safety First!* triangle was planted above his name.

Bob and I worked at desks side by side in the trailer. Dead center over his desk was a tool poster. Many construction equipment and service companies advertise their product by way of posters that feature young models, curvaceous and vulnerable. The woman above Bob's desk held a twenty-pound rivet buster between her parted legs, her red nails flexed as she held the penetrating steel with an innocent touch, while courting the camera with an effusive, fuck-me smile. Seeing her did not make me feel safe.

When Bob was on vacation, Gary and I worked hard to maintain the productivity of the pipe-laying operation. We were always looking out for each other. One day, as he sat in Bob's chair waiting for me to run numbers, Gary leaned close to me. He inclined his head toward the poster, and said, "When Roger was alive, he wouldn't have allowed that. Roger would have said, 'This is a place of business,' and torn that right off the wall."

"This is a place of business!" I declared and deposited Bob's insult in the dumpster outside.

In my mind, my action was applauded by a group of women like those I had known in college—feminists who marched through San Francisco to take back the night, who staffed battered women's hotlines, who sat in silence with heads bowed honoring confessions of violations of body and soul. These women stood up and cheered as the poster fell into the trash.

When I returned to the trailer, Gary looked at me for a moment, then said without emotion, "You act on impulse."

I stood taller, proud of my impulse.

Gary shook his head. "What do you think Bob will do when he gets back? You think that was bad? Wait till you see what he puts up in its place."

I hadn't thought that far.

Gary backhanded my knee, as he stood to go. "Figure it out, girl." From his full height, he looked me in the eye and strode out.

I remember thinking this is why I love construction. The directness. I will look Bob in the eye and own what I did.

"You're a woman, not a girl," the feminists crooned.

Yes, I am a woman—in a construction trailer where your puritanical proclamations are of no use. You wouldn't last a day.

"Nor would we want to," scoffed these women who disparaged the state of a world controlled by men.

I held the door open for women who sought refuge in the arms of women or in the arms of a different man—an emasculated man with whom they felt safe. As they filed past, a voice branded me, "male-identified." Women who nurtured separate worlds.

I stayed in the trailer, in part, because of my mother. Because of a psychologist's insistence that every voice be heard, that every life be of equal value. She engrained in me her egalitarian gospel. With what license could the feminists discount the lives of the men with whom I worked?

I stayed in the trailer, a sometimes stunted, sometimes expansive place. As Bessie put it, "I . . . am just thinking how I can organize myself in future so that I spend the rest of my life with rough loud swearing men. I don't like hypocrisy and pretense and malice and there's really none of it here."

CHAPTER THIRTY-TWO

Ɛte sɛn, Idrissu?" I shout from the top of the embankment.
"Ɛyɛ, Akua, ɛyɛ!" Idrissu rushes out from behind his sew-ing machine, motioning for me to come. "Akua, bra, bra."

I move down to the bottom step and Idrissu squares off oppo-site, like an opponent, one foot on the lip of his gutter. We both look to and fro, gauging the evening traffic for a suitable break. I mark a blue and yellow taxi billowing a ribbon of black exhaust worse than any cartoon. As I step into the road, I glance at Idrissu who waves his confirmation.

"Yes, Akua. Yes, how?" Idrissu welcomes me.

"Ɛyɛ."

"Maadwo, Akua," calls Fathia from her low stool beside the charcoal stove.

"Maadwo, awuraa."

"Dat man from the Peace Corpse come today," Idrissu says, excited.

"Which man?"

"A white lady Peace Corpse, he come today and leave dis for you." Idrissu produces a sealed manila envelope with my name on it.

"Genevieve?" I ask. "Was it Genevieve?"

"Dat's right, de white lady Peace Corpse, he bring dis for you. I tell him I think you at office at Old Council or maybe you go for WAG. I tell him I see you go dat way. He say he no have time. He is for Tekyiman today—dat my town! I tell him, dat my town! He is for Tekyiman today and he cannot take time for you, Akua. Dat white lady ask me to keep dis for you. I tell him, I keep it safe for you, Akua. I keep it safe for you."

"Medaase, Idrissu. Medaase pa ara. This is my mail from Accra."

Idrissu scratches his beard and studies the fat envelope. "Maybe in dere you have a letter from your mother. Or from your father."

"Yes, Idrissu, maybe I do."

"Your mother, she worry for you coming to Africa. She worry maybe something bad happen to you, Akua. But we thank you for leaving America and coming to Africa to help de black man. We thank you for coming to help de black man. If de white man never come to Africa, I feel very sorry for de black man . . ."

"Thank you for this, Idrissu," I say, holding up the package.

"I tell him I keep it safe for you, Akua."

"I will tell her when I see her that you kept the mail safe for me."

"Yes."

"Medaase. Idrissu, have you heard the news of Owens Wiwa?" Idrissu has an intricate network of sources.

He furrows his brow. "Eh," he grunts. It pains him to admit that I've got the jump on him.

"You probably know, but I have it straight from a man who has just returned from Nigeria."

Idrissu grows angry as I share the story. "How can Owens Wiwa stop de protests in Europe? De WAG cannot even stop farmers with rifles. Shell thinks one man can stop Europe?" He snorts, "Dat is not for Owens Wiwa."

"And how is it for Mr. Vaughn to stop Nigeria from prosecuting a murderer?" I ask.

"It is de oil, Akua. De oil! Mr. Vaughn has a pocket full of money. Dat money is how Nigeria got brave enough to make a murder." He clicks his tongue in Ghanaian fashion, loud and disapproving, far back in his throat. "I am sorry for Owens Wiwa. He cannot help his brother."

"But Mr. Vaughn can." I think of all the geologists I have known in my life. Maybe I have even met this Vaughn or fallen asleep to his laughter.

More tongue clucking.

"I am hungry, Idrissu. Mekɔ."

Idrissu steps up to the curb beside me and watches the traffic. When he feels it is safe, he motions for me to go. I run across the road and up the steps to the top of the retaining wall where I wave. Fathia and Idrissu both wave, "Good night."

The envelope feels heavy in my hand. I reach through the piquets for the Chinese padlock. Inside the compound, one of my neighbor's pigeons flutters away. Bird droppings spatter the concrete in an artist's frenzy.

I place the manila envelope on the corner of my desk, aligning its edges in parallel with the edges of the desk top. Still warm, the bundle of newspaper and banana leaf emerges from my duffel bag. Ozwald scrawled my name across the gold envelope with a heavy, black felt tip marker. My tongue relishes the heavy body of the hot yam. A wide piece of tape has been pinched around the edges of the envelope at the sealed end. There cannot be a better meal in all the world than golden, fried yam chips with pepe sauce too hot for me, washed down with boiled, filtered water.

The thick envelope contains four issues of *Newsweek* magazine, a Peace Corps volunteer newsletter, a book-sized package, and two letters. The package is from Mom. The letters are from Carol and Aunt Rachel. I line them up along the front edge of the desk: Mom, Carol, Aunt Rachel. A hard ridge runs along the bottom of Carol's envelope in the shape of a soda straw. Sitting with my legs running the full length of the couch, I look at the gifts on the desk beyond the tips of my toes. This angle betrays the dullness of the desk top.

Everything must come off to brush away the endless accumulation of Obuasi dust. The gifts are returned to their places along the front edge of the shining desk: Mom, Carol, Aunt Rachel.

I know Aunt Rachel's gift without opening it. Every one of her letters traverses the same terrain—the recent and anticipated St. Louis weather, developments in the maladies of my other aunts and uncles, a catalogue of Aunt Rachel's ailments, mention of the last time she spoke to my parents, and a few inquisitive questions about what I'm doing in Ghana, coupled with proud encouragement and a "God bless." Aunt Rachel has proven my most loyal correspondent. I read every word of her letters.

Carol and I have known each other since junior high. The instant I saw her I knew she was special. Her first smile opened my heart. We used to ride our bikes out to the ranches west of town and eat sandwiches under a huge oak in a horse pasture. Inspired by the magnificence of the grey stallion, we braided each other's hair—every kind of braid. We read articles and studied fashion photos, always looking for a new edge.

I love the silk of her flaxen strands. I know how it fans from static electricity and how to matte her peacock's comb with clay, not wax, so it doesn't darken. I know how her bangs fall without the slightest wave. And I know how to weave a fine braid that pulls her bangs out of hapless and into evocative. By our sophomore year, people had grown to expect our intricate coiffures.

I know every millimeter of Carol's head, her pointed peak, the flat spot above her right ear, the tender hollow at the base. And she knows me. I love the pull of her fingers through my hair, the mastery with which she manipulates my thick locks.

In our junior year, we got into dyes and played with punk cuts. Nothing was too outrageous. It wasn't just fun. It was our ritual. The sacred submission of one's head into the hands of another. Trusting each other to remake our selves.

The last time I saw Carol, she wove my sacrificial strands into a single long braid down the center of my back. Metal scissors abraded the bone of her thumb as she forced the blades to slice the thick root. She placed my femininity on white tissue in a narrow box. "I will keep this safe for you. Go, change the world."

I don't need to know the contents of Carol's letter. The envelope on the desk with Carol's handwriting spelling my name opens a chasm that rips apart the earth from Obuasi to Bakersfield.

I insert the soothing cream. Carol and I were ecstatic when we discovered we could buy yeast cream without a prescription. That was empowering. To be able to handle it on our own. Gyimiso Kakraba has no control. They are at the mercy of the multinational.

V

THE OLD COUNCIL

Where and when I was growing up, children, especially daughters, accepted their parents' authority completely, without question or resentment.

—Dympna Ugwu-Oju, *What Will My Mother Say—A Tribal African Girl Comes of Age in America*

CHAPTER THIRTY-THREE

Michael Vaughn can stop the murder of Ken Saro-Wiwa.

What is my father doing right now?

All of the oil companies for whom my father has worked—what are they doing right now?

Old Man Antoine used to say, "Authority is a privilege and an obligation."

If Michael Vaughn flaunts his privilege and abandons his obligation to be decent, where do the other oil companies stand? Do they notify Shell that its conduct is intolerable? Do they tell Michael Vaughn he is a stain upon their profession? Do they demand that a good man's life be saved? Do they stand on their honor and self-regulate their industry? Or do they watch in silence, ready to live by the lowest standard to which the world dares hold them?

All of the oil companies for whom my father has worked—what are they doing right now?

What is my father doing right now?

Michael Vaughn can stop the murder of Ken Saro-Wiwa.

When we were kids living in Tripoli, our parents took us to ruins in North Africa and Rome. Our father acted as tour guide, pronouncing the age and purpose of each edifice. He reveled in historical detail, throwing in anecdotes to reveal a ruler's hubris, a culture's idiosyncrasy. I stood on ancient, hewn stones, long toppled from their glory drinking in my father's intoxication with the visionary and the powerful.

For years after, my brother and I watched slides and listened to our father's reconstruction of the past. His monologue never varied. Dad loved that he could know the truth of history. I loved revisiting those sites of my childhood. Every showing rekindled my passion to return. Art seldom commented. Libya isn't sacred to him. It's as if we lived separate lives.

In high school, photographs of St. Peter's Basilica and the catacombs startled me from the pages of my Western Civilization textbook. Lou's domain! I brought the family slides to class and delivered Lou's oration. Without thought, words toppled forth in Pavlovian response to the familiar images . . . till there appeared the northwest apse of the Severan Basilica at Leptis Magna. In the foreground a small girl stood on a massive carved column segment, one of several dragged into rows. Heat flushed my face as I tried to rub the sweat from my palms. I had thought this scene a part of my genuine memory. But the description spilling from my mouth, the voice of the photographer, could not have been mine.

I carried the presentation to its end. Carol knew me well enough to perceive my shame at realizing that Lou's authority had superimposed itself upon my memory. I didn't know whether my recollections were of actual experiences or my father's narrative, repeated so many times it could not be forgotten or stripped away.

To this day, mention a civilization or ancient city and my father's words fly to my lips corroborated by images that may be my first-hand reality or the propagation of Lou's perceptions. Between the two, I long ago lost the capacity to distinguish.

Carol teases in her letter that my descriptions of Ghana read like a textbook. I suppose it's the engineer in me who needs to construct a foundation of facts. In part, it's my father's voice that inhabited me so young.

It's in creating a legend for the map that I begin to understand what's happening. Some villages are calm and have no
interaction with West Africa Gold. Others have longstand-
ing grievances, which the mine seems to ignore. Others have
pipe-borne systems installed by WAG. I could not decipher
an underlying principle that would predict the character of a
village. Outlying villages, in general, have less interaction with
WAG and are less disposed to assert claims. But this doesn't
always hold true. Some remote villages have received boreholes
from WAG. Other villages near the mine continue to petition
an unresponsive corporation.

It seemed a jumble of circumstances, until I labeled each village
by its type of water source and viewed this against the backdrop
of WAG's mining operations. It became clear that all of the pipe-
borne systems are in villages near the open pits—like Sansu and
Bediem. These residents bear the brunt of the daily dynamiting
and the subsequent dust thrown into the air and water. The borehole distribution correlates with villages that either constitute con-
tiguous suburbs with Obuasi or which lie along the Gyimi River
into which the mine discharges its effluent. Villages impacted by
the mine's continuing exploration activities accrue to an unpub-
lished list of those due to receive a water point. WAG doesn't share
this list, not even with Illiasu and Ankrah. However, West Africa
Gold voices its intentions in my presence, putting the Advocacy
in the peculiar situation of having to maintain silence.

Asasebomebosia is an island of mud-block homes in the forest.
We reach this remote village via an exploration road cut through
the bush by WAG. The villagers try to maintain vehicular access
by hacking away at new growth with their cutlasses, a practice
that leaves sudden protruding branches that hinder our narrow,
rutted, winding progress.

About three hundred people live in Asasebomebosia. More than half are children, who claim proportional representation at today's durbar of about sixty people. We sit in a concrete court-yard beneath an overcast sky. We're reviewing the mechanics of administering their village water project—community donations, a constitution to open a bank account, the terms of the funding sponsorship agreement. I read each paragraph of each document, Agyeman translates, the villagers discuss.

A question arises about placing a handpump in the well. I try to explain the considerations—the maintenance cost versus the benefit of a sealed well. Thomas feels that bucketed wells are des-tined to be contaminated and encourages the use of a handpump. I add that women and children will spend less time fetching water if they use a handpump. While Agyeman translates this advice, Thomas frowns, causing me to doubt the merit of saving time.

There is something peaceful about the process in this village. Although many questions are asked, there is no raging debate. There are no passionate opinions puncturing the quiet. A small man with a moustache sitting off to the side tells Agyeman that the village will inform the Advocacy of its decision. This man is our guide. He is that person we find in every successful village who mediates with the outside world on behalf of his people.

Asasebomebosia's guide is always serious, eyes wide to catch every detail. He is a mixture of trust and uncertainty. He has no choice but to trust, if he wishes to better the life of his village. I should like the chance to earn his trust, but Asasebomebosia is slated to receive a dug well. Other than cutting the road, explora-tion activity in the area is not apparent and WAG has not informed the village of their status. Until it is made public, the Advocacy must treat Asasebomebosia like any other village.

After the durbar, our guide leads us to the spring where the villagers draw their water. We enter a forest of cocoa palms. Thick foliage overhead filters the sunlight. Our eyes adapt to varying degrees of shadow dappling the rich earth. The spring emerges unannounced from dark soil, a tiny unprotected pool of crystal clear water. Here, the people draw their drinking water. Further on, a muddier pool serves as their source for nonpotable water. We take photos as part of our documentation to show to prospective donors.

The land in Ghana's forest belt is rich and fertile. I have heard expatriates at the mine complain that that is what is wrong with this country. If a person is hungry, they can wander into the forest and live off wild fruits and tubers. The supposed "problem" is that Ghanaians are not compelled to earn money in order to survive. The lack of a captive pool of wage labor has plagued the development of Ghana's mining industry.

Cocoa is Ghana's largest cash crop. The population of Asasebomebosia maintains the cocoa plantation of an absentee owner. In addition to the plantation, each subsistence farmer plants their own cocoa on a small plot intermingled with food crops. These mixed farms are not cleared of wild vegetation. Forest growth is left all around. Unlike in California's San Joaquin Valley, the eye does not meet a vast geometry of orderly cultivation.

We stand beside Asasebomebosia's spring, breathing air thick with vegetation, shadow, and silence, where earth and human hands midwife potent, inarticulate forms, precursors of all known things. Political realities cannot penetrate this place. In every pore swells the dank taste of afterbirth.

Our guide, this small man in a tee shirt and shorts, seems a creature of this forest. A lissome grace transports him over the damp earth. His solemnity betrays the strain of evaluating what we bring. I cannot help wishing we could somehow protect a life so pure. He leads us back through the cocoa plantation, past our truck, to the school on the far side of the village.

"This is Asasebomebosia's community project, Akua," says Thomas.

We are interrupting a class session. We look at the half-height walls sheltered by tin roofing sheets. The two end walls are full height and one is black for use as a chalkboard.

"The women dug the earth for the mud blocks. The men cast the blocks and built the walls. Every adult contributed to the cost of the roofing sheets," Thomas explains.

We want to show prospective donors that the village has demonstrated its ability to complete a communal project.

"Can the children stand in front of the school?" I ask.

Thomas speaks to our guide, who speaks to the teacher, who shepherds the children. The teacher and our guide stand at each side of a small assortment of students in simple dress. One has a tattered brown and yellow uniform like the students in larger villages and Obuasi town. The degree to which this village is isolated from our world announces itself in the unrehearsed, unselfconscious expressions on these children's faces. I snap a picture of something precious and fragile.

"Please wait." Our guide holds up a hand when we arrive back at the truck. He lets a smile break his mask.

While another man prepares coconuts with a cutlass, our guide relaxes a bit in conversation with the team. The thick air swallows their voices. We drink the coconut milk under a sky dramatic with gathering clouds. Lush hills answer the roiling clouds with vibrant green. Tangible quiet mutes the sounds of children and chickens. Our drained coconuts are cracked open with a few deft strokes. We eat the sweet meat.

CHAPTER THIRTY-FOUR

It takes a good half hour to wind our way back along the exploration road. Another tedious half hour of potholed tarmac brings us close to Obuasi town. We swing by Mamiriwa to follow up on rumors of a palaver regarding their water project. Though unscheduled, the villagers seem happy to see us. Nananom and a few villagers assemble in the chief's courtyard for an impromptu durbar.

Following introductions and some discussion in Twi, Agyeman says, "Akua, some of them are still not certain about the fundraising. Can you try once more?"

"What is it they don't understand?"

"Eh." He looks down to gather his thoughts. "It seems there has been trouble in the village. Everywhere there was trash in the village and the people objected to the filth everywhere around them. The people took their objection to the chief. The chief and elders met and as they had heard the will of the people that this garbage throughout the village was intolerable, so the chief and elders resolved to put an end to the situation. The chief and elders considered what to do and decided to clear one area of the forest to make a garbage dump that the whole community should use. They wanted the garbage dump to be away from the center of the village, but not so far that the distance to travel would discourage the women from going there.

"It seems that the site that was chosen met their criteria all right.

The site was near the home of a certain old man who didn't like to have the thing so close. The schoolboys were sent with cutlasses to clear the site and this action distressed the old man, even to tears. This is an old man who has lived in the village all his life. When he was a young man he worked at the mine. There was an accident . . ." As an aside, Agyeman offers, "In those days, Akua, fatalities were common, almost daily. . . . Eh, and he injured his foot. A great collapse in the shaft killed the man's brother and one other. The man injured his foot and could no longer work."

"Was the man his real brother?" I'm onto this. Ghanaian references to family do not necessarily reflect bloodlines.

Thomas and Agyeman look taken aback, bringing home that this is a poor context in which to ask for clarification.

"Never mind." I shake my head and brush away the question with my hand.

One of the villagers says something to Agyeman in Twi.

"Please, tell her I'm sorry."

"This woman is the old man's daughter. She wants to know why you are asking."

I look to Agyeman for an indication of whether to continue this conversation. He seems to be waiting for me. "Mepa wo kyεw, please tell her that I'm sorry. It was indiscreet of me."

The woman speaks again in Twi. She must understand my English.

"Akua, it is all right. The woman can answer, but she wants to know why you ask."

I can see the price of my crassness is to suffer making a bigger ass of myself. "In America, we do not refer to friends as 'brother' or 'sister.' 'Brother' would mean the two men shared the same father and mother."

The woman speaks and Agyeman translates. "The woman asks if you have a brother."

I'm surprised by the personal question. Tit for tat, I suppose. "I do."

"She asks if you are concerned about his death."

The woman must be a seer. She wears a tee shirt tucked into a wrap. She might be thirty and has the ebullience of a healthy village woman.

"No, there is no trouble with his health."

"She says his health is not the matter. Are you concerned about his death?"

"Why does she ask this?"

The woman throws up her hands. Agyeman and Thomas join her laughter.

I feel excluded and embarrassed. "May we continue?"

Agyeman says something to the woman, who wears a satisfied expression and does not reply.

"Eh." Agyeman retraces his thread. "Since that time the man has farmed just a small piece of land for himself, not too far from his house. He has never been any trouble to anyone and so the people say he should not be troubled in his old age. The people, with the chief and elders, met at a durbar and decided to build a fence to protect the old man's farm from encroachment of the garbage dump. The old man agreed this would protect him, but pointed out the very poor state of his roof, which was made of thatch and leaked when it rained. He said his greatest need was to have roofing sheets, and, if it was not too much trouble, the people should consider this.

"Some people objected, but in the end, it was agreed to purchase roofing sheets for the old man. Now a collection was taken up to pay for the materials. Each adult was to contribute twenty cedis. Many people paid their share and many others dodged the thing. Then the man collecting the money reported that the money was stolen. Many people became suspicious of the collector and life in the village became very tense. Before the matter could be resolved, the man disappeared. Anyway, he was not from here and some people say he returned to his village. There has been difficulty raising money for community projects since that time. The people are not saying they will not do it, but they want to know more about how it will work."

"You have had some experiences that have damaged the trust in your village," I say. "We are sorry for this. We hope it will not weaken your resolve to complete the water project, but this matter is in your hands. You must decide whether you can proceed with confidence. The village health committee has been formed for the purpose of health education and administering the water project. The health committee should collect the tariffs and deposit them in a bank account in Obuasi. You will have three signatories on the bank account, so that three people must sign in order to withdraw money from the account. These can be any three people the village chooses, but we would like one of the three to be a health committee member.

"It seems you need some means of accountability for the tariffs that will be collected. The Advocacy could provide you with tariff cards. Each paying adult would have their own card. Each month, when they pay their tariff, the collector would initial the card indicating that the money was received. The person would also sign their name in the collector's book, so that both the collector and the person have a record of the payment. Would this help?"

Agyeman translates and nods to me in the affirmative.

"Okay, we will work on making the tariff cards. We will bring them after your health committee has come to our office and completed a funding proposal. The project you have selected is two, four-inch boreholes and one, six-inch borehole, is this correct?"

The ɔkyeame nods.

"You do not have to decide on the amount of your contribution right now, but you must do it before the funding proposal can be written."

Agyeman translates. "They want to know how much, Akua."

"You must decide what is an appropriate amount. The total project cost is seventeen million five hundred thousand cedis. You know you cannot afford to pay the full amount. But there is some amount that you can afford to pay. If you make the amount very small in relation to what you are able to pay, when we go to donors asking for help, they will see that the project is not important to you. They will ask us why they should give money to a community that does not care to give that amount of which it is capable.

"If you make the amount too high, it will be too great a burden upon you. You will not succeed in raising all the money and the project will fail. You must decide what is reasonable."

On the drive back to Obuasi, the men talk while I feel the shame of their laughter—the seer, Agyeman and Thomas—all perceiving something about me to which I am blind.

Are you concerned about your brother's death?

I wrote to Art when I first arrived in country. He hasn't replied. My brother is not dead. Is there a difference?

The old man's brother was killed. Was it even the man's brother? No one in Ghana cares.

Art is my blood brother. Does that mean anything? Were Art and I ever close? *She says his health is not the issue.*

The familial distinction means less to Ghanaians. The distance between Art and me has always felt an emblem of my inadequacy, proof of my inherent failure to connect because it existed from the earliest time, even in Libya. *Are you concerned about his death?* Does it matter that I don't know Art? Is my concern only an engineer's compulsion to hold every piece?

The woman throwing up her hands and laughing so that her whole body shook. *Why does she ask this?*

What killed my brother?

A great collapse in the shaft.

CHAPTER THIRTY-FIVE

Several vehicles crowd the asphalt that fans around the back of the Old Council. Today is the first day of the District Assembly's quarterly meeting. The Advocacy's office is upstairs across from the Assembly Hall. A myriad of transactions are in progress in and around the parked vehicles, in the stairwell, and in the hallway in front of our office.

Businessmen in suits with briefcases, chiefs in cloth, assemblymen and women taking a recess from the ongoing proceedings take advantage of the occasion to press their concerns, both public and private. Thomas, Agyeman, Takyi, and Osei melt into the throng as they renew acquaintances.

I make slow progress, catching a couple of references in passing that "the trial has started." I penetrate as far as the office door where people direct my attention down to the vehicles. Mr. Moses stands flat-footed, looking up at the balcony. When he sees me, his wide palm deserts its post at the base of his chest and rotates out to the side in a semi-mechanical greeting. His words cannot pierce the din. I thread my way back downstairs.

"Hello, Akua." Moses clasps my hand in his large paw. Henry Moses is a tall, lean man whose careful motions suggest a need to coordinate long limbs. "I thought I would try to find you before returning to Kumasi." He offers a gentle smile.

"Yes, Mr. Moses, thank you for stopping. I just missed you yesterday at Yeboah Estates."

"Ah, yes," he says, his voice slow and apologetic. "The head driller did mention this. I have had to rush back to Kumasi lately. There are many meetings, much is happening these days. What did you want to discuss?" Henry Moses has a continuous moustache and beard that encircle his long lips like a clown's makeup. The effect is not comical, but rather, when combined with his concerned manner, gives him a comfortable appearance like a much-loved teddy bear.

"Yes, but first may I confirm . . . I overheard someone saying that the trial has started?"

Mr. Moses's camaraderie fades into reverence for the poignance of what is happening in Nigeria.

"I just wanted to be sure," I say. "They mean the trial of . . ."

"Yes."

It is unusual for a Ghanaian to display the discourtesy of interrupting. It is certainly not the nature of Mr. Moses. I understand it is a painful and complex subject into which he does not wish to digress. "Thank you. So, we pulled the drilling records from some of the boreholes you drilled for WAG. The one for Nyameso shows the borehole goes down fifty meters. But when we pulled the pump, it was down fifty feet. Do you drill a hundred feet past the pump setting?"

"Yes. We want to ensure a continuous water supply. If we can, we drill fifty meters to pierce multiple aquifers. This way, the well receives water from many different layers." Moses gestures as he speaks, the broad, open palm curling to create a well in the air, cutting through permeable layers at different depths. "What has caused your concern?"

"I went to Accra last week and met with Tao Bronson and Jim Kelly at the World Bank."

"I know Tao."

"Kelly is his boss from America, in town for a few weeks to

review the proposal for the new rural water programme." I plant my sandal on the front bumper of the Advocacy's truck, leaning an elbow on my raised knee. "They need some place to establish a pilot program and are thinking of working with the Advocacy. But when I told them that most of our water projects right now are boreholes due to population size, they said, 'Nonsense,' that you should always put in dug wells because they're more economical. A larger population just gets more wells."

Moses leans over the hood of the truck.

"I came back and discussed this with Kwasi and he was pretty excited about the savings, until he thought of Kokotenten. West Africa Gold dug two wells there, both of them dry. Then they drilled a borehole. The dug wells ended up being a wasted expense. So, he's asked me if I'm sure that dug wells will guarantee a source of water all year round, even in the dry season. I feel stupid, after talking to the World Bank, to have leapt for a high-tech solution. But, I don't know the answer to Kwasi's question, either."

Moses casts his gaze beyond the political machinations spilling out of the Hall and enveloping us, focusing on the tip of the winding gear at Attakpah Shaft. "It is true, what Kwasi is saying. Wells do not have the depth of boreholes and are, therefore, more subject to fluctuations in the groundwater table, to environmental conditions like droughts and even annual dry seasons. The well may yield water when it is dug, but throughout the year or even a few years later, you cannot be certain that it's a lasting solution. But boreholes, the first borehole drilled in Ghana fifty years ago still produces water. I am not saying that the people you spoke to are wrong, but you must consider the interests of the people speaking."

Mr. Moses is the chief hydrologist out of Ghana Water and Sewerage Corporation's regional office in Kumasi. He manages the crew that is sinking boreholes for WAG and that would sink boreholes for the Advocacy, if we were to get funding. My eyes tell him that I am well aware of his interests.

"Akua." He rearranges his gangly limbs. "I own a company that constructs dug wells. It would be in my interest, if you were to select dug wells over boreholes. This would be good for my business. But I am telling you what I know to be true; boreholes are superior to dug wells. You must realize that the people who are making these decisions are interested in preserving their jobs. The World Bank money will come. They will have a ten-year program and they can appear to be aiding a much greater number of people by constructing dug wells. But when the money is spent and the wells are dry, the problem of good drinking water for the majority of the population will still exist. They will all still have jobs because there will still be a problem. Their interest is in preserving their jobs."

"Tao Bronson?" I ask, not wanting to believe.

"Yes."

"Yeah," I say, picking myself off the hood of the truck. "A lot of things don't make sense about this program. They want Ghana's rural water needs to be met by a private sector that doesn't exist. They expect people like my team to quit their civil service jobs. They expect them to form private businesses that will contract with the district assemblies to educate rural villagers about safe drinking water and create a demand for what the World Bank is selling.

"In ten years, eighty percent of Ghana's rural water needs are supposed to be met. Then what happens to my team? There is no more demand for their services and they've lost the security of their civil service jobs. Even if they get into handpump maintenance, the market can't absorb all the people who are needed up front to mobilize the rural communities. Is anyone thinking about what will happen to these people?"

Moses massages the woolly scruff on his chin.

"Excuse me, Akua." It's Takyi at my side. "Hello, Mr. Moses, it is good to see you. We were looking for you only yesterday."

"Yes." Mr. Moses extends a hand to Takyi.

"Excuse me, Mr. Moses. Akua, Mr. Illiasu would like to see you. Mr. Illiasu has asked me to find you and tell you to come to see him. He's in the Assembly Hall. He's expecting you."

"Ah." Moses shrugs. "I must get to Kumasi. There're people waiting for me in Kumasi."

"Thank you for your thoughts," I say, as we clasp hands.

CHAPTER THIRTY-SIX

The Assembly Hall is a dignified chamber. Three u-shaped tiers of bench seats beneath continuous desktops open toward a two-tiered dais hosting desks at varying elevations. The furnishings are of polished, yellow wawa wood. Wood paneling covers the walls with equal luster. This room stands empty most of the year. Once each quarter, the Assembly meets to conduct its business.

During this convening the Assembly will hammer out the details of administering the upcoming presidential election, the first since a Rawlings-led coup in 1981. For the past eleven years, Chairman Rawlings has presided over the stabilization of the revolution. It's unclear to me whether he has the popularity to win a fair vote or whether Rawlings's apparent favor is the residue of silence. Ghana's embracing of democratic practice comes at the behest of the international finance community, principally, the World Bank.

The main doors to the Assembly Hall are closed. I weave through many small, private meetings in the open air hallway to the balcony that overlooks the front of the Old Council. A door from the Assembly Hall is open onto the balcony for ventilation. An usher keeps the balcony clear to minimize the noise filtering into the Assembly. He waves me to his side at the open door.

Mr. Ankrah conducts the Assembly meeting in Twi from the highest desk in the center of the highest tier of the dais. To his right, at the second highest desk, sits Mr. Illiasu. Chiefs in full regalia, others in political suits, as well as Western business suits, fill the u-shaped tiers.

"Go ahead," whispers the usher.

I approach Illiasu, who sits on the near side of the dais. We speak in quiet tones.

"You are back," he says in a voice both friendly and unrevealing. "I enquired of your whereabouts this morning before the meeting. They said you had gone to the villages."

"Yes."

"To which villages did you go?"

"Asasebomebosia and Mamiriwa. We were also scheduled to go to Adubensasu, but no one was there to meet us."

"Adubensasu?"

"Mile 9." I correct, giving the familiar name that originated with WAG's road-cutting crew.

"Ah, they are poor farmers. You travel so far to meet them, but they've gone to farm. Asasebomebosia and, what is it, Mamiriwa? That's nice. What happened to you yesterday? I was expecting you. You didn't return."

"No." I seek refuge in the drone of the meeting. An assembly-man in the first tier slouches over the desktop, his head cradled in his arms. His mouth hangs open and his eyelids flutter on the verge of relinquishing the battle. To Illiasu, I offer, "I did not think my attitude was conducive . . ."

"No," he laugh-sighs in high pitch. "You were not in good shape."

I smile in apology.

"We must get together soon. When can you come? Tomorrow I must attend the Assembly. Can you come the day after?"

"All right."

"And bring someone who can sign the contract, someone from your team."

The usher nods as I leave. The team accesses the Advocacy office from the rear stairs and I usually don't venture down the hall to this balcony. I take a moment to survey the view. Off to the far left is the bright green of the golf course, below that the spire of the Catholic church, ahead is the main expanse of corrugated tin rooves that comprise Obuasi. To the right is the tip of Attakpah Shaft. Between the shaft and the Old Council are the railroad tracks and the Miner's Circle.

Not the village in the Peace Corps brochure. I'd imagined a slower pace, quiet, playing with children under a clear sky far from civilization. The scene of my two-year hiatus from the craziness of America, the insanity of my profession, bears none of the comforts I'd sought. The muezzin calls from the mosque, whose minaret rises from the carpet of rusted roofing. There is no escaping oneself.

At the Miner's Circle, Ned Clyde lifts steel round stock up to a crewman standing in the bed of his truck. Ned jumps behind the wheel and disappears down the chute road. A memory comes of another truck, another Old Man whipping the tailgate down before I cut the engine. His crew had busted a fire main at the abutment of a freeway bridge.

On the eve of Labor Day weekend, the Old Man waited four hours for me to crawl through holiday traffic with parts to make up a joint. In the dusk, the Old Man dragged the box of fittings across the bed. He knew I would do my best and expected, given Murphy's Law, that I would bring the wrong parts.

Antoine took stock of my delivery and, without looking up, said, "You are a true friend."

Watching Ned's truck disappear around the Catholic church, I wipe a tear. Why did I leave a world of such clarity? Where I knew the right thing to do. Where our mission was always accomplished.

I take the truck up to Safety to find Kwasi and give him the keys. Although the Advocacy's budget indicates that we will purchase our own vehicle, the mine has never billed us for the truck. WAG prefers to retain ownership. Kwasi's promotion to senior environmental officer entitled him to a company vehicle. Harrigan assigned to Kwasi the Advocacy's vehicle, meaning that we must begin and end each day exchanging the keys.

"Thank you, have a seat." Kwasi accepts the keys and stretches in his modern, wheeled executive chair.

"This is a nice office, Kwasi."

"Yes. It's a bit large. It's difficult to get used to this large room."

Finn Harrigan has been busy the past few months constructing offices for his new Safety Department just west of the Environmental Lab. Kwasi is the last to move in, due to miscalculation at WAG's furniture shop.

"How did it go today?" Kwasi speaks in a husky voice that sounds too soft for his large frame.

"Pretty well. We had durbars at Asasebomebosia and Mamiriwa." I adjust my balance on the new, high-backed, wooden chair, custom-made in WAG's shop.

"Asasebomebosia. I think they are on our list to receive a dug well. I'll have to check."

"Yes, they are."

"Hm, and what are you doing in that village?" Kwasi scratches the tip of his moustache and pushes up his glasses.

"They are a very motivated village. They want to improve their drinking water and we're taking them through the steps to implement a water project."

"What kind of water project?"

"They want one dug well. Today the debate was over whether or not to add a handpump. We're waiting for them to make that decision and come to town to open a bank account."

"How soon would you begin construction of the well?"

"The villagers have to raise their part of the funding first, which will take six months and then we want to build the well in the dry season . . ."

"They aren't going to pay for the well, are they? I don't think West Africa Gold would like that." Kwasi opens his eyes in distress.

"The village doesn't know it's getting a well from WAG. Until they know, we've got to go along with preparations for their water project. It's okay. They'll be well-prepared to maintain the well after you give it to them."

"So six months to perhaps a year?"

"Yes."

"Hm." Kwasi looks at his desk, as if trying to remember where he left something. "There are some other small villages along the Dunkwa Road that should receive dug wells. I need to look into finding contractors who build wells. Do you know of any?"

"WaterCore builds wells. And, Mr. Moses has a well-constructing company. I don't know if WaterCore contracts out or if their service is limited to villages served by their programs."

"What was the other village you visited?"

"Mamiriwa?"

"Yes, Mamiriwa. We have to investigate a claim by Mamiriwa. They say our exploration crews have somehow spoiled their stream. Do you know about this?"

"No."

"Well, someone will have to investigate." Kwasi stares at his broad, polished desktop. He is gradually being given charge of Jim Hansen's duties—all of WAG's air and water quality monitoring, as well as all environmental operations. He's the individual most depended upon by Harrigan. The last time I dropped the truck, he was just rushing out in response to a call from the Bediako Treatment Plant. They wanted to know what should be done with the piles of fine powder occupying every inch of the roof of the plant—arsenic trioxide that had been pulled from the smokestack by a state-of-the-art vacuum and left to blow in the wind.

"You only went to two villages today?" Kwasi inquires.

"We were scheduled to monitor health education at Mile 9, but the people were not ready for us."

"You try to help the villagers. You do the best you can, but it's difficult in a country like Ghana," Kwasi muses aloud. "Look at your team members. They are all civil servants. Everyone knows the government doesn't pay civil servants enough to live on. Maybe they pay half what it takes to live on. So, right away, you know you cannot expect to find civil servants working all the time. If they work full time, they are really donating fifty percent of their time because they will never be paid for it.

"Civil servants must always be running schemes on the side to make money. That is why you cannot find them at their jobs—they're busy attending to personal affairs. But in a country like Ghana even university professors don't have the kind of income to attend professional conferences or even to subscribe to professional journals. You cannot even keep up with developments in your field. It's depressing. You cannot blame them for losing their motivation . . ."

Kwasi carries on in this vein, occasionally returning to an earlier point and repeating the subsequent logic. I don't know what has prompted his philosophical mood—a frustrated attempt to conduct civic business, a conversation with a colleague at the University of Science and Technology, a need to bolster his own rationale for staying at WAG? I listen without sympathy. He's not speaking to me, after all. I'm just a body at which he can project.

"Eh, Louisa." Kwasi's tone changes. "Ah, we are drilling for the boreholes at Gyimiso Kakraba tomorrow."

"That's great." Better late than never. "I just saw Mr. Moses. He says boreholes are more reliable in the long term."

"Yes. We will stick with boreholes in the larger villages. Eh, Louisa, would you know if the Advocacy contract has been signed?"

I say nothing and look away. I resent being caught in the middle.

"No? Well . . ." It's late. Kwasi pushes some files into his briefcase. Though he'll drive past my house, he doesn't offer me a lift.

Before I am out the door, the phone rings. When Kwasi cradles the receiver, he says, "The audit report is in. Finn would like to see you."

"Now?"

"Yes. He is waiting."

Finn looks like a caricature behind his room-wide desk in his executive chair, the back of which rises almost two feet above his head. He is not a tall man and the oversized dimensions of the interior do not serve him. At my previous visit, his pair of Fu lions had at least concealed the full width of the desk and framed him in a more complimentary manner.

Finn holds up the report, saying, "This is an audit of your accounts." He does not offer it to me, but slaps it onto his desk.

He waits, I suppose for some sign of agitation from me. I avert my gaze to minimize the impact of my nonchalance.

"I have audited your accounts, Louisa. I know."

Know what? Finn has a pair of new, four-drawer file cabinets behind his desk. What I would give for one of those.

"You are skimming money."

I look at him with raised brows. He's going to frame me?

Finn takes a long drag on his cigarette and plays with his wedding ring. "You may come clean and step down now without anyone else knowing. Otherwise . . ."

The Rifleman swing cocks the Winchester. "You have not even given me a copy of the report. I have no idea the basis of such an accusation."

"Louisa, be smart. I'm giving you an out."

The Rifleman fires high into the seat back above Finn's head. "Out of what? Out of a charge that you cannot defend, else you'd let me see the report."

"Louisa, there are irregularities. Whatever you may think of me, the audit was conducted independently. The accountants do not answer to me. Think about the Advocacy. You have worked to build the organization. The damage to the Advocacy's reputation will be irreparable."

"If there are irregularities, I should have the opportunity to address them. I am not an accountant. Errors can be made."

"I'm letting you handle this quietly. Releasing the document outside of WAG must be authorized by Madame Tettey. Do you want the attention of the General Manager on your . . . *irregularities?* Madame Tettey is an attorney. Embezzlement is a crime under the laws of Ghana. Your volunteer status does not shelter you from trial."

I smile with incredulity. Agyeman was wrong. Things are not serious; they're ludicrous. *Don't let them take you out of here in a straitjacket.* Hansen had it right.

"Do you need a minute to think about it? Would you like to consider all the good your team can still do, even without your leadership? Would you like to accept my gracious offer?"

In the backroom of your office? "No. I'll take my chances in the light of day." I stand to my full height and look down upon this small man. "Please have the complete audit report sent to the Advocacy office."

Finn takes a drag and flicks ashes. "We will have to suspend any further disbursements to the Advocacy until this is cleared up, you understand."

I do. You just conceded that it can and will be cleared up. The Rifleman lowers the Winchester. "The truck?" If he pulls the money and the truck, he is shutting us down. I'm not sure that's in his interest.

"You may use the truck. Only to make scheduled village visits. You will notify Dr. Kwarteng-Badu where you are going in the truck every day."

I already publish our schedule in advance, and Kwasi and I meet every day to exchange the truck keys. This is nothing new.

"If the doctor reports any untoward activity, you will forfeit use of the truck."

CHAPTER THIRTY-SEVEN

Bracing my weight along the steep slope of the fifth hole, fear flutters in my belly. I cannot control lies. The bold patterned cloths drying on the banks of the small river startle me. I avert my gaze, remembering the insanity of Del undercutting me on the pier job. The prospect of watching my back every minute depresses me. It's a bleak existence.

Could Illiasu help? If he and Ankrah sacrifice villages for political ends, they certainly aren't coming to my aid at the risk of their relationship with West Africa Gold. Ei! Ankrah will never meet with World Bank. He does not want them to see WAG's impact on the villages and the environment. He does not want things blown wide open.

My balance on the slope of the green feels precarious. The Advocacy will never be a Watsan Collaborator. Ankrah will ensure that World Bank never comes to Obuasi. Sobered by this realization, I comprehend that I will never have support in dealing with WAG.

There remains the contract to sign. I hope Illiasu will be expedient. I can't sit through a forced march over every item in my letter. Can we just sign and be done with it? I plot a path via the least saturated mounds of soil at the swampy downhill edge of the course. Osei will sign. I can't imagine in which war he served, but he retains a martial obedience. Takyi would have doubts. Thomas is new to this region and Agyeman is already too embroiled in local politics.

Stepping sideways through the gap in the wrought iron, I emerge onto Obuasi's main road. I might stop at the Dazzle store. They sell household items. I've never checked out their wares.

"Need a lift?" Joy washes through me at the sight of Peter Clayton's friendly face. He hangs his head out the driver's window from the far side of the road.

I scamper through a break in traffic and clamber into the passenger seat. "Thank you. I don't usually see you about town."

"Ah, they've a bit of a palaver down at Ashanti Shaft. Not my specialty, but they called for reinforcements." Peter pulls his eyes from the road to shoot me a smile that's a little crooked and gapped, and full of life. "How've you been, Lou?" He asks with a sincerity that cannot help but sound eccentric.

"Good, thanks." It feels good to have another human being treat me with respect, as if I matter. "How's Evelyn?"

"Nice of you to ask, Lou." Peter brakes. "She's doing well. Why don't you come round for supper, Thursday? We can catch up."

"I'd love to." I enjoy responding with gusto.

Peter crawls around a stalled vehicle. Through his open window, I glance at the alley that houses the mural of unpatriotic Kofi. There's never been the possibility of speaking to anyone of this enigma. "Why does Kofi hold the Union Jack?"

"The saints," Peter says.

"What?" I ask.

"The saints. Amadu al-Attar is like a patron saint to Obuasi . . ."

"Exactly. Why the hell would he brandish that blatant symbol of colonialism?"

"The saints, Lou. St. George, St. Andrew, St. Patrick. Don't you know what the flag is? It's the crosses of the three saints."

"The British flag is a religious emblem?"

"Hey, we never claimed to want separation of church and state. That's your side of the Atlantic."

"Huh," I mutter. The things I don't know. I don't even know what I'm looking at when I see a flag I've known since elementary school. How will I ever understand Ghanaian culture?

"The trial started," Peter offers in a somber tone.

"Yeah. It's all the buzz at the Old Council."

Peter pulls to the curb in front of Idrissu's. As I get out, Idrissu hustles out from behind his sewing machine. He and Peter exchange enthusiastic greetings.

"Six o'clock, Thursday, Lou." Peter flashes a hand toward me, already looking over his shoulder to judge the chaotic road.

"I'll be there." I wave him off, as he cuts into the heavy traffic.

"Akua, dis man give you a ride!" Idrissu exclaims.

"Yes."

Idrissu swings his head in jubilance. "Dis man give you a ride!"

"Yes." I sit on the bench eager to hear Idrissu's story, aware of how precious it feels to have a neighbor receive me.

"Akua, you know dis man?"

"Yes."

Idrissu sits on the bench beside me. "I know dis man. He work for de WAG. Many years I see him go by. One day, he stop. He say, 'You, Tailor, can you make men's trousers?' I say, 'You show me, I make for you.' He want I make trousers for him. I tell him, 'You show me. I make for you.'" Idrissu's face beams.

"Dis man." Idrissu points at the road in the direction taken by the truck. "Dis man bring trousers, finest quality, made in Europe. Dis man say, 'You make dese trousers for me?' I tell him, 'Yes, I make for you, very good.' Dis man bring cloth, finest quality. I make for him trousers, two pair, three pair, I make for him. Best quality, just like trousers dis man bring."

Kwadwo, who irons at the table behind Idrissu, turns to catch my eye. We exchange a silent greeting, not wishing to interrupt Idrissu.

"De man come," says Idrissu. "He say, 'You, Tailor, do good work.' I do best work for him. He tell me, 'Make two more trousers.' I make three trousers for dis man. Always he come to me when he need new trousers. I make for him best quality, just like in Europe."

"You are Peter's tailor?"

"I make best quality trousers for him, just like trousers made in Europe."

"You are a fine tailor," I echo.

"Akua, you know dis man?"

"Yes."

"He give you ride?"

"Yes, from the Catholic church. Have you heard that the trial started?"

"Dat's right. Akua, you go to village today?"

"Yes, today we went to Asasebomebosia down Dunkwa Road, and Mamiriwa. We had durbars to discuss their water projects."

"Dat's right. Just two villages?"

"We were supposed to go to Mile 9, but the people were not there to meet us. They had gone to farm."

Idrissu looks at the ground, shaking his head from side to side. "Africans," he says. "I feel sorry for Africa, if de white man never come. I feel sorry for Africa, if de white man never come. You come all de way from America to help de African. You leave your mother and your father in America. In America, de life is very good. You leave America to come here and help de African and dese people, dey cannot make time for you?" He clicks his tongue and shakes his head. "I feel sorry for Africa, if de white man never come."

Kwadwo looks at me from behind Idrissu's shoulder. He squeezes his face, rolls his eyes, and shakes his head. It seems he does not feel sorry.

"You have shaved!" I say, studying the face revealed.

Kwadwo says nothing. Idrissu turns to look at his friend.

"You've shaved your beard!" I repeat.

"Yes." Kwadwo holds up his head, refusing to admit his wound.

"Why?"

"My father told me it is disrespectful," he speaks without betraying emotion.

A man in his forties with a family of his own whose father tells him how to cut his hair. This obedience to elders inculcated in children cannot be cast aside with age. Kwadwo and Idrissu would be mortified by my challenging of Finn.

I was raised to have a voice. For Dad it was a matter of intellectual rigor. But Mom knew one day I would be in a position to finish the conversation. She intended that I speak.

CHAPTER THIRTY-EIGHT

Idrissu, I have a *Newsweek* for you," I say.

"Dat's right."

"I'll bring it."

"Go, come."

I wait for a break in the evening traffic and dash across. The touch of the metal padlock sends my thoughts to the treasure. A flat, rectangular gift wrapped in peach-colored petals because my mom cares about making things beautiful. It sits on the corner of the desk, book hard, its edges aligned with the desktop edges. I deliver the magazine and return to let my eyes feast upon the peach-colored petals.

I suspect the wrapping offers much greater pleasure than the intended gift. I can't say that I've learned not to trust Mom's judgment in books. I don't know what her judgment is. I don't know what she feels when she reads. She knows I don't know. She can sense my frustration and begins already apologizing for what she won't say or what I won't hear. Frail apologies.

But Mom keeps trying to give me something. Today, she gives me peach-colored petals and *The Measure of Our Success*, by Marian Wright Edelman. Perusing the jacket, my teeth clench. Mom's inscription brings a familiar feeling of distance.

Dear Dear Louisa, How I miss you! I am so proud of you. What courage you have to help the Ghanaians! May you find

inspiration in the strength of this brave woman's convictions.
May God keep you safe.

I love you very, very much,
Mom

I can see Mom sitting in the breakfast nook, sunlight filtering through sheer curtains onto the crisp, cream page upon which she writes. My mom loves me, would do anything for me . . . and I want more.

I want the voice of a mother who knows her daughter, who knows that she raised me to be who I am and there is nothing remarkable in my choice to be here. I want a mother who knows I am here to save myself because she has already saved herself. Because she knows the imperative to find one's ground. I want a mother who calls to me from land that she has claimed, paid for with her life, and her words reach my ears like a symphony rising to heaven reflecting to the Goddess her magnificence.

I turn the page. Despite my instinct, I begin reading because I'm in Obuasi and this is a book. I've descended already to that genre of spy novel born of businessmen and transcontinental flights. How much worse could *The Measure of Our Success* be?

Much. An appeal to do what is right and insist that everyone around you do the same. Confront every instance of sexism, racism, ageism, . . . -ism's ad nauseam. Vanquish evil and the righteous shall live in glory. Up in the ceiling, I can see the university feminists and my mother rallying to the cry. Of what use? Puritanical dictums will not bring water to Gyimiso Kakraba. They will not melt Finn Harrigan's heart. The fierceness of these women's forebears made my life possible. How is it that between this book and the reality of my life, the connection is lost?

The photographer caught Bessie mid-word. Oh, to have

heard the sound of her voice. Bessie's was a life forged by –ism's. Apartheid. Bi-racial. Woman. Exile. Writer. Addict. Violation and identity guided her pen to an unsparing honesty. Bessie never knew her mother. She would find no comfort in the sentimentality of mine. She sits here with me, measuring her success by survival, by every word inked upon the page.

I once worked a job drafting field layouts for utility crews. One morning, the superintendent entered the trailer with a big grin on his face. "Louisa," he said, standing beside me at the drafting table, "Why did the woman cross the road?"

I set down my pencil. "Is she surveying?"

"No. That's not the point." He leaned in with a mischievous twitch. "The point is . . . what is she doing out of the kitchen?"

Touching my hand to his arm, I said, "She's building a better road."

Jake flushed bright red and left my office with a sheepish grin.

There is no better way to show affection on a construction site than by giving someone a hard time. I cannot see the simple world in which these intolerant women survive. Their sermons are no help to me.

I smooth the paper against the fibers of the wood. The Muslim looks at me. The pale grey and soft lines of the sketch cannot compare to my memory of the bold black line of the frames set off by the striking white gown impassioned with flecks of red. My memory remains as vivid as the actual encounter, the brief moment when our eyes met.

How long does it take to walk past someone who is walking toward you? What is the margin for making contact just as two are abreast? I was not conscious of him before our eyes met. Something caused me to look up in the only possible instant.

This man I'd never seen before. I haven't seen him since. Though I walk that street every time I go to market, I'm not surprised that I don't meet him.

I find him every day in the image that met my eyes in that brief moment. We did not stop or slow our steps. In one glance, the gift was given. A gift too large. I cannot comprehend. Further contact would be greater waste.

I remember the urgency of the Muslim's eyes. Imperative amplified by stark black spectacles. The harsh eyes and frames made holy by the purest white cloth abjuring the filth of Obuasi. Red diamonds bleeding into white, pulling God down to earth.

I stare at the frames sketched on the paper. Pencil cannot hold the reality of black. Ink is permanent. I can always erase pencil, reapply it. What if the ink is too much? There will be no undoing it.

The fourth night of the exquisite cream. Symptoms did not return at all today. It is just a matter of finishing out the medicine to be sure the infection is eliminated. In less than a week, I am pain free. It is approaching two months that Gyimiso Kakraba has gone without fresh water.

A jumble of steel crashes in the night. My body recoils from the threat of a haul truck smashing through the bedroom wall.

Sounds of night swirl in the wake of the truck's tumultuous passage. The drone of my neighbor's television. A live quarrel in Twi, clear, as if they are in my room. Truncated paternal tones chop the voices. A high-pitched, tear-soaked explanation dies in the slap of a hand against the woman's face.

My eyes snap open and I stare at the darkness. The same darkness on the same continent where my parents shouted their way to compromise. Silence now from my neighbors' side. But I hear arguments, the torpedoes with which my parents would sink their marriage. A thick limestone wall muffled their words. Nothing disguised their venom. Accusations, pleas, indignation thrust in rapid exchange.

Every night, my ten-year-old self lay awake listening to the demise of our family. Was it always there? Mom's silence had concealed the ugliness. The flaw exposed by the crisis. I have always blamed her for wanting to return to the U.S. But she helped us to see the truth. Not the kind of truth Lou loves. The truth of who we are.

Drumbeats, steady and reassuring, float down from Presby church. I turn over and close my eyes, letting the rhythm enter. Words and thoughts dissolve in the unending, unbroken pattern. An involuntary contraction expels a breath, air that has been trapped for eons, on which rides a moan, a coarse, malformed sound laden with earth. Tears gush, mixing with soil with the beating beating beating. My cheek nestles in the mud of incoherent memory, coursing with the dense, unrelenting rhythm.

VI

GYIMISO KAKRABA

Spirits of various pantheons often establish their masculinity or femininity as fluid rather than fixed, offering gender as a continuum of qualities found in both females and males. . . . The self, the body, and the person are not unitary concepts but open to a constant reformulation through mutable entanglements with others.

—Heike Behrend and Ute Luig,
Spirit Possession—Modernity & Power in Africa

The Akans did not conceive the world in terms of the supposition of an unbridgeable distance between two worlds, the temporal and the non-temporal. . . . Because we were all religious objects, there was not sufficient externality and profundity to call for worship and religion in that sense. As men, that is to say, as accidents, we owed our existence to God; as spirits, that is to say, in our essence, we were uncreated.

—W. E. Abraham, *The Mind of Africa*

CHAPTER THIRTY-NINE

Two gentlemen confer under the awning of a shop. To dodge a funeral caravan, I leap onto their porch. It is said that in years past there were several funerals every week for mine fatalities, even daily. As the blaring horns diminish, one of the men approaches me. Though I don't know him, I know what he will say. Despite my inability to comprehend the Ghanaian mind, I have no difficulty perceiving when my sex is in question.

The man opens both palms before him to present his plea. "Ah, excuse me . . ."

I do not respond to his jovial mood.

". . . We see you walk past here every day." He gestures toward his friend. "We see you every day and we cannot agree. You must tell us, are you a man or are you a woman?"

I lower my eyes to gain some distance from his rudeness.

"We cannot agree." He says, as if he thinks I should care. As if it matters that they know my sex. Misinterpreting my silence, he elaborates. "He says you are a man. I say you are a woman. Tell us," he demands. "Are you a man or are you a woman?"

I step into the road.

The man takes offense. "Ha, I am talking to you." He spits the words in disbelief at my departure.

I don't look back.

"I am talking to you." In a culture that holds courtesy paramount, they would roll me over to see if I have balls. The man's friend begins to laugh. They laugh together. I am less than human.

I wave to Idrissu, toss my duffel bag inside, and peer into the mirror. It's hard to see my whole face in the tiny glass. It doesn't matter. I know how naked I feel. Why have I done this?

It was something when only one side of my head was shaved. When Carol wove a fine whisper braid to fall in front of my unsheltered ear. When the other half of my head spiked purple. That was trick. It was a joy to be seen.

This . . . I slide my hands against my scalp, letting the tufts gather in the crevices between my fingers, making a fist and pulling . . . this is not style. If my brutal appearance possesses coherence, it eludes me. I suffer the intensity when it grows too long. Bow to the imperative to cut. Cry for the release of the shearing.

Man or woman?

That is not the question.

The Measure of Our Success lies on the desk. One minute adjustment aligns the spine with the bullnose edge. The half-read manifesto no longer stirs anticipation, but the gift means something. Someone knows I exist. My mother cared enough to wrap a book in peach-colored petals.

The isolation of Obuasi magnifies the significance of every human connection. I grab the book and flop on the sofa. With my knees up, I let Edelman lean against my thighs and open to Mom's inscription. How many idiotic things have I said to the team? Should they slam me every time as racist? They do not. Have we failed?

I believe the team measures our success as I do, by the quality of service we provide to the villagers, by the number of people we educate about preventing water-related diseases, by the number of sanitation facilities and water points we will, one day, help the villagers construct. I hope that despite my blindness to my own racial folly, the team recognizes that my heart is in the right place, that my dedication to our mission earns me some latitude. We are here every day together doing our jobs. Isn't that a measure of success?

Mom tries to give me something. Her heart is in the right place. She ignores my chafing against her doctrine of inclusion. I skim a few pages. My head spins from all the –isms. Dirty beige-thread grey-sworl brown-CAPITAL green black red white-Gere grey. I stow *The Measure* in an empty suitcase. When all things are included, I cannot find my bearings, cannot stop spinning. Dirty beige-thread grey-sworl brown-CAPITAL green black red white-Gere grey.

From the end table, I retrieve the wrapping paper. The beauty my mother gives me. I smooth the crisp, clean sheet against the grain of the table. Peach-colored petals. I can wrap them around a gift for Carol.

If nothing keeps me whole, Carol, at least, keeps me honest. I have always loved her for that. That and the beauty of a mind that doesn't dwell on minutia . . . and the miracle that she loves me. I cannot imagine life without her. Carol is the one to whom I show my insanity. Not that I can hide it from her. We are sisters, confidantes, and, above all, uncompromising in our quest for truth. No matter where I stand in the world, she is my touchstone.

My recovery feels complete. I could almost forget to take the last few doses of the cream. But the residue of humiliation inspires me to finish. Instead of relief, I feel inconvenienced by having to accommodate the night time application. How arrogant I would seem to those who languish in Gyimiso Kakraba without medicine—without clean water—to cure their latest malady, dysentery.

"Ah, there you are." Jim Hansen stops pacing when I arrive at his door. "You've heard?"

"No," I say, surprised by his gravity.

"We need you to get to Gyimiso Kakraba. There's been some palaver. They sent the drill rig away. We need you to find out why."

It saddens me to see the degree to which Jim is marginalized. Kwasi should be handling this. But today is the interdepartmental safety meeting. As evidenced by Jim standing before me, Harrigan has bumped him in favor of Kwasi.

In the meeting of our eyes, I suspect Jim recognizes my consciousness of his fate. However, he stands on form, betraying no feeling. "Louisa, can the Advocacy investigate?"

"Of course," I say with solemn reassurance. "We'll divert from our schedule. I'll report to you as soon as we get back."

"Kwasi."

"What?"

"Kwasi should be available by then."

"Well, I guess I shouldn't delay."

"Thank you, Louisa." Despite his stiff lip, Jim's voice carries a trace of gratitude, perhaps, for bearing witness.

Along the road to Gyimiso Kakraba, while the men chat amongst themselves, I review the political landscape. The Advocacy is asked to serve as proxy to protect West Africa Gold from an explosive confrontation. What were Illiasu's words? "You should have seen WAG the day Bediem stopped their equipment with guns." Is it out of line for WAG to send us into this situation? Damn right. But the residents of Gyimiso Kakraba—they're not to be feared. The relaxed energy of the men confirms this.

There is a part of me that wants this. That wants to be the one who can get the job done, the one to whom others turn—the kind of thing that happens a dozen times a day on a construction site. Rarely does Obuasi afford me such satisfaction. Soon enough, crushed rock crunches beneath our tires.

Takyi notes, "WAG has finished repairing the road."

We park at the bare mound of the durbar ground and wait small near the truck. I love the dramatic grey clouds gathering overhead. A villager should arrive in short order, but today no one comes. I roll up my sleeves and peel my tee shirt from my back. Thomas and Agyeman wander into the village proper to locate the Chairman of the Committee for the Defense of the Revolution. Osei, Takyi, and I take shelter in the shade of banana leaves on the bench where I met my small. The forest on the far side of the durbar ground glistens in the moist air.

Takyi draws a handkerchief under his armpits. Osei unfastens the upper button of his political suit and speaks with concern. An urgent, "haw," lands in my ear. Takyi responds with laughter, a somersaulting rumble that puts me at ease. I tap my watch and hold it to my ear. The packed earth of the meeting ground spans more than a football field to the forest's edge, beyond which lie trails to the village and outlying subsistence plots. I savor the rich scent of damp, red soil.

Takyi volunteers. "Akua, Mr. Osei is worried about the absence of the villagers. Mr. Osei fears the absence of the villagers is because of a serious matter. I told him I do not think this is so."

Osei rebuts in earnest. "It can happen in the villages that all the people flee. The people can flee to escape a curse. They can flee out of fear that a serious transgression may bring the wrath of the gods upon all."

Amused, I say, "I thought you were a preacher, Mr. Osei."

"Eh, yes, I am."

"Yet you speak of 'the gods.'"

"Eh, Akua." He shakes his head. "Akua, I speak of the villagers.

I speak of the villagers and their ways. It is not right that no one has come to greet us."

We all watch a man emerge from the forest. He wears traditional cloth over one shoulder, the other shoulder bare. The cloth falls to his knees. Osei and Takyi stand and face the man who remains motionless, the forest rising behind him. I stand, too. When the man comes toward us, I step forward to match his stride.

"No, Akua." Takyi warns. "That is not how it is done."

I see Osei's outstretched hand, as if to call me back. Embarrassed, I return to my position. We stand—Takyi on the left, Osei, then me—shoulder to shoulder, facing the stranger.

About two yards away, the man pauses. I try to match Osei and Takyi, who receive the man with soft eyes, not the penetrating stares of cowboys who may need to draw their guns.

The lanky man stands over six feet tall. A moustache trims his upper lip. His skin is the deeper hue of coconut after rain. Cords of sinew shape his arms and calves. On his feet are stout sandals. After about a minute, the man closes the remaining distance. He takes our hands, holding our three in his, and peers into my eyes, then Osei's and Takyi's. Without dropping our hands, the man speaks in a hushed voice.

When he finishes, Osei and Takyi look at each other.

Osei translates. "Akua, it is as I feared." Osei tries to soften his rough voice. "The people are meeting on a grave matter and have gone to the forest." He bows in apology to the man, as words violate the solemnity into which we have been drawn. "This man was left to guard the village. He . . ."

I hold up my free hand. I understand enough and want to honor the protocol of silence. Osei gives a faint nod of approval. Takyi stands as I have never seen him. A nobility of purpose has displaced his frailty. The guard's gravity and ritualistic approach have opened Takyi's heart to the drama unfolding in the forest.

I look to the guard who returns my gaze. Who might he be? Has he lived in the village all his life? Does he have a degree from Oxford or Cornell? Home for the Christmas holiday? He has an intelligent face that reveals nothing. Form dictates his reservation. He lets down our hands and turns to the forest.

CHAPTER FORTY

I know that I am to follow. Osei and Takyi gesture that they'll pick up the rear. We cross the expanse of the durbar ground in single file. Our guide pauses on the periphery of the lush vegetation. His grey cloth shimmers with threads of silver. He stares into the wild tangle of trees and vines. What he sees I cannot imagine. My vision cannot penetrate the dense growth.

At some unknown signal, the guard picks up his cutlass and enters the forest, trotting with the poise and pulse of another world. My eyes strain in the darkness. Striving to match our guide's pace, I scan the vicinity for hazards, while tracking his lithe movements for clues to what lies ahead. Pungent scents of iron and tropical decay dew our nostrils and lick our shins. Ducking low under a thick branch laden with vines, I rise too soon and butt into another limb. Osei clasps my shoulder and pushes me forward. It is uncommon for the men to touch me, but we cannot afford to lose our guide.

I redouble my concentration on the guard's agile form. The silver threads no longer glimmer. The cloth moves as a shadow around a fallen palm, through tendrils of vines hosting other odd species dangling, pausing at the thrashing sound of an animal, avoiding a bramble of thorns. An arm flies out and wields the cutlass in a severe arc. I improve at molding my form to match the rising then dropping, knife-edged then sidestepping contortions of the silhouette that now represents the guard.

Tripping on something unseen, I break my fall by shooting out a hand. Whatever I grasp bites into the fleshy pad of my palm. Osei's hand at my upper back sends me hastening on. The dim shades of the forest underworld grow more distinct. How far we've traveled or how much time has passed, I cannot say. Such measures feel irrelevant. I cannot explain the devotion I feel for our unnamed mission.

Moving with speed and in silence is contrary to my experience of Ghanaians. How could anyone await us at our destination? They cannot be expecting us. Something sharp cuts above my left ankle. I stifle the cry that rises, picking up my pace in anticipation of Osei's prodding.

We move faster. The air is cooler and damper. My heart pounds in my ears. Sweat covers my body. The pad of my hand aches. A burning pricks above my ankle. My toe screams every time I push off with that foot. I feel fierce in response to the pain. I will not quit. I will not be the one to kill this adventure. What a blessing that Agyeman and Thomas left. They would have interceded. It's rare for us to see something genuine. Normally, the villagers are reacting to our programme. I've never had the privilege of arriving unannounced and being invited to witness their affairs.

This way of passing through the forest exalts my soul. My body has learned to anticipate the dance of the shadowy guard. He leads by a few meters, and it's impossible to know the obstacles inspiring his spontaneous maneuvers. Some intuitive perception governs my fluid form. The clumsy stumbling of my initiation has melted into a finesse that I can sustain for hours.

I wonder at the growing awareness that our journey is the necessary preparation for what is to come. This breaking down of the body, yielding of intellect to instinct, opening of the soul—this is the Ghana for which I came. Show me what I have never seen.

Our guide stops, a move I fail to anticipate. My reverie ends as I land close on his heels, trying to not crash into him. While he peers, once again, beyond the impenetrable mass of vegetation, I bend over to catch my breath, hands to knees, head drooping.

Osei, half a step behind, places a hand on my back, leans near my shoulder, and whispers, "Ɛte sɛn, Akua?" . . . Or that is what I expected him to say. He slices the knife blade of his hand across my shin. Thrusting me forward, he says, "Ants, Akua. We must keep moving."

Exhausted, I hadn't noticed the guard's departure. I'd supposed we'd reached our destination and were pausing to contact the perimeter guard for our final passage to the sacred site. Having embraced the notion of our imminent arrival, I find it difficult to rekindle my former dedication. Leaves smother till I push through. Vines catch a hand or foot, pitching me into trunks and tangled thickets. Twigs scrape my shins and branches deliver unexpected blows. Foreign flora emit stinging fluids. The raunchy odor of carcass bloats and suffocates.

At every stumble and fall, Osei is there righting my balance or picking me up, always pushing me ahead. Even when I'm not tripping, Osei nudges my lower back to indicate shifts in direction. How he can read a trail over my shoulder in this realm of shadow, I cannot imagine. It is all too much for me. What I lack in heart, I try to muster in physicality, pitching myself along each new alignment charted by Osei.

Each touch upon the base of my spine brings the thought, "Who is Osei?" He has always seemed to me a simple man. Not lacking intelligence, but bound by rules and possessing a character that relishes constraint rather than resists it. Reliable, knowledgeable, unsophisticated. Whose hand guides from the small of my back? A man of stamina and razor sight, with a willingness to endure nature's wounding en route to the sacred.

Every breath roars in my ears. I grow exasperated at the frequency of my stumbling. Does Osei see the guard? I've abandoned the effort of discerning his form. My thirst clamors for relief. I'm numb to the cuts, stings, burns, gouges perpetrated upon my flesh by this ignominious tangle of life.

My breathing grows louder. Inhalations and exhalations assail my eardrums, obliterating other sounds. I wonder if I'm delirious. Osei's hand braces my shoulder. I stop and raise my eyes. For some immeasurable period of time, I've studied the ground, keen to select the optimal footing for my haphazard gait, too beaten to question Osei's navigation.

Straightening, I see we've come to a fast-flowing river about thirty feet across. Our guard stands on the far side with three men dressed in the same grey cloth. For this water to flow, it must be a good distance upstream of the dam. We've circumnavigated the reservoir. In all likelihood, a more direct, better worn route lies submerged.

"Here, Akua." Osei points to a flat rock upon which he wants me to stand.

Hoping for refuge from the assaults of plant and insect life, I lean over and pant, hands to knees. Though trees grow close overhead, the river creates openings through which light cascades. The men on the far shore appear to be waiting, as does Osei, who looks toward the way from which we came. My breaths still thunder in my ears.

Takyi, of course. How could I have forgotten? The journey seemed interminable, my concern reduced to survival. Takyi's delicate constitution—how did he fare? I shudder at the thought of the ants.

Osei's political suit will never be redeemed. Twigs and thistles have caught the thick fabric. His crisp cuffs have disintegrated into stained shreds. A white undershirt testifies that buttons have gone missing. In response to a cue I cannot perceive, he shouts, "Ah, we are here!"

The men across the river point as Takyi emerges from a wall of vines. I stand. Osei rushes to catch his friend, clasping him to his chest. Upon releasing Takyi, he takes his hand. The two continue to hold hands as Takyi hobbles to my side near the water's edge.

"Akua." Takyi lifts a gentle hand. Tufts of his hair have been pulled out of his neat coiffure. His right sleeve is split from elbow to wrist. The cuffs of his trousers are muddy and ragged. Takyi glances at me, then looks to our guide. In that moment of meeting his gaze, the beauty of his being pours forth. He is not a man in need of verbal reassurance. Whatever the physical challenge, it cannot compare with the magnificence of our mission which emanates from his tattered soul.

CHAPTER FORTY-ONE

This is no time for words. The incessant pounding in my ears! Will my breathing never quiet? Perhaps it has been my heart all along.

Osei and Takyi move along the bank following the gesticulations of the men of the grey cloth. I follow them to a small dugout destined to be flotsam in the battering current.

"It's all right, Akua." Osei gestures for me to join them in the vessel.

Someone, no doubt an enthusiast on the far shore, has attached lines to either end of the canoe. It is absurd. I don't bother to inspect the connections before stepping into the shaky rig. The priests—priests they must be, for they hold our lives in their hands—pull us through the thrashing waters.

I do not confirm whether vines or ropes tether our bobbing, twisting craft. Curiosity does not turn my head to search for the pulleys necessary for the rigging to function. Osei bails water with a half calabash. Takyi clutches the edge of the dugout. Is it desperation or determination to prevent being pitched overboard that whitens his knuckles? One foot he has wedged under the gunnel, forcing his knee to his chest. I am crouched on the bottom of our peripatetic craft, my hands pressing with all my might into the sides. Shivers run through me with each slap of the chill river topping our dugout. I keep my head down, my eyes on level with Takyi's trouser leg, which sticks to the blood of a gash down his calf.

Shocked at the pain he must bear, I twist around Takyi's knee to catch his eye. But his head is thrown back, his gaze up to the shroud of treetops and shafts of piercing light. I feel abashed at my callowness.

Remember why you came.

Gritting my teeth, I flip and wedge both feet under the opposite gunnel, dreading the brace of water as I drive my back into the sloshing hull. "Uh." The bitter plunge pries a cry from my locked jaw. Osei intensifies his bailing effort. I lift my face to the striking brilliance of pure spirit penetrating this morbid realm. Takyi jeopardizes stability to place a hand on my wrist. Our eyes meet. The craft surges and Takyi makes a panicked grab for the gunnel. I turn back to the light with gratitude for Takyi's friendship and the sacrament of yielding to God.

The thunderous beating of my heart intensifies the nearer we come to sacred ground. At the bank, two priests hold the dugout steady, while the others haul us to shore.

Without a word, they line us up. Osei, Takyi, me. Looking solemn, the priests administer their benediction. Or perhaps it is a medical inspection. Two palms flat to the top of the head—a real pressure. Dropping to the ears and squeezing, twisting the head to one side, then the other. Down to the shoulders, pressing quite hard and slipping the compression along the arms to elbows and wrists. A hard squeeze of the hands. Grabbing the hips as they had the ears, twisting the pelvis as they had the head, passing the constriction down the thighs to knees and ankles.

Stopping at our feet, which in every case are cut, swollen, bruised. The priests remove our sopping sandals. One priest kneels to apply a brown paste. Never mind the stink, that cool concoction soothes the throbbing in my toe, eases the burn of insect bites, pulls heat out of the swelling.

When my feet are coated in the dark ointment, I take a deep

breath. For the first time, I hear drumming—or was it the drumming all along that I mistook for my pained breathing and frantic heart? The priests restore our shoes. I'm mesmerized by the pounding pounding pounding.

One priest, our original guide, leads the way toward the source of that overwhelming sound. The remaining priests take our hands, so that we move in pairs. Though deep in the forest, the path has no obstructions. A world of shadow swallows the river's hallowed light.

Our priests act as caretakers, holding a slow pace, watching for further signs of injury. Their concern and the cleared path contrast with the survive-as-you-can, erratic scramble from Gyimiso Kakraba. The deserted village feels like a memory of a distant life. Thomas and Agyeman?

A glowing light resolves into a flaming torch at the entrance to a small structure. Osei and Takyi are led inside. I am led further toward the glow of a second torch. My priest stops at the threshold. I catch the briefest glimpse of a woman inside before the door flap drops. She could be my age and wears a tight wrap that covers her chest.

The woman takes my hand and pulls me down till I find myself sitting on a stool. Her touch feels firm and practiced. Little light enters the hut around the edges of the mat covering the doorway. The smoke filtering in from the torch triggers a cough. I command myself to adjust, as years ago I forced myself not to notice the cigarette-induced pall in construction trailers.

The woman removes my sandals, then pulls up on my forearm till I stand. She lifts the hem of my soaked shirt. I take the cue to remove it, shuddering at the cold lick that chases the peel of wet cloth. I feel the woman tug at the pocket of my shorts and oblige by removing what remains of my soggy clothes. She passes her hands over my sweaty, battered body. Although her contact is not disrespectful, I feel—as I do when seeing Ghanaian smalls being bathed—that the body is treated as communal.

The woman tugs my leg toward one side of the hut. Grabbing my ankle, she halts my progress. With care, she places my foot on a pile of pebbles. I'm standing in a soak away pit. Feeling pressure under my chin, I lift my head, at which she pours water over me.

I gasp at the chill followed by the stinging of every wound, inflicting memories of the stumbling, stabbing, endless, unnavigable flight through the shadow forest. The woman takes me in her arms and holds me to her chest, enveloping me in scents of shea butter and hair gel. She squeezes me as if to force any remaining air from my lungs.

"Ah," I exhale and cry out, clinging to the woman. How long since I've felt human contact?

Her arms are strong, as a nurse's might be from lifting patients. She pushes my face into her neck and whispers something in Twi. I have no idea what she says, but the sound of her voice stills me. Her touch is that of a healer, communicating confidence, serenity, tenderness. She sends me the energy of her body. I understand she is preparing me for what lies ahead.

The priestess relaxes her hand at the back of my head and feathers her fingers across the nape of my neck. "Kojobesia," she whispers again.

Kojo—a man's name. *-besia. Bɛhyia*, as in *Yɛbɛhyia bio*? "We shall meet again." *Bɛhyia* is "will meet." Kojo will meet. I don't know what she's saying. *Asasebomebosia* is one of our villages. *-bosia* sounds closer to the sounds she made. *Kofikrom* is another tiny village. *Kofi*, a man's name; *krom*—town. Kofi's town. Could *bosia* be similar to *krom*? Kojo's bosia? Kojo's place? Is the priestess telling me the name of the place to which I have come?

She steps back and grazes her finger under my chin. I tilt my head up and brace myself for the cold, stinging slap, after which she soaps a plastic mesh bathing cloth. Though she softens near lacerations, the abrasive rubbing feels merciless. Eyes closed, I lean into powerful rhythms, grateful for the intensity, the continuity, the renewal. After a final frigid dowsing, the priestess leads me out of the bathing pit. I rake my fingers through my wet hair, while she pats me with a thin towel.

The priestess's hand traces my form—head, neck, torso and limbs, reapplying the healing ointment. I choke on the stink of that brown paste mixed with smoke. When every wound and insect bite is smeared, she says, "Ɛyɛ," in a quiet voice.

I step into a skirt that she holds open for me. The untailored fit of the drawstring waist is hidden by the top that falls to my lower thigh. The top fits me well. Though I cannot see, I know the top is tailored. The smocking of the fabric creates an elaborate texture. A bulbous sleeve fills my palm. A small sash demarcates the finished edge of the sleeve at my bicep, accentuated by a cloth-covered button.

She places traditional leather sandals on my feet. I feel the weight of the thick soles, the rigid leather between my toes. The crowning touch is a headcloth, presumably of matching fabric, riding high on my forehead and tied behind my right ear.

The priestess pulls back the mat at the entrance. In the torch-light, her face appears neither young nor old. She wears a simple wrap, exposing muscular shoulders and dark, satin skin at her clavicle. She looks at me with a worldliness rare in a village woman. Does she make her home in Paris or Rome? Her eyes hold respect and a vision of something I can't yet know.

"Medaase," I say, closing my eyes and bowing my head.

"O ɛnna ase," she replies. As I step over the threshold, she lowers her head and says, "Kojobesia."

CHAPTER FORTY-TWO

Smoke hangs thick in the air, causing me to gag. I clear my throat to stifle the reflex. My priest stands in the flickering torchlight, his gaze running up and down my form. He pulls a cloth from his shoulder. As a costume designer primps his model, the priest drapes the cloth across my right hip and over my left shoulder—in the customary manner for men.

I feel certain that for a Ghanaian man to dress a woman is beyond cultural norms, especially one to whom he is not related, not to mention with the priestess here. I look over my shoulder, but the mat hangs over the doorway. Moreover, the outer cloth should match the pattern of the dress. My top and skirt are a gold and brown print with an underside accent of royal blue. My outer cloth is white with a pattern woven in black and grey.

I feel confused. The Ashanti have a bold sense of fashion. They would not commit such an error. I'm tired, thirsty, and hungry. Every drumbeat hits the mark. Intentional blows beating me to the pliable consistency demanded by what is to come.

The priest stands back and appraises me. He taps my arm, indicating I should mimic the way his arm supports his cloth. I gather some folds of the fabric, at which the priest turns and disappears into the surrounding darkness. I try to follow but find walking in the sandals laborious. I cannot bear the thought of another high-speed chase and decide to stay.

Uncertain that asphyxia was the better choice, I'm relieved when my priest reappears, followed by the rest of our band. Osei and Takyi beam at me. They have received similar treatment. Ornate sandals, flowing cloth, and bare shoulders reveal their dignity to a degree unattainable in Western attire. I find it reassuring that my outer cloth matches theirs.

My priest points into the darkness and sets out in that direction. I am to follow, but my body refuses. I lower my eyes. I can't force any more. Osei clasps my shoulder through the white cloth. I stiffen my lip before looking up.

"Akua Kojobesia," Osei says in a coarse, admiring whisper.

My ears are pricked by that word, with which I cannot argue. We travel neither far nor fast. I struggle with the challenges of my raiment, picking up my whole foot and laying it flat upon the ground minimizes the cutting of the leather into the soft flesh between my toes. Though unlit, our path is free of impediments. Drumbeats pummel and penetrate, usurping my heart's rhythm. Impossible to discern the origin of the resonance—within or without?

Our brief excursion ends at a shelter. Osei, Takyi, and I are enjoined to enter and partake of fresh coconuts ready for drinking, roasted groundnuts and bananas. A banquet could not compete with the sating of our hunger by this simple fare. But it's no proper reception for guests, suggesting we're being fortified for the next leg of our journey.

Out of respect for our hosts, we maintain silence, though I doubt human voices could carry above the pervasive drumming. Osei and Takyi exchange looks that convey anticipation and awe. I am accustomed to relying upon Agyeman and Thomas, the more articulate of the four, but I feel trusting of this place without words. I am captivated by Takyi's openness and radiance, a silent testimony to the compelling nature of our mission. I feel dependent on Osei as a child might for instruction and assurance, a surprising twist in our relationship. I have always found Osei's earnestness amusing. Today I stake my life on it.

Having completed our meal, we step outside. I look to Osei and Takyi, who study the distant exchange of the priests. The torchlight reveals men willing to meet their fate. I look at the regal fabric in which I've been dressed. It's as if these clothes were made for me. How could they have known we would come?

The pounding pounding pounding of gods stampeding.

It is for this that I came. To touch something greater, that presence animating the sands of Libya, whose conspicuous absence rendered trite the suburbs of my adolescence. It is this for which one hopes. To be pitched out of one's self. To be shown something greater and one's purpose in relation to it.

We wait shoulder to shoulder, Takyi, Osei, me. We could be three gods. We could be sacrificial lambs. Is there a difference?

I am ready. I watch the priests and try to match the bearing of the men beside me. The guard priest looks at us, unmoving, as when he first revealed himself. He again looks each of us in the eye.

What does he see? We cannot be the same three he met on the durbar ground. He speaks in Twi. How can anyone hear above the din? It matters not. Now is the time. We are to play our role.

The pace of the drumming accelerates. All of us, the priests included, hasten to a clearing where the durbar is underway. I stumble. The guard priest grabs my wrist and pulls me up. I have no experience with this cumbersome footwear.

A large clearing is filled with people. They face the chief, queen mother, and nananom, who sit in a broad line facing the people. The chief and queen mother wear fine cloth and gold adornments.

Younger men and women sit in the foreground and stand to the sides with fans of ostrich feathers.

The fans must be more ceremonial than functional. Though light washes the clearing, the cool damp of the forest permeates all. Most of the nananom are men who wear white cloth with varying patterns of black and grey. Two women sit behind the queen mother, regal in elaborate styles cut from the same cloth as my dress.

The akyerɛmma sit to the side in the foreground facing the people. Three men, bare chested, their hands a rapturous love-making releasing the ecstatic voices of those fierce energies once incarnate in the bestial dance, whose horrific orgasms summon the gods, dissolve the veil, thrust human consciousness into the earth. The center drummer is the elder, a short, thin man who stands on a pile of skins. With hooked sticks he plays lover to a pair of talking drums. Thin bands encircle his rock biceps, another crosses his brow and bald head.

Our small assembly stands offstage. Smoke from the perimeter torches hangs heavy in the air. At some undetected signal, the frenetic drumming slows and simplifies, distilling the sound of a single drum, the beat of my heart. Three priests escort Osei and Takyi to the center. They bow to the chief, queen mother, and nananom, then turn and bow to the people.

The guard priest brings me to the center. I'm relieved to move beyond the smoke. Osei, Takyi, and the other priests wait on the far side. The guard priest bows, then presents me to the chief and queen mother. I bow in imitation, a part of me doubting I could ever exhibit the proper grace, another part aware that the preparation given, the potency of the gathering, the masterful drumming, the bearing of my guide, and the majesty of those to whom I bow transport me beyond the stratum of my normal self.

CHAPTER FORTY-THREE

I have an image of the guard priest delivering me to the rest of our group, but I'm not sure that happens. It may be only my expectation—displaced by realities beyond my ken.

Fragments of scenes, numinous voices, scents that belong to altars, the heated frenzy of the devoted—an ocean of sensuality in which I swim. I cannot attest to a sequence of events. Much comes as a simultaneous collage of experience. It seems certain that the original guard priest never leaves my side . . . except when I dance my own dance.

His intermittent messages are sometimes explanations, sometimes prompts. "We are here for the boreholes. Water is powerful. It cannot be neglected." ". . . to your right . . ." "One, one-two; one, one-two. You may look at him and at the people . . ."

. . . The chief stands and addresses the durbar through his ɔkyeame: "The people of Gyimiso Kakraba are desperate for good water. Yet, we must not succumb to rash acts. For generations we have taken our water from the Gyimi River.

"West Africa Gold has spoiled the Gyimi. How can we trust WAG to provide the new boreholes? WAG's engineers could not anticipate the flooding. What does WAG know of water?

"Water comes from the river. The river swells and recedes, as does a woman's belly. The River Goddess is respected and honored. Her beauty and power are evident to all.

"How will the River Goddess live in a pipe? How can Her full aspect be known to those who cannot see her? Her life has been swallowed by WAG's dam. How can we accept water from those who fouled the home of the River Goddess?"

. . . smoky haze . . . thunderous drumming—many gods speaking . . . the people dancing . . . fright surging as the guard priest steers me out of the path of a fetish priestess; the priestess crouched low, her feet pounding shuffling shifting, her eyes wide and unblinking . . .

. . . the chief and his ɔkyeame: "No machine was needed to make the river. WAG brings a huge machine to drill for water. They bring engineers who say that they know how to find water under the ground. We have seen their talent with water on the ground!"

. . . a ritual dance of the chief, queen mother, and nananom. All the people form a circle in which the elders dance. The nananom circle counterclockwise inside the people's circle. The guard priest's voice, ". . . an honoring of the River Goddess. Affirming that She is not forgotten . . ." A second inner circling, into which the guard priest nudges me. I walk-dance between the chief and queen mother . . . one, one-two . . .

. . . always the drumming. Many women click castanets. Clappers, bells accentuate the pulsing beats. A flurry of colorful cloth, arms in the air, clicking and rattling of improvised percussion, stomping and clapping. I dance in the crowd, exhausted and exhilarated . . .

. . . the chief and his ɔkyeame: "Water flows freely in the river. Water in a pipe appears a servant rather than a goddess. We cannot risk further offense of the River Goddess. We suffer from skin diseases and dysentery. Our health is in jeopardy. We cannot continue to drink the water spoiled by WAG."

. . . the voice of the guard priest: "The well is the Source. It cannot be blocked or contaminated. A well unattended is a desecration."

... the chief and his ɔkyeame: "There must be a consecration of this act. For the new water to be clean and not cursed, the receiving of the boreholes must be consecrated. We have tried to talk to West Africa Gold. Our lack of success is evident in the flooding. We cannot speak the language of WAG. We cannot speak to the drilling machine. We need the consecration to come from one who moves in both worlds.

"We asked the River Goddess to send such a one and She has answered by sending Akua Kojobesia. Akua Kojobesia is an engineer. Unlike the WAG engineers, she sees our plight. She cares for the health of our people. She advocates on our behalf.

"Akua Kojobesia is an engineer. She understands the machine. Yet, we see her heart in her dealings with us. She also sees Nature and respects our ways. We thank the River Goddess for sending Akua Kojobesia to our aid. Our prayers are answered."

... energy building in the drumming ... a movement of the people who had gathered to hear their chief ... the guard priest's vice grip crushing my bicep: "Do as I do. Face the people and do as I do."

We are dancing even as the people are spreading to the edges of the clearing. We find the new rhythms of the drums. At first our expressions are simple, slow and repetitive—a raising and arcing of hands, slight bending of knees, a gentle side-to-side swaying. We move counterclockwise in the circle facing the people.

We complete two revolutions and the drumming accelerates. My guard priest becomes more fluid and dynamic. I remember following him in the forest, the period in which all difficulty melted and I could match, even anticipate his shadowy form. My body knows how to do this. Delighting in the connection, I loosen into larger, more confident gestures. We are now crouching and leaping and spinning, some madness perhaps of storm waters crashing down a riverbed.

The earlier gestures reveal themselves as preludes to our exultation. The gentle swaying and slight bending beget an integrity of motion grounding in our hips, swinging our fists past our knees, exploding across the waist with the force of that low energy hands flung open bursting overhead in a grand arc evoking an indescribable immensity.

The guard priest smiles—his first smile. My heart soars! A swelling in my chest explodes in lustful zeal. The crowd is all men. We dance for royalty, then move to the women. When they separated, I cannot say.

The guard priest looks me in the eye and shouts above the drumming and the clapping, "Kojobesia." We spin. When we face each other, he points to the men. "Ɔbarima." We crouch and leap. "Ɔbaa." He points to the women. "Transcend, Akua Kojobesia. Two worlds." As he says this last, he stands still and holds his fingers in a V toward my head, the custom for praising a dancer.

The crowd roars its approval. Many hands fly up forming Vs that flutter in my direction. In the thunder of so many voices I ride the crest and some part of me dances a dance never danced before.

I cannot map the choreography, for my mind cannot keep up with my body. It is a dialogue of the feminine and the masculine. My hips lead with gyrations and thrusts. My loins burn. I desire union. My gestures may be crude. I cannot judge. I surrender to my body announcing its purpose on this earth. I dance to the men to stir something deep within. I dance to the women to touch their fire.

The men and the women answer me with guttural and shrill cries, with a powerful stomping and clapping. I catch glimpses of my hands arcing high overhead, now a symbol of joining the women and the men. What had split, merges. The elaborate prints and solid cloths flow into each other.

Their response fills me till I feel I might expand to touch the uppermost boughs. I come close to committing to the unending dance when the drummers rescue me, modulating a gradual descent in pace, letting me find ground in one, one-two; one, one-two.

Concluding before the chief, queen mother, and nananom, I take a low bow.

CHAPTER FORTY-FOUR

When I rise, people rise with me, exalted, into the center of the clearing. They come near to touch. With every gentle contact, I look into their eyes and feel my feet deepen into the ground. Osei and Takyi and the three priests escort me through the crowd to a house with tables and benches.

The priests exude a hearty satisfaction, as if they've just played the match of their lives. One of them points at me, saying, "Your cloth."

I look at my white cloth which has been bound over my shoulder.

"I tied it for you," says the priest. "You do not remember. You needed to dance! I fastened your cloth and took your sandals." This priest was my escort from the river, my costumier. He hands me a bundle in which I feel the distinctive shape of sandals.

I look down at my bare feet, dirty, my left big toe swollen, numerous scrapes and dried blood. None of the healing paste remains. "I am sorry I do not remember," I say.

Glowing with pride, he bows his head, saying, "Akua Kojobesia."

The others bow. I feel buoyant, as if a great ocean supports me and no effort is required.

"Do you know this word, *kojobesia*?" asks my escort priest.

My being opens to receive.

"No?" He gestures for me to sit and takes the place beside me. His presence feels protective, an intimacy balanced by the respectful presence of the others, and one heretofore not accorded in my relations with Ghanaians. "*Kojobesia* is 'androgyne'—the one who moves in the duality of man and woman. *Kojobesia* is the expression of those who possess the quality of transcendence necessary for the invocation of deities and the efficacy of the sacred rites."

My eyes fall as I try to take this in.

The escort priest places a light hand on my shoulder. "Do not think, Akua Kojobesia. There will be time for that. Eat now and rest."

Women set before us a full meal of coconut water and nkontommire with boiled eggs. After eating, I feel less light-headed, but still find it impossible to think. I cannot fathom returning through the forest. Nor could I have dreamed of the provisions that have been made for us.

We are led to a four-by-four. There must be a road to the east by which we can circle back. Our driver soon joins us, a man in Western garb. I am slow to recognize him. The gradual realization shakes me to the core—our guard priest now passes for an American suburbanite. I mean to study his transformation, but feel my eyes close as soon as the vehicle starts to move.

We find Agyeman and Thomas sitting in twilight beneath the banana palm. They have enjoyed the company of three guards who assured them we would return but offered no information. We share the joy of reunion and they compliment our regal attire. I feel an inkling of insight into our adventure. All along, the villagers intended I should come with Osei and Takyi. They perceived the potential for interference from the more educated of our team.

Agyeman's gaze meets mine. I'm sure he has reached the same conclusion. Had Agyeman and Thomas not paired off to search the village, the guards would have induced a separation.

Before piling into the truck, the guards peel and slice the tops off oranges. I decline, but Agyeman insists.

"You must stay hydrated, Akua."

I feel fine, but the gravity of his concern reaches me. I suck down four oranges before reaching for the truck keys—or rather before realizing that I lost everything when I undressed in the hut.

The guard priest hands two bags to Takyi. In one, we find our tattered clothes which have been washed, pressed with a coal iron, and folded. Our shoes fill the second bag. The guard priest holds the truck keys, shooting a pointed look at Agyeman.

Agyeman opens a passenger door for me, saying, "Let him drive."

"No, that's ridiculous. I can drive." Though my voice cracks, I try to appear nonchalant, extending my hand for the keys.

The guard priest's jaw hardens. His moustache underscores humorless eyes. "No. You cannot."

It dawns on me that my superb dancing may be the product of something other than my ravished soul. I look to the men. None has a driver's license. Seeing no one backing me, I concede, taking the seat behind the driver.

When I wake, we're parked in front of my duplex in Obuasi. I am leaning into Osei's shoulder. Everyone else is across the street at Idrissu's.

"Medaase." I offer a slight bow to Osei.

He looks relieved to be no longer in a compromising position. Without comment, he departs to join the others. I open my door to get out, but am met with a great deal of shouting. Looking across the traffic in the darkness, I see all of the men, including the guard priest and Idrissu, waving their arms and shouting. I comprehend Idrissu.

He stands with a foot braced on the lip of the gutter with palms outstretched above his head. While forcing his palms forward, as if shoving a great wall of water, he shouts with all his might, "Dabi, Akua!"

Like a child's, my adrenalin spikes at the fear in my parent's voice. I shift my weight back onto the seat and close the door. A Zion train whips past, inches away. My heart races and sobs erupt. I want my mind back. It's my inclination to exit by the opposite door, but I no longer trust my judgement. I drop my head in my hands, shaking.

CHAPTER FORTY-FIVE

I wake with a splitting headache. Removing my head from
the bare wooden armrest of my sofa eases the pain. Sitting
up is a different matter. I wait for the ocean to stop sloshing
in my head.

No light through the shutters. It must be well into night. That
is the worst sleep I've ever had—out cold, but no feeling of deep
rest. As if my mind just checked out.

I'm wearing a tee shirt and shorts. Images come back to
me . . . Idrissu's daughter Hasna helping me out of my regalia;
Takyi coaxing me to suck a million oranges before he would leave;
the men stopping by in the morning . . . it must have been today.
But today must be tomorrow. Have I lost an entire day?

I stand and take a delicate step toward the kitchen. My feet
hurt. I prefer to not look at the damage.

Oral rehydration salts. My savior. Bless Peace Corps. The
greatest invention. I think I shall always keep a drawer full, no
matter where I live.

I settle back on the couch nursing my liter bottle of rehydration
salts. I feel better with every life-giving swallow.

My journal before me. How can this story ever be written?
Who will believe it? Can I recall the details? Despite my hangover,
I feel I'm still in the drama of the ceremony. How can I return to
my old life? The world cannot be the same.

My palms flat to the grain of the table. Pain shoots through my left palm and wrist. I inspect the dark, dried blood, the swollen flesh. I can't recall the injury. Whose hand is this?

Picking up the pen and opening to a blank page, the pristine page, brings tears. I have to write before more is forgotten. My night passes in this way—writing, crying, luxuriating in the otherworldly quality of my perceptions, preparing batches of rehydration salts. By morning, real sleep comes.

At midday, I wake with a clear mind. I bathe, dress, and head to market, first visiting Idrissu.

"Akua, you are all right?" He examines the cuts and bruises on my feet, arms, and legs, pausing at the deepest laceration above my ankle.

I rotate my left hand to hide the swelling. "Yes, Idrissu." Afraid the magic will dissipate, I don't wish to speak.

"Akua, I am afraid. Your team should not let dis happen. I tell your team, dey are putting you in danger."

"No, Idrissu," I say. "It was my choice."

"Ei, Akua, you cannot choose." He crushes my glory. "How you know? You cannot choose."

"Idrissu, I must go to market."

"Yes, Akua. Dat man leave dis for you."

I unfold the note:

> *Lou, Idrissu tells me you're laid up and wouldn't want a man visitor. I hope it's not too severe. Missed you last night. Let's reschedule. Cheers, Peter.*

Ah, I had forgotten. And Idrissu did me a solid. "Medaase." I look him in the eye with gratitude.

He scratches his beard.

I do my shopping and return home feeling insulated from

Obuasi. The sounds of the street are muted. My reactions are slow. Speech less comprehensible, as I make no effort to hear.

Everything is trivial relative to what I know. "Kojobesia. Ɔbarima—ɔbaa. Two worlds." "Transcend, Akua." I see the face of the guard priest. Undoubtedly, he is an educated man . . . and a priest. I must ask the team who he is.

I must ask the team so many things. The priestess—who is she? Why did we not see the Chairman of the Committee for the Defense of the Revolution? All of the elders, the chief and queen mother, the priests—I had never met before. Why? Where were the children? The team . . . Today must be Saturday. Good. That gives me time to not speak.

The dance. The drumming. My breathing deepens at the memory. At the way my body moved. The guard priest putting his *V* to my head, "Two worlds," and the roar of the crowd. Everyone waving *V*s at me. At once praising my dancing, affirming the consecration, and celebrating my fluid gender—invoking transcendence of gender. I never imagined Ghana could give me such a gift. I feel someone has made love to me. Tender. Passionate. I move now in an altered state, in a dream from which I have no desire to wake.

Monday morning I cannot wait to get to the office. There is so much I want to know. The team must feel the same, as they're all present and seated when I enter. They scrutinize my arrival without extending a greeting.

Their lack of decorum doesn't daunt my spirits. "Ɛte sɛn?" I ask, looking around the table.

"Ɛyɛ, medaase," Osei and Takyi say together.

"Good," Thomas says in a soft voice, dropping his eyes, then looking at Agyeman.

"We are all well, Akua," Agyeman responds. "How are you this morning?"

"Ɛyɛ pa ara."

"Are you sure?" Agyeman presses.

"Absolutely. Do you think I should not be?"

Agyeman weaves his head from side to side, as is his way when choosing his words. "Perhaps you are suffering from the strain of the work?"

I sit down and look at each in turn, saying, "You should not worry. I did not come to Ghana to sit in an office. I am honored to have been included in Gyimiso Kakraba's ceremony. It is something I shall never forget."

"You are not feeling ill?" asks Takyi.

"I did wake with a terrific headache. But a day's hydration seemed to put that to rights. I—have a vague memory of your stopping by."

"Yes, Akua. That is right. You remember! We came the following morning to be certain you were all right. But we could see we were disturbing you. We could see you needed to rest. We left so you could rest."

"Thank you for your concern."

"O, Akua, you have tried!" Takyi exclaims with pride.

You have tried! is Ghanaian high praise, but the expression always strikes me sideways. I didn't just try, I succeeded. "As you can see," I say, "all is well. But I have many questions . . ."

They explain to me that Gyimiso Kakraba is a satellite village of Akrofuom. That most of the nananom are persons of note, few of whom reside full time in the village. They would conduct business in the cities at the normal time of the Advocacy's visits. In their absence, the Chairman of the Committee for the Defense of the Revolution administers routine matters. Although he has no standing in such rites, he attended as part of the community. He greeted us; you do not remember? Because of the upcoming Christmas holiday, it is likely that many are returning to the village.

Even from out of the country. That could be why so many faces were unfamiliar. Children were there, did you not see them?

"It is possible," adds Agyeman, "that some of the roles are rare, such as the akyerɛmma and those you call 'priests.' Each small village cannot support them. These holy people may attend to all who live on the stool land. It is likely they do not reside in Gyimiso Kakraba. The one you call the 'guard priest' is the ɔkyeame."

"But, the linguist stood with the chief."

"There can be more than one ɔkyeame. Anyway, we may enquire to see what we may learn."

"Medaase," I respond. "Well, shall we plan our week? We'll need to make up the villages we missed."

The men again are quiet.

Agyeman addresses me with solemn eyes. "Akua, we would suggest—it is possible—we would suggest it may be well to not speak of what happened . . ."

"But I must tell Hansen or . . . Kwasi . . ."

"We have spoken to Doctor. We felt it best since you were resting that Doctor should not be kept waiting. We informed Doctor that Gyimiso Kakraba will soon welcome the return of the drill rig."

I take this in. There is nothing wrong with their action. I suppose I feel deflated because I was looking forward to telling someone what happened—even if it was Kwasi, even if it was an abridged version.

Agyeman clears his throat. "Akua, we appreciate that you possess the spirit of adventure. Others may not. Our superiors, perhaps, might feel you were put in harm's way. They may feel we did not perform our duty . . ."

"But you and Thomas didn't even know. And Osei and Takyi followed my lead. I don't think anyone can blame you. Besides, I am not blaming you."

341

The men are silent.

"In addition," Agyeman continues, "West Africa Gold may not appreciate such a rite. In particular the role that the Advocacy performed may be misunderstood. It is possible that there may be confusion and the Advocacy's participation may not be viewed favorably . . ."

By "the Advocacy's participation," he obscures what WAG may perceive as a gross indiscretion on my part. It's rare that Agyeman's gift for subtlety is intended to shield me. Once anyone outside our office is told, all of Obuasi will know. "Idrissu?" I ask.

"We did not tell him everything," Agyeman responds. "Anyway, he could see your dress and your condition. He has a good idea, all right. We appealed to him for his prudence. Anyway, Idrissu is in it now. He persuaded a WAG driver to return the truck. Now he's in our boat."

That driver would be Kwadwo. Idrissu is quick to brag about the favors he procures—odd that he said nothing. Proof that Idrissu concurs it is unwise to speak of it.

"The villagers themselves . . ." I don't see how so many tongues can be kept silent.

"Do not worry, Akua. The villagers have been dealing with WAG for many years. They love you for coming to their aid. They will not put you in jeopardy. Anyhow, commonly such rites belong to those present. To speak of sacred things can be arrogance."

A low rumble emanates from Takyi's throat. He shoots a warning glance to Agyeman.

"There are those who believe," Agyeman goes on, "that to speak of such things is profanity, that such a travesty the gods will punish. Even the rite for which so many sacrificed may be nullified."

They are taking it away. I close my eyes. This gift they want me to swallow as if it never existed. I cannot look at them without crying. My jaw clenches. The Rifleman pumps his Winchester as he strides to the center of Main Street. He stands tall and surveys the deserted town, keen to spot his foe.

After a pause, I open my eyes, saying in a firm tone, "We shall have to work some long days to make up the villages missed. Takyi, why don't you go to the lab and see if we have the truck today?"

"I should go to the lab?"

"Yes, to Safety. Is that all right?"

"Yes, Akua. I shall enquire after the truck."

"Medaase."

Takyi rises and limps toward the door. I remember the tangle of forest yielding his battered form. I feel the heat of his beatific glow. The others do not realize we are in the presence of the Divine. Thomas peruses a copy of the week's schedule. Osei produces a bundle from his bag. Agyeman writes in his personal notebook.

"Could I . . . ask just one thing?" My voice breaks.

Takyi turns in the doorway. The others look up.

"How did they know we would come?"

All of the men burst with laughter.

"Akua!" Takyi shakes his head near tears, as if I have made a joke.

I look to Agyeman. It seems he no longer finds the situation compelling enough to necessitate that he play spokesman. Although chuckling, he does not meet my eyes. With all that has happened, I had forgotten his debt, his remoteness.

When the laughter subsides, I try again. This may be my only opportunity. "What is obvious to one may be indecipherable to another."

My hero, Osei, collects gravel in his throat to deliver his sermon. "Of course you would come, Akua. You are the water man, water lady."

He calls me by a woman's name and in the next breath calls me a man. I see Osei in the torchlight outside the hut. I see the pride with which he looks at me and hear the respect in his voice.

"Akua Kojobesia." He does not use that word in the light of a normal day. But what I would have assumed before was gender confusion—"water man, water lady"—is it actually acknowledgement of the presence of both? An honoring of non-static gender?

Takyi departs. Osei unwraps his bundle to reveal the ornate gift of Gyimiso Kakraba. He shows the sandals to Agyeman and Thomas, who marvel at their artistry.

An image comes to me of another bundle. I see the kind face of the escort priest. His words—"androgyne" . . . "one who moves in duality" . . . "necessary for the invocation of deities." And he handed me my sandals! He tied my man cloth . . . over my woman dress.

CHAPTER FORTY-SIX

We swing through Obuasi en route to the afternoon villages. On our way out of town, I buy tea bread for everyone. As I pull the bills from my pocket, I'm reminded of my impoverished state and that Agyeman's note comes due tomorrow. For many reasons, I pray he honors it.

We have a long day in the villages, finishing at Nyameso, a suburb of Obuasi. The village received a borehole from WAG before the Advocacy could conduct educational outreach. The residents have not taken a great interest in our program. We tour the village, pointing out poor sanitation practices and recommending alternatives. Before leaving, the villagers ask us to wait small at the truck. While they gather oranges and plantain, the team gathers round a few men who seem to have a story to tell.

On our way back to Obuasi, Thomas volunteers. "Akua, the people say there has been trouble in Sansu. The people say the house of the chief has burned."

I turn to meet Agyeman's eyes, but he doesn't look at me. I feel annoyed by his reticence.

Returning my gaze to the road, I ask, "When did this happen?"

"Just this morning, Akua, in the very early hours."

"Was anyone hurt?"

"No. But it's possible that was the intention. Some say it was expected the chief would be there, but he stayed the night at the home of his first wife." Thomas sucks his teeth. "It may be someone's imagination because others say the house isn't ready for habitation."

"No matter," Osei interjects. "Burning the chief's house is serious pa ara."

"The chief cannot control his people," Takyi pronounces.

I look to Agyeman to get his read on the situation. He faces the dusty windshield in silence. He has no right to punish me.

"What will happen?" I ask.

"The police will investigate," says Thomas.

"Will the police discover who did this?"

After some time, Thomas replies, "No. The people are not for the chief. They will not come to his aid."

Lying in bed listening to the ceaseless rumble of Obuasi. Swathed in new perceptions of myself for which I have no words. The gift of Gyimiso Kakraba. From the midst of their suffering, they infused me with grace. Did I consecrate their new water source or did they consecrate me?

At two a.m., a pounding rain wakes me. The drowning rush of the relentless drumming of tin courses through my body and transports me to a clearing in a forest. My being reverberates with the drumming drumming drumming, with the invocation by masters of the River Goddess, with the transcendence of worlds.

At four a.m., I realize my mind is racing. Osei is to stay in town with me. They'll need to find a driver. Takyi. The contract. Perhaps we can be done with it. Dinner tonight with Peter, that's a break. Will Agyeman repay his loan today? I dread his betrayal. My mind returns to the top of the loop . . . Osei . . .

No. Whatever may be forgotten, whatever the cost, it is not worth the clenching in my gut, the tightness of my jaw, the lack of air, my perpetual cycling in fear of dropping something. I let my breath travel to my perineum. One, one-two. Again, one, one-two. I push my cheek into the pillow and welcome sleep.

The town bursts with life. Crews of men in hard hats and grey coveralls unsnapped to their waists clutch the sideboards of pickup trucks lurching from pothole to pothole. As well as possible, I avoid the spray from speeding Land Rovers throwing up puddles of last night's rain. A pregnant goat scuttles out of the way of a taxi. Shopkeepers set up tables on porches along the road's edge and balance the precise geometry of their wares. The seamstresses who work next to the buroni store haven't arrived yet.

"Maakye, Akua!"

"Maakye, awuraa!" I call across the road to the yam chip lady. She sits on a low wooden stool peeling the bark from a pile of yams. I must be late if she is already at work. She wields the machete with ease. Her thick, stiff hair fans away from her face, looking soft and windblown. My heart swells at the sight of her. There is beauty in labor, in the constancy of her presence. This woman—I don't know her name—finding her every day anchors me, as a daughter reassures herself by glancing back at her mother.

"Akua, ɛte sɛn?" She wears a buroni waawu shirt that has pulled loose from her wrap. The teal blue, satin top hangs low across her breast. The skewed hang of the neckline gives her an unintentional sexiness. Her full, white smile warms me, the tilt of her head conveying awareness that her beauty inspires me.

I blush, calling, "Ɛyɛ, medaase," and walk on knowing that I am a man speaking language that a woman understands. I know it to a depth as never before. Gyimiso Kakraba has participated in my gender reality and it changes everything. I don't ever want to be a country of one. Self-affirmation, stubborn insistence upon what I know, this cannot compare to effortless, exuberant knowing, the gift of Gyimiso Kakraba reflecting back to me who I am.

With apprehension, I climb the chute road, so named for its likeness to the streets of Pamplona. Except, instead of bulls goring drunken thrill seekers, this narrow lane sports massive haul trucks flattening guileless pedestrians.

I recall Osei's cavalier reference to me as a man, then a woman. He works with me every day and cannot sustain a clear perception of my gender. Or so I had thought.

I move along the top of a soggy berm of gutter muck, parallel to the open gutter. The customary stench has abated. The typical stagnant, grey froth, disguised as rain runoff, overflows into the street.

Perhaps there is no confusion. Perhaps Osei makes no attempt at clarity regarding details of no relevance. The hill is steep and homes on the high side are built ten feet above the level of the road with narrow, steep steps leading up. There's nowhere beyond the gutter to dodge an errant vehicle.

Like his telling of the exact time—does Osei offer gender identifiers that he perceives to be of value to me? His errors—do they betray effort to remember the eccentric needs of a guest? Are they not errors at all, but compensations for the inadequacy of the language of gender?

Taxis and trucks pass within inches. I keep my eyes on the top of the slope, where the narrow lane ends and the road fans out at the Miner's Circle.

"Ɔbaa." "Ɔbarima."—Osei does not mind . . . these are meaningless categories in regard to me. Osei sees me better than I see myself. Akua Kojobesia exists outside of a clearing in a forest.

The Old Council sits back from the main road, just off the side road that angles up to the Environmental Lab. Agyeman is downstairs talking to Assembly employees. There may be time to check whether Peace Corps has transferred money to my account. I glance at my watch, finding only my bare wrist. The scar of absence jogs memories of the vicissitudes of an unforgiving forest. I shudder and force my steps toward the bank. The same teller who disbursed my loan money for Agyeman shakes his head.

I resent the haughty judgment issued to me by this suited gentleman along with the balance of my savings. He imagines me a bleeding heart of whom his countryman has taken advantage. I was not naïve. I made my choice. However, I need to assess how I'm going to eat next month. Peace Corps can't leave us all in the lurch much longer. Before stepping outside, I adjust the stacks of money to even the load in my duffel bag.

"Maakye," I call, as I enter the office.

Thomas, Osei, and Agyeman are transferring notes about yesterday's villages to the files.

"Good morning, Akua," Thomas replies. Ordinarily, I would ponder the way Thomas's politeness rides the edge of the perfunctory. How, within the context of Ghanaian graciousness, it feels an intentional slight. How his being of another tribe may account for the contrast with the gregariousness of the Ashanti . . . ordinarily, the River Goddess does not command my heart.

"Maakye, Akua. I saw you going to the bank." Kind deference buffers Osei's rough voice.

"Yes."

"You have made a withdrawal." He gestures toward my bulging duffel bag. "It is not wise to carry this around town."

"Did the Peace Corps come through, then?" Thomas asks with cheer.

"No. Peace Corps has not come through. This is the last of my savings."

"O. I'm sorry." Thomas now sounds very Ashanti.

"Thank you." I glance at Agyeman, who continues writing without the slightest flinch to betray his contribution to my financial ruin. To Osei, I offer, "Well, I can drop it at my house on our way to the Administration."

"Are we going to the Administration?" Osei looks puzzled.

"Yes, I need you to stay in town with me today. We need to meet with Mr. Illiasu regarding WAG's contract. He would like you to sign on behalf of the Advocacy. Is that all right?"

Osei stands at attention and furrows his brow. "I am to sign the contract with the Advocacy?"

"Yes, it isn't appropriate for a Peace Corps volunteer to sign."

"All right."

"Then you're not going to the villages with us today?" asks Thomas, closing the file on which he's been working.

"No."

"We'll need a driver." Thomas's statement of the obvious strikes me as a sign of the team's growing sensitivity to our transportation predicament.

"Yes," I say. "Have you seen Takyi this morning?"

"He's there."

Takyi limps in. "Maakye, Akua."

"Maakye," I reply too loud in a poor attempt to conceal that my heart stands beside a thrashing river and watches a tattered soul emerge from a wall of vines.

"You are invited." He tilts toward me his mineral bottle of ice kenkey. Takyi knows that I have not developed a taste for the milky drink made from fermented corn dough. But, his offer is sincere.

Takyi's gentle soul plunges mine into memory. The gift of his beatific presence in a hut where banana, groundnuts, and coconuts were laid for our consumption. Our last supper. A way station between worlds. Takyi and Osei in their finery, in awe of what the day had bestowed upon us and what the ceremony had yet to bring. I glance at Osei, who scratches his nose, while reading his diary. "Dabi, medaase," I reply to Takyi. "Osei and I are staying in town today. You'll need to get a driver."

"Have you spoken to Mr. Mensah?"

"No."

"Are you certain that we have the truck today?"

"I'll go up to Safety, now."

"I'll go with you," says Takyi.

We're not far along, when we see our truck barreling toward us. It slams to a stop and the driver's window lowers.

Anthony, one of Harrigan's new safety staff, announces, "Finn Harrigan wishes to see you."

"When?"

"Now, I believe."

"Well, I have a meeting at the District Administration."

"I believe it cannot wait."

"The truck . . . ?"

Anthony's bold declarations disintegrate to mumbling. "I am taking Ethan to Rupert Wickinham Shaft, where there's been a fatality. Your vehicle was the only one available. I'll drop him and return. Is that all right?"

Going along with the farce that I have choice in the matter, I say, "You're going to Wickinham, so it'll be about forty-five minutes." Despite the Advocacy's helplessness, I try to maintain a sense of accountability.

"Or an hour." Concedes Anthony. His face lacks animation. He would like to be on his way.

"Good morning, Akua." Ethan Acquah waves from the passenger side. Ethan is one of Safety's new inspectors with whom I've had little contact. "I hope we're not causing too much of a problem for the Advocacy. We know you have your schedule in the villages. We're sorry, but it's urgent that I get to the scene as quickly as possible."

Ethan's courtesy withers beside a memory of bowing before the chief and queen mother. "Do not let us delay you."

Ethan accepts with a slight bow of his head and waves farewell, as Anthony guns the engine.

"As they're going to Wickinham, it'll be some time before they return. I shall ask Mr. Mensah if he can find a driver." Takyi states his plan as a suggestion.

"Tell him you'll be ready to go in an hour."

Takyi continues to the Transport Yard and I return to the office. The drivers will all be committed by now, except those least desirable. Perhaps, with an hour's notice, we may get a good driver whose vehicle is in for repairs . . . or a guard priest disguised as a suburbanite.

I haven't had a chance to thank Kwadwo for returning the truck . . . but . . . even that is not to be spoken of.

Upstairs, Agyeman and Thomas are talking across the large conference table. "Good morning, Mr. Agyeman," I say.

"Good morning, Akua. Do you have news of the truck?"

"Yes. Safety has borrowed the truck to get to a fatality at Wickinham. They should have it back in less than an hour. Takyi's seeing about a driver."

"You think we'll have the truck in an hour?" Agyeman and Thomas exchange cynical smiles.

"I hope you will. If not, take a taxi."

"We're going to Bobriase, Old Akrofuom, Sodua, and Old Edubiase today," says Thomas.

That's a rough road for a low-bottomed Peugeot taxi. I ignore the inference. "Do you have enough money to hire a taxi?" I hold my tone steady and look at Agyeman, with this mention of money.

He looks away with no hint of acknowledging his debt.

"I have four hundred," says Thomas.

"Mine is finished," says Agyeman.

"How much do you need?"

Thomas calculates. "It is four hundred cedis per hour, so three thousand two hundred. Akua, my notebook is finished."

"Buy a new one."

"There are no more on the shelf."

"Buy a new one. Buy several." It irritates me that they ask to buy supplies. We're here for two years, we have plenty of funding, and they won't buy a pen without asking for permission. Well, we used to have plenty of funding.

I pull the last five thousand cedis of WAG money out of my duffel bag and give it to Agyeman. He initials in my notebook that he received the sum.

"Where's Osei?" I ask.

"He will return," says Thomas.

"Where'd he go?"

Thomas shrugs. I sit at my desk and rummage through a stack of village files. "Where's the Pomposo file?"

"Pomposo . . ." Thomas searches the files spread on the table near him. "Here it is."

Lynn had the foresight to have a beautiful, full-height bookcase built. Unfortunately, there's no way to store our village files, except in stacks. There are stacks of files on my desk, on the conference table, and on the bookshelf. Could I update Gyimiso Kakraba's file with a tale of a trek through an impenetrable forest, a river crossing of pure faith, a dance . . . my dance . . . the dance of a lifetime?

Osei's voice fills the office. "Ah, Akua, I had wanted to conduct my business, but I could see I was keeping long. As I did not wish to delay our meeting with Mr. Illiasu, I have returned. I will conduct my business after our meeting."

"That may not be necessary. I have been called to meet with Finn Harrigan. Perhaps you could conduct your business and we could meet back here at the office."

Thomas and Agyeman exchange a glance. "Perhaps Finn Harrigan will finally give you a copy of the audit report?" Thomas speaks on behalf of both.

"Perhaps."

Walking up the hill, I feel closed to what awaits me. Finn will hand me a bullshit report, or maybe the accountants have found a legitimate discrepancy that can, no doubt, be explained by my poor accounting practices. It doesn't matter. Finn has predetermined the outcome. He wants me gone.

I catch a glimpse of the ladies through the oleanders, sporting about the fifth hole. Past the lab, I enter the tomb of Safety. My footsteps trip a gauntlet of reverberating chaos. At the end of the tumult looms Finn's office. The antechamber remains unoccupied, though a tiny desk and typewriter reflect some attempt to accommodate a future secretary. My heart goes out to the hapless woman who will cater to Finn Harrigan.

I knock and receive an, "Enter, please," from the opposite side. Opening the door just enough, I stick my head in.

"Ah, Louisa, there you are." Finn stands and scrapes his way through the slit between the wall and the side of his desk. He comes to the door and opens it fully. "Come in. Have a seat," his voice warm and welcoming.

"Thank you?" I say, with a question in my voice. I take my customary seat, front and center.

Finn sets his hip on the front edge of his desk and claps his hands. "Good to see you, Louisa. Thank you for coming on short notice. I hope this isn't interrupting the Advocacy's schedule. We know you have important work to do in the villages."

"Yes," I try to say, but no sound comes out. I'm not inspired to follow him down the rabbit hole.

Rubbing his hands, then bowing his head near the steeple of his mated palms, Finn announces, "We are hosting visitors from the International Finance Corporation. They are very interested in our operations, our mining activities and outreach to the local communities. They would love to talk with you about the work you are doing in the villages." Finn looks at me with an expression of suspended joy, as if he has proposed a winning idea for my enthusiastic concurrence.

"What is the context?"

"What?"

"I don't understand the context."

"Our visitors would just like to learn about the work that the Advocacy is doing. They would just like to chat with you. We could set up an office here and you could meet them. I'm sure it wouldn't take more than half an hour. Maybe an hour. Well, your work is so interesting and you are helping so many villages, they probably will have many questions for you."

"But what is the reason for their interest? Are they wanting to set up similar programs in other places? Why have they come to WAG and the Advocacy? Are these personnel of the International Finance Corporation involved with the loan given to West Africa Gold?"

Finn's face falls. He reaches back to take a long drag and retrieve his paternal, cajoling persona. "Well, that's right. The International Finance Corporation audits the operations that it funds. They chose to arrive unannounced and we did not have the opportunity to plan their itinerary. We are doing our best to provide all that they are asking for. Would you be willing to sit for an interview with them?" His tone is quiet, an appeal to a friend.

"Why not Robert Obeng or Dr. Kwarteng-Badu? They are familiar with the Advocacy's operations. Obeng sits on the steering committee."

"As I said, we're trying to answer their requests. They would like to speak to you."

"They said no when you offered Obeng and no to Kwasi."

Finn meets my eyes without panic. He still thinks he can turn this his way. "Very good, Louisa, you have caught me out. Now, will you give us a hand?"

"I know how seriously you take audits."

Finn smiles. "There's no reason why we can't help each other."

"I've never seen your audit report. There is no proof that I need your help."

Finn drums his fingers on the polished wood. He drags his posterior off the edge of the desk, squeezes against the wall to reach his seat, and digs in his drawer for a box of cigarettes. "You're too smart for your own good."

He flicks open his lighter and puffs to draw the burn to his fag. "I'll take care of the Advocacy audit. You help WAG with the interview." There's tension in his voice from the effort to sound casual, to help me believe we are working out a deal for our mutual benefit. He's run out of cards to play.

"You have accused me of improprieties worthy of my resignation, that you claim merit criminal prosecution. I want to see the evidence."

"It's immaterial, if you go along with the interview."

"You would abet a criminal?"

"Louisa, save us all the trouble. This all goes away for a minor effort on your part. Talk to the auditors and tell them about the effective collaboration between the District and WAG to improve water and sanitation conditions in the villages."

Ei. That's straight out of my letter. He does read. A sarcastic breath escapes with the roll of my eyes. "Whenever it's convenient, Finn, right?"

He smiles, pleased with himself, reminiscent of my father swilling wine in victory over my mother's meek protestations.

I feel my mother's heart. She could have said nothing, saved herself the slaughter. But she has compassion for people. She cares about something larger than herself. "If you recognize the benefit, why don't you take the collaborative approach? It's good for WAG, good for everyone. What stops you?"

"We don't need it." Seeing the disappointment on my face, he says, "Grow up, Louisa. Live in the real world. West Africa Gold owns this land. We don't need to collaborate with anyone. We can do what we want. We can kick all the villagers off our land anytime we want."

"Maybe on paper you can. I'm sure it's legal. But, in the *real world*, you can't. If you could, you would have done it years ago. You wouldn't be funding the Advocacy, and you wouldn't need my interview. And if you can't, if the villagers stay on the land, why can't you treat them with dignity? Why can't you collaborate with the District? What stops you?"

"Enough." Finn's face is flushed. "Will you do it?"

"No."

Finn's hand tightens around a heavy cube paperweight.

"You accused me of embezzlement. You threatened to see me rot in a Ghanaian prison. You personally suck down an incomprehensible salary and refuse the responsibility incumbent upon your office. You think I'd do you a favor?"

Finn's arm flinches, as if he has to hold back the impulse to nail me with the paperweight.

I jut my chin toward his clenched hand. "Want to step outside?"

"I can take you out anytime I like." His voice is steel.

"Not today. You need me. Send me a signed, certified copy of the audit report with the conclusion that the Advocacy has responsibly managed its funds. Include a statement that audits will be conducted no more frequently than every twelve months. And reinstate the flow of funding." I nudge my duffel bag with my foot. "I've had to subsidize our good work out of my own pocket." A lie, but close.

Finn responds with an almost imperceptible nod.

"I'll meet with them."

Osei and I catch a taxi. The driver stops after a short distance to pick up a man, woman, and child. It's a squeeze for Osei and the newcomers in the back. The woman tries to hand me the girl to hold in my lap. The child could be two years old. Wide-eyed, she stares at me. When she realizes there's to be a transfer, her cavernous mouth opens.

"She's afraid of buroni," Osei says in response to her screams.

Is she? Or is she unaccustomed to transcendence? I get out and invite the mother to sit up front with her daughter. The girl peers over her mother's shoulder, trembling with fright.

When we arrive at the District building, Osei asks, "Akua, I should just like to check on the men. The men are to pull the pump at Fomena, today."

Why not? I'm in no hurry to listen to Illiasu's rendition of my contract letter. Osei's boss was part of a recent, nationwide layoff of senior staff at Ghana Water and Sewerage Corporation. It is called, "retrenchment," and has its origins in International Monetary Fund/World Bank policies. One of the senior staff has been assigned as acting district head and greater responsibility has devolved to Mr. Osei, as the senior-most junior man. Osei can never be senior staff because his education did not take place in a classroom. He possesses, however, irreplaceable knowledge about the pipe-borne systems in Adansi West District and is becoming an expert on handpumps through his work with the Advocacy.

Osei undertakes his new duties with more than his customary vigor. I cannot begrudge his joy at the challenge life has brought him.

As Osei heads across the street to the District offices of the water company, I wander over to the short block of offices that houses, among others, the Department of Community Development. I may as well use the time to see if Helen Boateng, Takyi's boss, will be able to make our next steering committee meeting. The door to her office is open. No one is there. In fact, nothing is there, except two barren desks. There's not one scrap of paper or a pen, not a remnant of chalk, not one publication.

I've seen people here on other occasions. Once, Helen Boateng sat behind the far desk reading a funeral announcement. It's no wonder the men ask permission to purchase supplies. Even something as basic as a pen they do not take for granted.

CHAPTER FORTY-SEVEN

Osei returns in short order. "Akua, the men've gone already. I had thought I might catch them. I'll meet them later."

We climb the steps to the third floor. No one is in the reception room, not even the receptionist. I knock on the door without hope and am surprised to receive a buzz-in from Illiasu.

"Ah, you've made it." Illiasu pulls a folder to the center of his desk.

"Yes."

"And you have brought . . ."

"Osei, sir." Osei extends a stiff soldier's hand.

"Osei. Please, have a seat." Illiasu speaks as he would to a dignitary. Not that he flatters. I imagine the demands of his career have cultivated a voice that maintains the requisite distance while conveying respect. "So, finally we meet. I am returned from my travels and you are looking well. You are recovered from your illness?"

"Yes, I'm much better. Thank you," I reply, glancing at Osei.

Illiasu opens the folder. "WAG has been asking about the contract. We've had it for a long time. They're asking if we're going to sign it."

He sets the contract aside and picks up my letter. "Should we finish this?"

Fresh from the confrontation with Harrigan, I understand Illiasu. The contract is meaningless. We will use whatever leverage we have, within or without the terms of the contract. The real world is not contained in a contract. "We're ready to sign," I reply.

"How is the audit?"

"About to come to a successful conclusion."

"Oh." The brows above Illiasu's sad eyes rise in curiosity.

I look at Osei, knowing he would find my confronting of Harrigan blasphemous.

"Ah," Illiasu says, as he and I lock eyes. "If WAG does anything we don't like, we'll terminate this. That's it. Signing the contract doesn't change anything." He turns the contract around for Osei to sign.

A world in which contract law has no meaning.

Osei springs from his chair and signs his name.

"Thank you for your service, Mr. Osei."

Osei perceives his dismissal and stands with military precision. "You're welcome, sir," he belts as if to be heard above a raging battle. Out of courtesy, he turns to me, "Akua . . . ?"

"Thank you for your assistance."

He departs and Illiasu observes, "He is a good man."

"Yes," I reply. "All four of them are reliable and they care about the work. For that, I'm grateful."

"Their commitment is a reflection of their respect for you."

I pause to let my eyes follow the billowing curtain behind Illiasu. "At least, we may conclude that my management has not been so poor as to quash the natural inclination of their hearts."

Illiasu looks at me—I feel, perhaps for the first time, seeing me. For a moment, I exist as a person apart from the endless stream of business to which he must attend.

"Tell me about the audit."

I recount the showdown, prepared to suffer his disapproval for backing WAG into a corner. When I finish, Illiasu's eyes shine through his melancholy.

"You are an engineer! Yet, you have learned."

Passing over his denigration of my profession, I respond, "Ghana is not America." It hits me that he is right, again. It has everything to do with my training as an engineer. "Right out of college, I went to work in construction. My first primer was on the rights and obligations conferred by a contract. In construction, we live and die by the meaning of contract language. Careers can be ruined, companies bankrupted, huge sums of money can change hands due to a word or a phrase.

"It is jarring to discover a world in which contract law has no meaning. Contractual relationships are irrelevant. Ghana is not America. To defend what matters, one has to be willing to lose everything."

"Europeans and Americans are fond of their documents." Illiasu spins the contract around. "They enjoy pretending that we come to the table as equal players. That we come of our own free will. In fact, we are impelled by a history in which Europeans and Americans play a large role." He studies Osei's signature. "This is not blame, you understand me. It is impossible to articulate the underlayment of history at the time of each engagement.

"Every culture has ways of organizing. We understand that European and American cultures require the signing of documents." Illiasu appends his own name. "It is not a poor practice. It is the hubris that pretends the words on the page possess finality.

"We sign the contract." He caps his pen. "But we are clear that the inherent complexity is not captured on these pages. When the inadequacy of the contract reaches absurdity, we do not honor folly.

"You have experienced it—the authority of truth."

"And truth comes from the present moment." I am struck by the magnitude of my own words.

"You have tried." While I remind myself that this is a compliment, Illiasu's hand moves to a stack of folders near the edge of his desk. "So, you're not going to the villages today?" It's over. My presence restored to its status as one of the many pressing affairs of his day.

"Oh, yes, the rest of the team went to Old Edubiase, Sodua, and Old Akrofuom. Or, that's where they will go as soon as WAG returns our truck. There was a fatality at Rupert Wickinham Shaft this morning, and the Safety Department took our truck to get their people to the site. When we left the office, the team was still waiting."

"Osabutey had to take my car to get to Wickinham. Perhaps, if the Advocacy's truck is available for such emergencies, it should also serve the Administration."

This was exactly the kind of chopping Lynn was trying to prevent by creating a quasi-independent agency in the Advocacy. It was the lack of reliable transport that had prevented her from implementing a consistent program in the villages.

As if reading my thoughts, Illiasu says, "Well, this is the Advocacy's truck and its first purpose is in service to your team. West Africa Gold took the Advocacy's truck that, it says right here in the contract, was purchased with Advocacy funds?" What lights Illiasu's face? Not cunning, nor smugness, nor an engineer's hegemony. He plays the long game.

"Yes."

He shakes his head. "They cannot have it both ways. They're breaking their own contract. When we meet with Dr. Kwarteng-Badu, we shall straighten out this situation."

Ah, the fabled meeting with Kwasi. Everything will happen, "when." The hypocrisy no longer burns. *Hypocrisy* now irrelevant to the intricacy of Illiasu's dance. Though there is much I will never understand, I finally feel trust in that thing beyond my comprehension.

A strong knock on the door is answered by the buzzing-in of

three suited gentlemen. Without Illiasu's notice, I take my leave. My steps follow the gutter in the direction of the school. The contract is meaningless. A reality anathema to the foundation of construction management. Contractors live and die by rights and obligations. Meaningless. How would roads get built?

For once, classes are in session. I make it halfway across the schoolyard before the screams begin.

"Oburoni!

"Oburoni!

"Oburoni!"

A chorus of boys and girls in yellow and brown uniforms hangs out of the classroom windows. I keep my head down, pressing through the gale of their chanting, which dies. I glance over to see teachers closing the shutters.

Rights and obligations. I loved the camaraderie of experienced colleagues who understood construction challenges and how best to meet them . . . how would they fare in this world?

A sweeping view of the empty school grounds makes me pause. Normally, I plow through, intent on outpacing the children. Red soil void of vegetation extends away from me in every direction. In Tripoli, our vast and featureless schoolyard was composed of Saharan powder. Children of expatriates from all over the world played endless games of football. My friend Deborah and I wouldn't let ourselves be separated. Throughout lunch period, we leaned on each other, never losing contact, and roamed the grounds laughing, singing, whispering to each other.

I felt I belonged—all of me belonged—in that world.

Ɔbaa. Ɔbarima. Oburoni. All of it and none of it. Who am I, if I cannot be perceived within a known category? Who is the District, if it signs a contract it does not feel obligated to uphold? The underlayment of history. The complexity of who I am cannot be articulated.

It's a relief to arrive home and get this duffel bag off my shoulder. Kojobesia. Ɔbarima. Ɔbaa. One who moves in the duality. What is the Twi word for one who moves beyond duality?

I unload stacks of bills onto my table. My situation is getting dire. If Agyeman doesn't deliver, I might make another month. Beyond that, if Peace Corps doesn't come through . . .

Bright inks liven the Ghanaian currency—strong reds, blues, purples, and greens. The designs are more imaginative and more beautiful than American dollars. By assisting my colleague with a loan, I've succeeded in losing my most trusted associate. Not to mention, the pleasure of a perceptive and poetic individual—a loss all the greater given the limited social milieu of Obuasi. I cannot make this right.

Crisp hundred-cedi notes corded in perfect alignment. A nurse holds her head high on the face of the bill, reminds me of no-nonsense Gladys at Peace Corps in Accra. Ghana's first nurse, Docia Angelina Naki Kisseih, born after World War I, achieving her doctorate in her sixties. It's the International Finance Corporation loan that led to WAG developing any kind of environmental programme in the first place. Even the multinational corporation is beholden. On the back of the bill, workers load produce.

Thin papers of two-hundred-cedi notes layered one upon another, their fibers grabbing like glue, act as one cohesive unit. An old man wearing traditional cloth looks off to his left from the face of the bill. West Africa Gold wants to dictate our agenda because they think they own us. They don't. But I squandered my leverage on Finn's red herring. What did I really gain? The Advocacy funds will flow again. A teacher engages students on the back of the note. What matters are Ankrah and Madam Tettey. Kwasi, Illiasu, Ankrah, and Harrigan, for some reason they're reluctant to meet. They will never meet. I will never know why.

A brick of five-hundred-cedi bills rests heavy on my chest. "Work and Industry" are proclaimed across the Ghana black star, supported by a fist, underscored by the words, "Gye Nyame." Ghana needs loans to transform its approach to rural water. Why else would World Bank/United Nations be the engine behind the Capital Investment Programme? On the back of the note, a grove of cocoa palms rises and a miner drills. Why does Tao Bronson, a Ghanaian, have to be employed by World Bank in order to draft and implement water policy in Ghana?

What did Illiasu say? "People who can draw their own pro-gramme will never become leaders. That is the curse of development. That's why we have a brain drain." Isn't that the same as silencing the voice of a country? As the debt between us has robbed me of Agyeman's poetry, what happens among nations?

Not a fraction of movement beneath the string. Impossible for sticky fingers to slide a bill.

A nurse.

Gyimiso Kakraba's refusal to pay for the skin ointment belies an entire community's sense of self, of integrity, its refusal to be intimidated by a modern world that has forsaken the art of human connection.

An old man.

Rejection of the pretense that the solution is money.

A teacher and students.

How did subsistence farmers, without exchanging a word, down to the last mother with an ailing child, insist upon framing the crisis in terms of human dignity?

A miner drilling.

Praying with all his heart, *Onyame, mepa wo kyɛw, spare the life of Ken Saro-Wiwa.*

A civil engineer surveying.

I live among gods.

CHAPTER FORTY-EIGHT

The change in environment is so dramatic, I feel I'm walking in the English countryside. His residence is set back from a verdant lane that rambles up, down, and around the neighborhood of the mine's senior staff. A yellow porch lamp glows in the quiet night. I pause, recalling another night, a torch beside a hut, the priestess waiting within, holding me to her. What honest thing can I say to Peter without profaning that night?

Peter greets me as if my visit is the most generous of gifts. "Welcome, Lou." He gives me a two-handed shake, beaming down at me. Without hesitation, I embrace the expatriate charade of presuming an ease that time has had no chance to nurture.

Stepping back so that I can step in, Peter claps his hands and raises his eyebrows. "We've got biscuit dough and corned beef. You know what that means . . . samosas!"

"Samosas? Great!" I respond.

"And," he raises a finger, "for dessert, we have cookies and ice cream!"

"Terrific!"

Rubbing his potbelly and mumbling to himself through a crooked grin, Peter disappears.

I follow to find him pacing in a kitchen with a sink, a full-sized refrigerator, built-in counters, and plumbing.

"Now, will samosas be enough?" He scratches his bearded chin. "Potatoes! We'll fry some potatoes to go with the samosas.

Ah! We'll put the potatoes in the samosas! What do you say, Lou?"

"I like it," I say, ready to support any plan in this fantasy kitchen.

"And . . . we have a can of peas. Corned beef, potatoes, and peas in the samosas or the potatoes and peas on the side?"

"Either seems . . ."

"Potatoes and peas on the side. Right. Lou, you wash and fry the potatoes. I'll get the samosas underway. Here's a pan."

Washing the potatoes, I ask, "Do you have any onion?"

Peter freezes. "What do you want onion for?"

"It'll go great with the potatoes. Potato and onion."

Peter is silent. Finally, he says, "I can't eat onion. It plays hell with my stomach. Of course, probably if I didn't drink so much alcohol . . ."

"Even if it's cooked?"

"Lou, I can't eat onion," Peter says, with the solemnity of one who lives alone and can no longer distinguish between idiosyncrasy and tragedy.

"We don't need onion," I say, as if correcting him, and pull a gleaming knife from a wooden block.

Peter twists the key to peel a strip of tin from the trapezoidal can of corned beef. It seems ancient technology. I love the British devotion to those who subsist in the outposts of empire.

"How goes the work, Lou?" he asks.

"Don't ask." The sharp blade halves a stack of thick potato slices in one clean motion.

Peter whacks the biscuit tube against the counter's edge, popping open the dough. "Harrigan giving you a hard time?" He tears apart the perforated squares.

"Both barrels."

"I'd expect no less from the devil." He plants a dollop of salty beef and pinches the first samosa closed with a fork.

As much as I like Peter, the mine is a small place and people talk. I'm reluctant to share my reactions to Finn, lest he gets wind and perceives his aggression as successful. On the other hand, that could be a good thing. The more confident Finn feels, the less likely he is to escalate. I pour oil into a pan. "When we met in Accra, Harrigan was busy auditing the Advocacy's accounts. I returned to bullshit charges of embezzlement. He threatened me with criminal prosecution."

Peter sets down his fork. "That's harsh. He's pissed at something you did?"

"Or didn't do. WAG wants to dictate the Advocacy's agenda."

"Well, we are funding you."

"They want us to serve only WAG-impacted villages, even if that means going outside Adansi West District. The District's mandate is to serve all villages in the district and only within the district."

Peter scrapes the backs of his fingers along his bearded jowl, pressing his face against the rub as a cat would.

"It's not even my call. They took it to the steering committee and got shot down. Now they're pressing me. It's not my place to overrule the steering committee." The potatoes sizzle and I lean into the scent of hot salt.

Peter grabs a skillet and turns a burner on high. "So what're you gonna do?"

"I've done it. I called his bluff."

Peter shakes his head. "Careful, Lou. These bastards have crazy power. Crazy power does crazy things."

I boast of my refusal to help Finn.

"You're gutsy. I'll give you that." He starts popping samosas into the hot oil. "But I'm afraid Finn is right. He can take you out anytime he likes. He is not your father. If he tires of you stonewalling him—one day your truck could break down, you might never return from the bush."

Genuine concern colors Peter's face. Admitting his point would open the door to paralysis. I cannot live from fear. "In the end, I agreed to the interview if he restored our funding."

"One hand washes the other. That's how you do it."

"Is it? What did I really gain? The Advocacy is back to zero. I'm fighting just to maintain normal operations. Was Harrigan a step ahead of me the whole time? Did he contrive the audit as leverage to impel my interview? I think these are done." I kill the heat under my pan.

"Don't you hate that?" Peter's face breaks into a devilish leer. "When they know they've got you by the short hairs?"

"Yes. What did you mean? When you said Finn is not my father?"

"Are you sure you're your father's daughter?" A playful grin twitches beneath his graying moustache.

"What?"

"Your father's a real stickler for facts. Everyone knew that. Never speak to Lou Lehmann before getting your facts straight." Peter executes a military salute.

"My dad loves the truth. That's for sure . . ."

"Your father is a realist. He practices the art of the possible." Peter scoops fried samosas with a slotted spoon, dropping them on a paper towel. "You know you're in Obuasi? This isn't the cinema. No one will rescue you."

I am pragmatic. Finn pushed me into a corner where I had nothing to lose. And Finn is my father. Peter doesn't understand. The complexity cannot be articulated at the time of each engagement.

Fresh samosas slide into the oil. "Besides, where is the Advocacy without WAG?" asks Peter.

I grasp this theme on which we can agree. "Yeah, what I wanted to tell you is the District signed the contract today. It's a horrible contract. If they ever decide to enforce the terms, the Advocacy is dead. Everyone at the District is acting like we don't need West Africa Gold."

"They don't. If they manage their affairs properly they don't need WAG. They're just looking for the handout." He stirs the skillet.

"That's not true, Peter. When WAG's effluent has killed the Gyimi River, WAG is responsible to provide alternative drinking water supplies. That's no handout."

"No, but what's the District doing to help? Those villages would be in bad shape with or without WAG, and it's the government's role to assist them."

"The District is assisting the villages. The District has dedicated four of its employees full-time to the Advocacy, and the District is responsible for bringing in a Peace Corps volunteer."

Both of us are yelling. I'm just getting warmed up. Peter looks as if he may be at the end of his patience. A samosa misses the paper towel and ricochets to the floor. I pick it up and Peter points to the trash.

"Maybe your case with the Advocacy is an exception." He concedes. "But how about the road? Every day my entire body is vibrated into oblivion. It feels like my teeth are going to rattle right out of my head. They should fix that bloody road."

"That road is used by haul trucks twenty-four hours a day. Those trucks are tearing up that road."

"That's right. In the U.K., I pay taxes and the government maintains the road. I don't pay a second time to repair the road. The District is responsible for that road."

I don't respond. I had never thought of it that way. Maybe the road is the District's responsibility. Maybe there's a reason that road isn't repaired. That road is this town's revenge.

"More lemonade, Lou?"

"Please."

"Isn't this great? I have a glass of fresh-squeezed lemonade every morning. The old man brings the lemons for me from his tree. More vitamin C than oranges."

"You were going to tell me how Evelyn's doing."

Peter goes still, hangs his head, and drowns in sympathy. "Bless her. She's an angel. Bless her, she's not the brightest, but she's tough. Lou, she'll do this. She'll get her degree. She's learning what a challenge this is. Bless her. She's determined.

"When she gets back, we'll be able to go into business together. We'll be unstoppable."

"How long will it take for her to complete the program?"

"Three years. It's a two-year degree, but coming from Ghana, she's got to take some additional courses to prove she has the U.K. foundation."

"You must miss her an awful lot," I say, noting how misty-eyed he's getting.

"It's tough, Lou," Peter says in a voice full of drama. "It's tough to be alone. But she's the woman for me and we'll get through this."

We settle into the living room in front of the television. Each of us has a plate of potatoes and peas and two samosas. As I raise my first forkful, Peter leaps out of his chair. He closes his eyes and raises a palm to forestall questions, then returns to the kitchen muttering to himself.

In his absence, I peruse the memorabilia mounted on the walls and laid upon shelves—stone sculptures, wood carvings, metal work—several bawdy phallic figurines of local craftsmanship, raw stones, polished wooden eggs. To an unpracticed eye, the deposition of objects may appear haphazard. But every expatriate curates their private collection, each memento aligned with no less care than the chewing gum packages comprising the meticulous pyramid of a roadside vendor.

An oil painting on a large canvas tugs at my memory. Two pastel camels race through a storm, their riders tossed in the graceless gallop, their robes a riot of color whipping in the tempest. The handwoven cloth; mastery on camel back; intrepid plunging into the unpredictable, uncontrollable sands celebrate a vibrant culture surviving across the desert's vastness. Magnificent and puny, at once.

"Ah, the ghibli," Peter moans in awe of the sublime energy, then places on the table between us a reserve plate of samosas. "It's erotic isn't it?"

"The style . . . it's familiar. . . . The artist?"

"Barudi. Libyan."

"My parents had a painting of a Libyan woman, gypsy looking. I grew up with her on our wall."

"Barudi was very popular at the time. It wouldn't surprise me if your parents had purchased one of his paintings. Do you remember Tripoli?" Peter asks. "You couldn't have been very old."

"Oh, yes." Mention of the site of my earliest intoxication unleashes the flood of my devotion. "I remember. I loved it, Peter. It was such a stimulating place. I never felt so alive as there. I always knew I'd come back." Feeling the story of Gyimiso Kakraba on my lips, I lapse into silence.

Peter squints at me and gives a satisfied snort. "No quibbling about it. You've definitely got the disease."

I hold up my hands and bow my head in surrender to his verdict. "One of the things that has me going about this place is Union Jack Kofi. Can you tell me more about the crosses on the Union Jack?"

"Well . . . they're the crosses of the Saints—George, Andrew, and Patrick—the patron saints of England, Ireland, and Scotland. The center cross is St. George. The red X cross is for St. An . . . No, the red cross is St. Patrick's. The saltire is for St. Andrew."

"What's a saltire?"

"The white *X* cross upon which St. Andrew was martyred."

"Oh, I always wondered why the *X* looked funny. It's two *X*s."

Peter rolls his eyes.

"Well, how would I know?" Receiving no give, I repeat, "How would I know? I've never studied flags."

"Every schoolchild in Britain knows what those crosses represent . . . and, they can tell you why there are thirteen stripes and fifty stars on the American flag."

"Ah, all right, I'm the boorish American."

"That's right, Lou. Eat up. Have you seen, *Heat?*"

All the American culture I abstained from in college finds great play overseas. The more action, the less intelligent the dialogue a film possesses, the greater its commercial value in the international market of pirated videos. A friend of Peter's in the U.K. taped this video off the television. After the movie, they continued to record a local newscast.

"Want to watch nine-month-old news?" asks Peter, while clearing the plates.

"Why not?"

A gentleman in a coat and tie stares into the camera. "Negotiators feel they are on the verge of a major breakthrough. Critical advances are being made in peace talks in Bosnia."

"Hey, this could be today's news," Peter scoffs, as he disappears into the kitchen.

He's right. Peace talks continue in war-razed Bosnia. Always you imagine you are on the verge of momentous change, when, in reality, very little changes.

The contract was our great promise of change. It has come and gone, and nothing has changed. Just that "fifty thousand dollars" is written in black and white. My proposal had asked West Africa Gold to reframe their relationship with the District. It had asked them to conceive of partnership. Too radical for transnational capitalists.

The news anchor turns stage right to provide an alternate view of monotone. "Arabs stage a hunger strike in the desert where they were left over one week ago by Israeli soldiers."

I call to Peter above the noise of his dishwashing, "And the Arabs are still on hunger strike." Very little changes and that which does, does so at a geologic pace.

A commercial touts the aphrodisiac quality of peppermint sweets. Peter crosses the living room to answer a knock at the door. "I'll bet it's the old man with my lemons." He rubs his palms together, grinning.

I'd held out hope that today Agyeman would salvage our friendship. I'd hoped he'd look me in the eye and acknowledge that he's late in repaying my loan.

The front door closes and I realize that Peter has stepped outside. The news anchor introduces a guest, an expert on medieval metallurgy, and invites him to comment on a recent archeological find.

I had hoped Agyeman would explain a new timetable for making good on his word. But he's left me outcast, making it clear what I am. First and foremost, I am white-skinned. Whatever my woes, they cannot compare to the financial strife of the Ghanaian. Whatever my goodness, I'm not deserving of an honest answer. I'm less than human. In Agyeman's eyes, I am more and I am less.

The front door opens and closes, but Peter does not gambol past gloating over his delicious lemons. I look over my shoulder to find him slumped in the hall, arms hanging at his sides, eyes on the floor, lip quivering. Aware of his flair for drama, I wonder if Peter has received some bad news about his fiancé or whether he will have to go a day without lemonade. He slogs over to his chair and sits. Crouching forward, Peter holds his face in his hands, then rubs his cheeks and looks up, saying, "Oh, God, they've done it." A tear rolls down his cheek. "They have sentenced him to death."

I feel the wind knocked out of me. The shift to certainty in the fate of Ken Saro-Wiwa, this change comes too fast. I drop to the floor, throw my arms around Peter's legs, and bury my face in his knee. I cry for a man I do not know. A man beloved by this Africa that I hold dear. A man who speaks truth in defense of his people, just like the Rifleman. A man who, if circumstances permitted, I think would listen to this engineer's tale.

Peter howls over my head, his body shaking.

His abandon draws the grief out of me. I cry for Gyimiso Kakraba. For my small and his village, who, through no action of their own, have been robbed of the most basic need. I cry for my profession that is my passion and pride. For civil engineers in the employ of West Africa Gold who have betrayed society's trust, dishonored the mantle of *Civil Engineer*. For those who afford themselves the luxury of ignorance or dispassionate observation or cruel disregard for the injury wrought by their miscalculation, who have stolen that which they are sworn to protect. For the lack of conscience that allows months to pass, months of needless suffering at the hands of my profession, the hands of those who know the vital nature of water.

I swivel till my back lands against his chair and pull Peter's knees into my chest. Peter folds himself over me, his arm draped down my arm.

I cry for myself. For a child's dream of discovering what makes her whole. For the richness of the answer given in a clearing in a forest. For the paradox of an impersonal sacred reaching into the most private spaces of my heart. For silence. I cry for the sanction to carry the most profound experience of my life without words. For the sad fact that there is no one in

Obuasi with whom I would share, if I could. I cry for the distance between Carol and me.

Peter slides back, sniffling. A spasm wracks his chest and ripples down his arms. The tremor quiets, as Peter brushes my cropped hair with his palm, over and over.

I cry for the scrawny, hairy legs against which my chest heaves. Heat and sweat and tears bathe my neck and cheek, slick against Peter's knees. The only physical contact I've known since coming to Obuasi. I cry in gratitude for release to cry in another's presence.

As my shuddering grows less intense, my cries less frequent, Peter rubs my back. I linger with my head down, reluctant to leave. When I look up, Peter is leaning back in his chair, closing and opening swollen, red eyes.

He looks at me and we sit for a while, just looking. A crooked, wistful grin spreads over his face. "Ah, Lou," his voice scratches, "you are more than your father's daughter."

CHAPTER FORTY-NINE

When the mason struck, the unequal distribution of plaster formed recesses in random shapes that give texture to the surface of the ceiling. Above the center of the table, the irregularity approximates an equilateral triangle. Delta. The symbol for change. Can truth change?

Delta. A mathematical symbol for a rational world. A world of parity. But this delta is different. It overturns the premise of my life. That I am helpless to find my voice beneath the timbre of my father's.

Conceived as a function of the blinding African sun.

Barbara spoke in her own voice. Her colleagues could not comprehend. My voice resonates with the authority of my father. What is lost? Is it possible to appropriate his style to convey a genuine message? Can my integrity survive the masquerade?

My eyes slide to the *X* in the plaster. The Union Jack. The absurdity that trivializes Kofi's noble personage. Does Kofi appropriate the flag? Do I look with the wrong eyes? Is the cartoonish aspect meant to trivialize the horrific?

I have felt less my father's daughter since the day he told me he could not change. I was home from college and found him in a pensive mood. Brimming with newfound feminist righteousness, I broached the issue of his treatment of Mom. He had responded with, "We . . ." "We find we cannot change." As if he had Mother's collusion, which, despite how much I wished otherwise, he did. This was my father's summary reflection on their marriage. From his recliner, the bastion from which he surveys and judges the world, Dad had pontificated in the same voice he might have used to describe the ascendency of a particular style of architecture.

I would not be standing in an Obuasi street if Lou's grace had not lifted me to stand upon ancient stones.

"We met very young, when we were in college . . . well, I guess we were your age, a little older. Anyway, when you're young, you see the world in a certain way. This worldview leads to certain behaviors. You fall into patterns with your wife—or husband. We fell into certain habits.

"These ways of treating each other become engrained. As we grow older and grow to see the world differently, one or both may wish to be treated differently. But after so many years, it's impossible. We find we cannot change."

Lou is not the Rifleman. He does not mourn the fate of Ken Saro-Wiwa.

I had looked with condescension upon the man who needed to bolster his view of his life with such crippling rationales. What truth is this? Lou's truth is the truth of history, words on pages about dead cultures, military battles, political maneouvers. When I was young I admired my father's lust for facts. I trusted the elevation of truth above all. With the naïveté of a child, I applied Lou's lessons to every realm, failing to notice his omission of human relationships.

He cannot help me make the Earth whole.

I am not content to know the fact of the geologic process that formed the mountain. I want the facts of how I treat people and vice versa. I want the facts of what I feel. Mom's world. Her persistence in trying to meet Lou's cold reason with her unsubstantiated insistence that desire, that preference holds equal weight with rational fact. Of who I am.

I stare at the darkness cloaking the wall. Nothing else sounds like the screeching of steel scraping steel. I press my hand to my heart and lie back down. With a deep breath, I go back to sleep.

Robert Obeng catches me as I leave the lab. It's unusual that he should seek my company.

Obeng is a short, square man, who totters more than walks. He stops at a safe distance, bursting with his victory. "The boreholes have been drilled at Gyimiso Kakraba."

"That's great. We'll go by there today. What shall we tell them about the pumps?"

Obeng's pride recedes behind a dull mask of rubbery flesh. He fumbles for words. I'm sure he regrets straying from the herd. In a twist of Ghanaian logic, he says, "Let them know we're still looking forward to receiving handpumps . . . but only if they ask you. Otherwise they may ask you many questions you cannot answer, like when the pumps will arrive."

I know the men are tired. Although most villages offer us fresh coconut or oranges or bananas, it's little to sustain us through a full day in the heat and humidity. I gave up bringing provisions when I discovered the men wouldn't squander their out-of-station allowance on lunch chop. It had felt absurd to eat in front of them. Pulling to the side of the road, I beckon to a woman selling tea bread.

"Akua," Thomas enquires, "did you say you wanted to visit Gyimiso Kakraba?"

Agyeman has abdicated his role of speaking for the team.

While the men eat, I cajole. "I know it's late, but I'd like to see what WAG has accomplished."

"We will go." Thomas ends the matter.

The drive to Gyimiso feels longer than it should, partly because of the congestion getting through Obuasi this late in the day, partly because our bodies have been tousled about on rough roads for the last six hours. Maybe also due to the anticipation I feel at returning. How might the people greet me? Will my small race out of a jubilant crowd? Osei and Thomas talk in Twi. Agyeman stares out the window. Takyi sleeps in the back with his head on his chest.

We arrive to find the Chairman of the Committee for the Defense of the Revolution isn't in. Of course, our visit is unscheduled. A young man offers to lead us. No guard priest. No priestess. I press my palm to the center of my chest. We follow the young man along a narrow forest path. I glance at my feet. The black gash along the nail of my big toe has softened to pink. Soon there will be no evidence. Two small concrete temples rise from the center of a clearing. The men hike up the wide steps on the back side of each structure.

These temples, or "civils," as Jim and Kwasi call them, are intended to permit clearance for a filter to reduce the high level of iron in the ground water. The villagers won't use the filters because they require back-flushing every two days. Jim and Kwasi learned this almost nine months ago when they experimented with the prototype. The filter idea hasn't been pursued since, but no one has bothered to modify the design of the civil, which elevates the base of the handpump six feet above grade. The ridiculousness of the design echoes the absurdity of my hope for some acknowledgement of that holy day.

As Takyi climbs the steps of a civil, I strain to catch his limp. If one did not know, one would not see it. He squats beside the plastic pipe extending a couple of feet above the platform. "Ho ho," Takyi sings, "Gyimiso Kakraba will have water soon."

The thrash of tree limbs and bush pulls our attention to an unbroken face of dense forest from which my small bursts into the clearing. With his typical ease, he throws himself against me, clasping his arms about my waist.

I kneel and ask his name.

He hangs his head.

"Yɛfrɛ wo sɛn?" I whisper.

The boy tries to stand straight. Sweat runs down his temples and drips off his nose. Putting his eyes on the ground, he says in a small voice, "Yɛfrɛ me Sebastian."

"Sebastian. Ɛyɛ." My hand light upon his back, I say, "Yɛfrɛ me Akua Kojobesia."

Sebastian looks up and my heart soars at his violation of the etiquette of addressing elders. Our gaze opens to the infinite.

Thomas interrupts our communion with the placement of his hand to Sebastian's forehead. "He has a fever." Sebastian bites his lip. He seems pale.

Who gets access to good water? Who does not? Who decides?

"The boy's mother . . ." Osei announces, as a woman pounces on Sebastian. She clutches both shoulders and pulls him to her, her voice scolding and concerned. She moves away with Sebastian pressed to her abdomen.

Questions you cannot answer.

At the sound of Thomas's query, Sebastian's mother half-turns. Her reply comes in a high-pitched cry.

She disappears into the forest and Thomas relays, "The boy has diarrhea and vomiting. This is the third day. It gets worse each day."

Who will tell Sebastian he does not warrant good water?

Shell Oil and the Nigerian government have told the Ogoni that they do not warrant good water or clean air or uncontaminated soil. They do not even warrant a voice of dissent. Their voice is to be murdered.

382

"Akua?" It's Takyi's voice from the backseat. I realize I've been staring through the dusty windshield, oblivious to the men's silence.

"Yes?" I take the left edge of a large pothole.

"Akua, ɛte sɛn?"

"Ɛyɛ . . . dabi. Me ho nyɛ. It is not right that Gyimiso Kakraba suffers. How long can a village go without water?" I toss my gaze toward Agyeman who rides shotgun. He does not look at me.

"WAG has installed the boreholes. It will not be long now," Takyi reassures.

"No, Takyi. It will still be long. WAG has no pumps. And another second is too long." I glance again at the vacuum on my right. A barreling trotro sends me scuttling to the shoulder. "We need to know what our role is. Can the Advocacy come to the aid of Gyimiso Kakraba?"

"Eh, Akua, that is not possible." Osei warns from behind my seat. "The Advocacy owes its life to West Africa Gold. We cannot displease WAG."

"Can the son challenge his father? Hmph," Takyi snorts.

Sebastian reached into the depth of his being, where we met as equals.

There is only one opinion I wish to hear. Looking straight through the windshield, I say, "Mr. Agyeman, it seems you have lost your voice."

"Why is that?" he replies. I bask in the gravel rush of his voice, the roughness as he accelerates from void into full sentence.

Splitting the difference between tarmac and dirt and keeping my sight ahead, I say, "I don't know. But you'd better find it. We need it."

Agyeman speaks without hesitation, "If we believe that World Bank will come to the aid of the Advocacy, we may risk offending WAG."

"The World Bank deal is dependent upon the District Secretary's cooperation. We cannot count on anything from him."

"Even so, it would be unwise. West Africa Gold is powerful and World Bank does not reside in Obuasi. WAG pulls the strings here."

I take a full breath, relieved to hear his thoughts. "Then what was the ritual worth? What can the Advocacy do for Gyimiso Kakraba?"

"Not the Advocacy." A grim note tinges Agyeman's voice. "Akua Kojobesia."

My heart swells at the sound of my name. Tears spring to my eyes. "I don't understand," I say, keeping my eyes on the road.

"It is too late for that."

The slap of Agyeman's words sends the Rifleman's finger to the trigger. I accelerate to pass an idle trotro. There has to be more than the ritual, more instruction. "Who am I to interfere?"

"You danced. You made your choice."

My eyes don't move from the ceiling and its scrawny rooster. In the texture of the plaster, I imagine touching a child's face. The face of my seven-year-old self savoring the extravagance of green pistachio gelato. An uninhibited soul enthralled by the magical realm of Tripoli.

The stick clutched in the rooster's claw widens into the wing of an airplane. The wing visible from the window through which my ten-year-old self stared in shock. 1973. The year my well ran dry. A stepped line in the ceiling, like the ascent to Gyimiso Kakraba's pipe rising from the top of the civil. How many days till they drink? How many days could Dr. Kwarteng-Badu or Illiasu or Ankrah go without water? I've lived nearly twenty years in the dry. Water is not so important.

Carol's letter lies on the desk beyond my toes. What did she say? I flip through the pages, my spirits lifting a little at the sight of her handwriting, a script that has borne to me much inspiration. Here it is, "Passion is the wound."

What does she mean? I thought I understood . . . I follow the line of her pen, hoping for the coherence I'd felt upon my first reading of her letter.

Just when I've won this chance to lead, I suddenly doubt my motivations. All these years of politicking — yes, the causes were right. (We cannot allow another Tyack!) I was right. I am right. But I can see now that my passion has always been fueled by the pain from the wounds of my family.

Thanks, Isa, for the congratulations. You know better than anyone it's been a long, hard haul! But honestly I feel a sham. When those women look at me, they see the confident head of the Democratic Women's Caucus, when I'm only a terrified girl.

All the fight in me is born of desperation. I begin to believe there's no such thing as compassion. I don't truly care about the abused and downtrodden. I take up the fight for the chance to scream in public — the screams that were silenced when I was a kid. It feels great to finally scream!! But even when we win, I'm not sure it changes anything. Can we ever rewrite the first chapter?

I unwrap the ornate leather sandals. A vivid orange tassel adorns the engraved leather. It was me who danced. I slip my hands into the stiff, painted leather. One, one-two, the sandals step on air. One, one-two. Akua Kojobesia.

To know something greater and one's relationship to it. That greater something is not about me. It doesn't give a damn about me. It doesn't even give a damn about Ken Saro-Wiwa. Someone as beloved and esteemed as he can die. Agyeman said he foretold his own death. He knew Abacha would come for him, but he did not flee.

Didn't I, for a moment, see something greater in me? I felt it to my core. Not Mother's sentimentality. Not feminist virtue. Not Edelman's purity. Vitality in my body from that extraordinary connection with the people of Gyimiso Kakraba, for a moment.

Gyimiso Kakraba's well isn't dry. But for a handpump, Sebastian could have water. Obuasi is one huge construction site. Somewhere in this town I could find a handpump. I don't doubt that. McKenna's prohibition persists, "Do not interfere with WAG's affairs."

Letting my gaze retrace the edge of the airplane wing to the stick in the rooster's claw brings my heart back to gelato, to my young trusting self . . . to Sebastian, a village boy who has no reason not to trust. My fingertips brush the line of Carol's script.

What was my first chapter? Was it the sacredness of Libya? The split? The dropping of connections?

"It is too late. You danced." Agyeman.

Has Gyimiso Kakraba rewritten my chapter? Is it possible?

Idrissu scoffing, "You cannot choose."

Is Carol right? Is compassion a euphemism for denying my own broken humanity?

"No one cares about a few subsistence farmers." If Carol is right, Harrigan is right.

It doesn't matter. I am none of these people. I am Akua Kojobesia. I made my choice. I can stop the suffering of Gyimiso Kakraba. If Michael Vaughn is obligated—and I am certain that he is—how can I doubt my obligation?

By what authority? That vested in me by Gyimiso Kakraba.

If this were a construction site, it would be clear that my mission is to obtain handpumps. "Do not interfere . . ." I would never challenge a direct order from my project manager.

What privilege defines my obligation? That of being Akua Kojobesia.

I know I could find pumps. "Ghana is not America." I don't want to be impulsive. This inscrutable culture. My instincts don't apply. I do not want to impose an engineer's hegemony.

I feel the insanity of cycling. I want to be free of my mother's injunction that every voice be heard. Every viewpoint be given equal weight. The pinball ricochets in my head from one voice to the next.

Dirty beige-thread grey-sworl brown-CAPITAL green black red white-Gere grey.

Dirty beige-thread grey-sworl brown-CAPITAL green black red white-Gere grey.

I take out my Swiss Army knife. How long can one live without good water? I grab clutches of hair. The grating scissors do not soothe. More. There is always more hair. Whose thirst?

It is always too long. I yearn for the ecstasy of the release. Make it shorter. To whose aid do I come? Although I stand in front of the tiny travel mirror, I don't look. My fingers tell me every time—cut more. Whose well is it, mine or Gyimiso Kakraba's?

A whimper slips from my throat. Strands alight on my shoulder. I brush away the excruciating wisp, a spider scurrying, a whisper. My fingers pinch their way across my scalp, feeling for excess. I cannot find the lie. The piece that needs to be shorn. I throw myself onto the sofa, burying my sobs in a cushion along with Mom's question, "What is the measure of this civil engineer's success?"

VII

TENDER OF WELLS

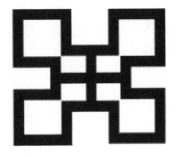

He looks straight ahead at the viewer—seeing but not being seen, present but not recognized.

—DAVID HECHT AND MALIQALIM SIMONE, *Invisible Governance — The Art of African Micropolitics*

CHAPTER FIFTY

Idrissu does not notice me approaching the stretch of duplexes. He argues with a man in the twilight. I love Idrissu's uncensored passion. But tonight in the dim light, without a trace of his words reaching me above the din of the road, I feel certain his passion has yielded to anger.

Perhaps the tell is in the body of the man at whom he directs his wrath. I recognize the erect posture, the deep blue shirt starched to stand in the heat. Reaching the tree in front of my duplex, I peer around. Once they grow aware of my presence, the encounter will dissolve.

I watch Agyeman in profile, rebuking Idrissu. No voice reaches my ear, but there is no trick to perceiving hostility. I have never seen Idrissu and Agyeman together. I don't know what they have in common.

Idrissu comes at Agyeman in his way, his face close, thumping his chest. Agyeman leaps back, flinging up an arm in warning. The two freeze, I imagine their eyes lock, and Agyeman scuttles into the maze of homes behind Idrissu's shop.

Without thought, I race up my side of the road, well beyond the range in which Idrissu would seek me. When a lull presents in the traffic, I dash across and cut back in the direction of Idrissu until finding a break in the row of frontage shops.

I find myself in a narrow, eroded lane. The close buildings block the already fading light. As my eyes adjust, I hustle around a corner and head in the general direction of Agyeman's disappearance. I've never explored this neighborhood, as I have no business here. Ghanaian miners live in the rectangular, one-story, windowless buildings with tiny, vertical slits set well above anyone's line of sight.

Pulling my duffel bag higher over my shoulder, I leap over a scummy thread of bathroom sullage. I run as if I know, weaving through the poorly-ventilated blocks of housing. I follow the guard priest, placing my feet in his steps. Osei's hand on my back steadies my gait.

I can do this forever. The guard priest stops short. This time, I pull in tight beside him and see what he sees—a wider street, chop ladies ladling out meals in plastic bowls. Throngs of miners patronizing their favorite kiosks. I meander through the crowds, stopping to take a gander at the chop plates served to the men whose labor is the engine of Obuasi. The quality and quantity of food beats anything on the main road. Why didn't Idrissu tell me about this?

A bowl of chopped salad piled high with grasscutter, chopped tomato, and boiled egg tempts me. I dig into the best street chop I've had since coming to Ghana—no offense to Kwabena's Tea Bar; egg sandwiches belong to a league of their own.

Loud music begins to play. The crowds thicken. I presume more are arriving off the day shift, hungry and exhausted. However, many in the throng seem fresh and clean.

"Akua, I did not expect to see you here." I know Agyeman's voice before turning.

"This is great street chop," I say.

Agyeman's advice feels like a command. "Ei, it is not good for you to stay here."

"What is here?"

"This . . ." He gestures above the miners' heads. "This is not a place for buroni, nor for a woman. Let me take you home."

A microphone whines, cutting off the music. Truck head-lamps shine upon two men who stand on a table. The crowds have merged into one audience that quiets to hear the speakers. I cannot catch their rapid Twi.

"Come, Akua." Agyeman pivots, as if to guide me away.

". . . Ken Saro-Wiwa . . ." As his name rings clear, the rally comes into focus. Agyeman is part of the Obuasi resistance.

"I saw you arguing with Idrissu," I say.

"He disapproves of my . . . activities."

"I do not disapprove." For a moment, I see Agyeman. He is present behind his eyes, unlike the many weeks of absence. Perhaps, away from the office, he is able to forget his debt and allow me some humanity.

"You here is what Idrissu did not . . ." Agyeman's last words are lost to the surge of the crowd. My bowl is knocked out of my hand. I feel frightened by the force with which my body is pressed. Loud, angry cries rise above the rumble of the men. My feet come off the ground. Agyeman grabs my arm and pulls me against the inclination of the crowd. My protest at the pain of his grip dies in a memory of my bicep crushed in the clutch of the guard priest.

Agyeman navigates the maze without stopping or looking at me. When we emerge onto the main road, he releases his charge. I rub my arm to stimulate blood flow. Agyeman points in the direction of my home. He calculated to deliver me well west of Idrissu.

"Medaase," I begin to say, but he has melted into the dark. His haste may come from many things—protectiveness of me, his desire to return to the rally, discomfort at being alone with me at night. A roiling wave in my gut overrides my disappointment at Agyeman's departure. "Squeeze those cheeks," as we used to say during training, when we all underwent an unpleasant adaptation to the gastrointestinal fauna of our new country. I maintain a fragile balance between speed and the capacity to prevent any discharge. Sometimes I stop in fear that I have failed, imagining the humiliation of soiling myself. But the gods treat me kindly. I make it to my gate without incident.

"Akua!" Idrissu waves a questioning hand. He wants to know why I'm not coming from the direction of the Advocacy office.

I clutch my gut and point to my house.

"Kɔ." Idrissu flicks the back of his hand to indicate I should hurry.

I fumble with the Chinese padlock, toss my duffel bag on the porch wall, and drop my shorts in time to let the first explosion hit porcelain. Sweat beads on my forehead, as a gut-wrenching spasm releases foul liquid into the toilet. I press both hands to my belly, awaiting the next salvo. Nothing comes. I am reluctant to leave. As soon as I dress and get comfortable inside, I'm sure a spasm will compel me to run back.

I rub my belly for a long while before deciding it's safe to leave. The timing suggests the world's most glorious street chop may not be sanitary. However, if that were the case, I would expect a much more intense experience, not just one shot. I mix up a batch of rehydration salts and sit down to my Muslim.

All of Obuasi could fit on this page. I had only wanted his face: bold lines flaring from a cloth flowing white and soft. The urgency of his eyes constellates in every cell of my body a fierce single-mindedness. To what end? The Muslim knows. Can my lead discover? I want his face. But, the empty space surrounding him demands definition. My pencil is trapped with the Muslim in more.

"Eh." Kwasi seems unsure how to introduce me from a distance. "Yanos Avayanakos and Martin Dupree," he gestures to the men at his left, "Louisa Lehmann." He gives a stunted wave in my direction, not wanting his hand to enter my supposed field of contagion.

The two men, in full business attire down to their cuff links and polished shoes, nod and wave. The Greek smiles.

"Please, have a seat." Mr. Dupree orchestrates, looking disturbed at the carnage atop my head.

I sit across the table from the auditors from the International Finance Corporation, one hand beneath the table rubbing my belly, and leaning back to ease the pressure on my explosive gut. Kwasi takes a seat by the door, as removed as he can be while complying with Finn's directive to chaperone the interview.

Mr. Avayanakos flips open a file, exposing a list of questions. Sprawling his palm across the script, his pen wedged under and over his first two fingers, he leans far enough to bring his sternum over his splayed hand, and says, "We are sorry to disturb you when you are ill." He tries to create some confidence between us, while protecting the imagined prize of his yet-to-be-completed document. "Unfortunately, our time is short." He pulls back to erect posture, dancing his fingertips on the page. "We have a few questions and will try to let you go as soon as possible." He glances at Dupree for concurrence.

I wipe sweat from my eye. Usually I cannot bear the air conditioning at Safety. Today, I wish it could penetrate my fever.

Mr. Dupree sits back, playing with the gold band on his finger. An open laptop blocks half his chest from view. "Thank you for coming."

There is no excuse to not be here. Finn has delivered the audit report and reinstituted the Advocacy's funds. "Of course." I try to smile, stopping at the pinch of my chapped lip splitting a little further.

"Please tell us your job title."

I swallow rehydration salts and struggle to thread the cap back on the bottle. Giving up, I set the cap on the table and hug the bottle to my abdomen. "I am the Coordinator of the Adansi West Rural Water, Sanitation, and Health Advocacy."

"Mhm." Mr. Avayanakos scribbles. Mr. Dupree types. Avayanakos continues. "The Adansi Advocacy?"

"Just, the 'Advocacy,'" I offer.

"Mhm." More scribbling. More typing.

"How long have you held this role?"

"Nine months."

Avayanakos plays the pen along the fulcrum of his finger, performing math in the air. "February." Scribbling and typing.

"And what does the Advocacy do?"

"The Advocacy . . ." I take a slow draw from the rehydration bottle. ". . . works to improve water and sanitation conditions in the villages of the Adansi West District. We are comprised of four Ghanaian staff and a Peace Corps volunteer."

Avayanakos shoots a piercing gaze at Kwasi, who tugs at his snug collar, but says nothing.

A vague wondering what I may have said wrong gives way to holding my breath, hoping for painful gas to pass without sound or odor.

The auditors both wait for me to continue. "Mm, we do health education, encourage the formation of village health committees, and support the villagers to implement projects to improve their water or sanitation facilities."

The Greek turns the page to record on the back. The Frenchman knocks his glasses up and pinches the bridge of his nose.

"How do you do this?"

I look at the Greek and wait. A vague question that requires too much effort.

"How does the Advocacy do its work?"

I mop my brow with a cloth. He will have to do better.

"Where do you meet the villagers?"

"In their villages."

"How do you get there?"

I mop my brow again. "Uh, we have a truck."

Scribbling. "And who drives?"

"I do, or sometimes we have a WAG driver, or a taxi driver."

"It is either you or a WAG driver driving the truck?"

"Yes, when the truck is available. Otherwise, we can take a taxi, if we have the money."

"So, the truck is not available because of maintenance or repairs?"

"I don't think so. I don't recall that happening. Usually the Safety Department—we are funded through WAG's Environmental Lab, which is part of Safety—usually, at those times when we don't use the truck, usually, Safety has needed to use it."

"So, the truck is not exclusively for the Advocacy?"

"No. Well, yes, uh . . ." I glance at Kwasi, who is looking at his shoes.

Avayanakos follows my gaze to Kwasi. I wipe my forehead with the back of my hand and swallow rehydration salts.

The Greek persists. "Is the truck exclusively for the Advocacy?"

"It is. It is meant to be. Uh, we share the truck with Dr. Kwarteng-Badu."

"Sometimes the Advocacy takes taxis to the villages because Dr. Kwarteng-Badu is using the truck?"

"No. He doesn't use the truck during the day."

Dupree lets out an impatient sigh.

"I'm sorry. I don't think I have the mental capacity to satisfy your inquiry."

"I think you do," Dupree says in a flat voice.

I'm not liking our guests. I squeeze my cheeks and wait for the gas to pass.

"Dr. Kwarteng-Badu." Dupree stands and goes to the door. "We are not in need of your assistance." He opens the door.

Kwasi tugs at his collar and departs without looking at me. The shutting of the door sets off a chain of echoes. I close my eyes, for once wishing I could be walking that gauntlet.

"Now, you may speak freely." Dupree returns to his computer. The auditors stare at me.

"Eh, is there a question?"

"Does Dr. Kwarteng-Badu's use of the truck compel the Advocacy to take taxis?"

"No."

The auditors glance at each other. It is over. No way out. Truth will displease the auditors or Finn Harrigan or both.

"Please speak freely. We can assure you there will be no consequences."

Like hell. I lick my chapped lips. "Sometimes, other Safety personnel need transportation and they borrow our truck."

"Can you give an example?"

I rub my belly under the table. An example . . . ? "For example . . ." I don't want to incriminate Finn, but the mine accidents must be on record. The auditors must know. ". . . if there might be an accident at one of the shafts, and Safety must investigate immediately."

"In this case, they would take your truck?" Dupree raises his brows.

"They might, yes."

"It has happened?"

"Yes."

"Often?"

I swallow rehydration salts.

"How many times?"

"It varies. Sometimes it could be once a month. Lately, it has been almost weekly."

Their scribble scribble scribble and type-a-tap-tap escort me to the gallows.

The interview continues as a lopsided maneuvering of partial answers to pointed questions, or no answers at all, as I surrender to the notion that illness protects me. From time to time, I feel the tension break, hear the auditors scratch the record of my poor discretion and WAG's incrimination, incompetent to perceive the meaning of my own words.

When they let me go, I suppose they've gotten what they came for. I feel dirty. Does Bessie think less of me? Before she fled to Botswana, did she name names? I trudge down the hall, down the hill to the Miner's Circle, and huddle in the back of a cab. The driver must see my distress, as he does not stop to take on other passengers.

After an uncomfortable night sticking to the sheets, I check my temperature. One hundred. Encouraged by the low grade, I take a hot bucket bath and lie on the sofa. Bessie died of hepatitis alone in Serowe. I am not dying. I shake out the cobwebs and pull the Muslim from the cupboard.

I hate every smudge of graphite forming the narrow, arched doorway in parallel with the drape of his gown. A discipline of inclusion compels me to sketch the road extending behind the Muslim, a pregnant goat pausing at his heels, cross gutters choked with Obuasi's waste, vacant land prepared for a building foundation, then abandoned, eroding into oblivion, a woman balancing a headpan of water walking past dozens of nondescript storefronts. I entrusted the Muslim to this page without conception of the consequences.

A loud rapping brings me to the gate. A man wearing a round helmet, the chin strap dangling, balances a small motorcycle at his side.

"Hello," I say, noting his attention to my hair.

"I'm Yusuf Salihu. We met in the road."

Another request for water. How many villages can we take on? I feel obligated to hear him. "Yes, from Kwabenakwakrom. I am Akua. Come in."

Yusuf wheels the tiny bike into my courtyard and takes a seat in my front room. I roll up the blueprint paper and set it aside.

"Would you like a glass of water?"

"Yes, please." He accepts the glass from a posture half out of the chair. He drinks down a third, and stares at the carpet and my writing table before speaking. Although Mr. Salihu hasn't smiled, he seems more thoughtful than stern. "I work at the mine. I'm a miner."

I nod. He's not a huge fellow, but he is healthy. He wears white WAG coveralls.

Mr. Salihu sets the glass on the small end table and glances at my bookcase. "As I mentioned, I would like to see about getting a borehole at Kwabenakwakrom. I just moved there and they're drinking water from a stream. It's not healthy."

"No." It's not healthy. Welcome to the modern world. Water everywhere, unfit to drink.

"Someone told me that you're the white lady helping the villages to get drinking water."

Or white man, depending on the day and who's speaking. I feel space in my head. Is my fever rising? "Yes, I work with the Advocacy."

"What is that?"

"The Advocacy. The Adansi West Rural Water, Sanitation, and Health Advocacy." Specializing in cameo appearances at water rituals. Did I say that aloud?

"What exactly do they do?"

"We conduct education about water-related diseases and, if the people are interested, we'll help them with a water or sanitation project—wells, boreholes, latrines."

"I see." Mr. Salihu studies his glass for a moment. "And where are you doing this work?"

"We're in about forty villages."

"And can you come to Kwabenakwakrom?"

Why not? What's one more? "We can. How's next Tuesday? I believe we'll be in your area that day."

"You must come at night. We're all miners. We work during the day."

Agyeman would know the merit of such claims. "Then let us say Thursday night, but I must check with the team to be sure they can make it. Can you stop by our office or we can leave a message in the village on Tuesday?"

"Let us do both. That way the people will believe you're coming."

"All right."

Mr. Salihu glances about the room, pausing at the photographs on the wall. "These are your mothers?" he asks. Idrissu has explained to me the importance of having more than one mother. When your biological mother dies, there will still be mothers to care for you.

"Yes," I reply, knowing I have never thought of Barbara and Bessie in that way. The complexity of what they represent cannot be conveyed. Or . . . could they . . . be my mothers? "Why did you move to Kwabenakwakrom?"

"Because of work in the mine. I'm from the North."

It is said that when the British arrived one hundred years ago, the local Ashanti refused to work. They were too proud to do menial labor for the whites, accustomed as they were to having slaves who mined gold for them or to receiving gold in tributes. Their agricultural livelihood offered an abundant alternative to wage labor. Those Ashanti who did work were to be found in less dangerous, aboveground occupations. WAG made many efforts, often unsuccessful, to recruit or conscript workers from what in the early days were known as the Northern Territories. When the gold market booms, as it is now, workers flock from all over. Many northern tribes are represented in Obuasi, most of them Muslim.

"Where's your village?" I ask.

"I'm from Wa."

"Ah, we have a Peace Corps volunteer there."

He raises his brows.

"Karen Morten. She's a health education volunteer."

"I've not been home in more than a year. I've been looking for work."

"Karen says Wa is a model town. They don't need her."

Mr. Salihu lifts a proud head.

"She is supposed to be a contraceptive counselor, but she says the people are educated and don't need her. She lives in a home belonging to a wealthy man. He doesn't reside there. Perhaps you know him? He has a collection of models of various solar heating systems and a library on contraception and family planning."

Mr. Salihu purses his lips. "Abdul Rafi wants to power Wa from solar panels. He is occupied at Parliament. His plan moves slowly, but he is a patient man. We are patient people."

"In our water and sanitation work, we see many villages. I wonder when we come upon a well-organized village, what makes them different? Why is Wa different?"

"It was not always as it is now. My grandmother told me how after Independence many people got the chance to go to school. Ghana is proud that at Independence we had the highest proportion of university-educated people of any African nation. While this was true for the Gold Coast, at that time most Northerners were illiterate. Nkrumah made it possible for village children to learn to read and write."

"That happened across the country. What makes Wa different today?"

"Akua, you said yourself you see many villages. They are like people. Not all are capable of seizing the opportunities before them. My grandmother speaks of her generation, the elders at that time. It was the early sixties. They truly sought to benefit their offspring . . . and themselves. What their children learned at school, they came home to teach their parents. My mother taught my grandmother how to read and write."

"But wasn't this happening all over Ghana?"

"I cannot speak for the rest of Ghana. I cannot even speak of history. I was not born. I can tell you what your friend says is true. My people value education."

"But it was not always so?"

"The opportunity to learn was not always there. Ignorance can be seen. You are teaching about water-related diseases and good sanitation. You are not the first to teach this. My grandmother knows of a time when Wa was ignorant of such things. But many things were taught to all of Ghana through the school programme launched by Nkrumah."

"But I don't see such awareness in the villages we visit."

"Villages are not different from people. Those who failed to learn about sanitation before, may have been occupied learning other things. Who is to say when change should occur?" Now he sounds like me, except Mr. Salihu is not aggravated. He has reserve.

"But we are scheduling change, are we not? Our Thursday appointment—you would like Kwabenakwakrom to be more like Wa?"

"I would like to answer my thirst without jeopardizing my health. I cannot say when Kwabenakwakrom will change. But I hold the belief that it will not happen without the first invitation. Thursday night is a beginning. Do you like it here?" he asks.

"Who likes living on the haul road of an open pit mine with trucks running twenty-four/seven?"

"You have many books about Africa."

When I received my Peace Corps posting, I had thought I knew nothing of sub-Saharan Africa. A memory of my grandmother takes form. She stands on the circular carpet, not looking at Mr. Salihu. She spits from her lips the words she uttered when she learned where I was going, "Al Aswad?" Did Salihu hear Grandma's condemnation? Her words . . . before . . . had reminded me that my Africa was Arab and Muslim. Sub-Saharan Africa—I knew nothing of this place.

Al Aswad. The black of the Muslim's glasses. That I deny. Al Aswad. Oburoni. Aswad-buroni. I look from Salihu to Grandma.

"Are you all right?"

I focus on the miner sitting in my living room. "I'm sorry. I've been ill. Though I think I'm recovering, it seems to overtake me without warning."

"Are you a student of Africa?" Mr. Salihu attempts again.

I'm discovering this is the same Africa where I left my childhood. "Africa is a great teacher. Who is not her student?"

Mr. Salihu stands and sets down his glass. His eyes meet mine, then drift up to the butchery of my hair. With a final nod, he grabs his helmet.

CHAPTER FIFTY-ONE

I escort my guest to the road. It feels good to walk, to get outside. Idrissu steps up to his curb to note the departing motorcycle and waves me over. Holding up a finger, I indicate he should wait small. After locating the latest magazine, I return to assuage his curiosity about my visitor.

"Maaha, Idrissu." Crossing the road seems a grand adventure in my state.

"Maaha. Ɛte sɛn?"

"Ɛyɛ. Medaase." I feel the bench under me, the comfort and safety of Idrissu's porch. "Na wo nso ɛ?"

"Ɛyɛ. You have a visitor, Akua?"

"Yes, Idrissu. Here is *Newsweek.*"

"Dat's right." He stows the magazine in the small space beside the sewing machine.

"The man is from Kwabenakwakrom." I volunteer. "He wants to help them get better drinking water."

"Dat man is for Kwabenakwakrom?"

"Yes."

"Ah, Kwabenakwakrom . . ."

"It's on the road that joins the Kumasi-Cape Coast road, past Pomposo."

"Yes, I know dere." Idrissu pulls a creased newspaper from behind his seat. Unfolding the thin paper, he studies the page, then extends it to me over the sewing machine. "Dis, Akua."

I read the headline, *Ancient Justice Triumphs*. "Read, Akua," Idrissu says. I take the paper, settling a little closer to him.

> *Mpraeso District, the scene of the tragedy, the loss of the lives of three good men. Nomotey Akam, twenty-eight years old, husband to Ama Natue and father of three, deceased. Cause of death: Digging a well to provide good water for his family. Antwi-Boasiko Manu, thirty years old, husband to Adiata Amankwah. Cause of death: Saving the life of his brother, Nomotey Akam.*

The brotherly reference feels right. I understand. Ghanaians choose their family. Blood is no guarantee of connection. There may be obligations to blood relations, but there need be no pretense of anything more. The person for whom I will jump into the well, he is my brother.

Idrissu clears his throat.

"Eh . . .

> *Saving the life of his brother, Nomotey Akam.*

I love reading those words.

> *Enoch Godlove Afriyie, forty-one years of age, husband to Rita Sekyere, father of five. Cause of death: Rescuing the fallen men in the line of duty.*
>
> *The bodies of three good men lie irretrievable at the bottom of a well.*

I pause for a horn to pass.

> *Upon last report, no one was to enter the well, upon the order of Fire Captain Tijani, for fear of further loss of life. The*

grieving widows, the devastated children now fatherless, the good people of Mpraeso District could not bear to leave the bodies unattended in death. They have stayed at the well, nay, the grave of these good men. Mourning, singing, dancing, the living tell the souls of the departed that they are not forgotten and they shall have their proper rites.

Thus did the people spend their days, awaiting the return of the Fire Department to extract the bodies. Did the FD make good on their word? This FD who last year legally embezzled from the general funds to pad their private coffers, did it at least prove its worth in time of need? I am sorry to say, Dear Reader, that not only did these self-serving thieves fail to rescue the dead, they made no attempt at same. Neither Captain Tijani, nor his superiors, nor his subordinates showed their faces again. In a reprehensible show of disrespect, word was sent to this community steeped in sorrow via a lorry driver. The message? 'Expect no more assistance from us (the FD!). Advise to fill in the well.'

Fill in the well! Dear Reader you must be as shocked as this Reporter. No mention of the dead. No consideration to honor the fallen or aid the mourners in the necessary fulfilling of their obligations. Fill in the well! I respectfully submit the obvious. The FD's proposal is indecent, inhuman, un-Ghanaian, un-African.

What has this band of scoundrels to say in its defense? How can anyone defend leaving the corpses of once-honorable men to rot in the maw of the evil forces that snuffed out the bright lights of their lives? The cowardice of the FD is indefensible and well they must know it. For they make no attempt to explain. This Reporter has tried every mouth from the lowliest janitor to the Regional Chief. None will speak. A source wishing to remain anonymous hinted that the order came down from the highest level. . . .

I skip several paragraphs of This Reporter's rant on that detestable institution, the FD. Idrissu raises an insistent chin. I pick up the story on the back of the next page.

> *Abandoned by those to whom one turns in need, the widows and their families determined to take matters into their own hands. You will understand, Dear Reader, if I omit names from this point. For there are those who condemn reliance on the ways of old. Those who would spurn, nay, exclude from proper society those who can still conjure the powers of our ancestors.*

Idrissu sits forward, nodding.

> *As for This Reporter, I cannot say whether I was present or informed in the second-hand. I cannot divulge the ceremony summoning the aid of those spirits and angels with whom our ancestors communicated daily. I cannot say how many or what kinds of livestock may have been slaughtered on the altar of a certain fetish priest, nor whether a virgin dedicated her remaining life to religious service. It is not for me to tread upon that hallowed moment of levitation . . .*

While massaging his beard, Idrissu cocks his jaw and narrows his eyes.

> *I can say only this. I saw the bodies of the three fallen men laid honorably. Adorned in the finest cloth, by the bond forged among the three families, as they met the same fate in life, so the three men shared a funeral forging their smooth and proper passage.*

"Dat's right," Idrissu says, rubbing his hands together.

*Dear Reader, we must never forget this is what it means to
be African, to be Ghanaian, to be human, to be decent. We do
not trifle with the matter of souls entering and leaving this world.
This is a matter of the gravest (pun intended!) importance! This
is This Reporter signing off.*

Idrissu shoots out of his seat, scraping through that narrow
gap between the doorjamb and his sewing machine. "Do you
get it, Akua? Do you get it?" He leans his face over the edge of
the newspaper.

"Wote asɛɛ?" Idrissu demands. He has never placed himself so
close.

I hold his eyes, not understanding what he wants.

"Akua, before de white man come, de black man can travel
from Obuasi to Accra in fifteen minutes! Fifteen minutes!"

Juju aswad. "Why don't you do that now?" I ask.

"Dat was before de white man. De black man could travel . . ."
He snaps his fingers. ". . . like dis."

"Why not now?" I ask.

"Because de white man come. He bring Bible and make us
ashamed."

Juju aswad-buroni shame. I feel space in my head. Is Idrissu
finally talking straight about his beloved white man?

"Dese peoples . . ." He raps the paper with his knuckles. "You
read it, Akua. Dese peoples save de men. Dese peoples use de old
ways. De African way.

"Akua, dis de way of Kofi."

Kofi. I wipe sweat from my brow. Idrissu has never spoken to
me of Amadu al-Attar. He uses the familiar, "Kofi," out of respect
for what cannot be named.

"You see de mystery of Kofi. De mystery is his protection."
Idrissu steps back and swings his arms above his head, as if dodging

evil spirits. "Like Dis Reporter." He taps a thick finger on the thin sheet. "Like Dis Reporter say. Dere are even Ghanaians who do not trust de old way. Kofi doesn't know who he can trust." Idrissu ducks his head to dodge the evil. "Kofi cannot walk like an ordinary man. De mystery protects him."

Kofi mystery. "Kofi is alive?"

Idrissu flips an impatient hand, returns to his seat behind the sewing machine, and says, "Wote aseɛ?"

CHAPTER FIFTY-TWO

I spend the rest of the day sipping rehydration salts, taking my temperature, deciding if I should be concerned about the strength of the sulphur odor emanating from my diarrhea, and roaming the geography of ceiling plaster.

Juju aswad-buroni shame-Kofi mystery.

"He bring the Bible and make us ashamed." Would that be the Bible of the religion whose saints' emblems Kofi displays in the alley? A flag of shame in the hands of the patron saint who relies upon African ways?

Grandma's Bible. Grandma's ways. "Al Aswad?" Shaming me. As if I should know better. "Al Aswad?" Judgment. Disbelief. Buroni shame. *My granddaughter in Africa?* Aswad.

The black of the Muslim's glasses.

Juju aswad. "Dis de way of Kofi." The African way. A flag of shame. How does one appropriate the symbol of one's own destruction?

Somehow . . . in this fast town void of any unifying chief, no one defiles the image. "De mystery is his protection." Does every local know that Union Jack Kofi is Ghanaian ingenuity? Aswad. Ingenuity.

Kofi mystery-Aswad ingenuity.

The last truck slams into the void. I wake and do not sit up. I do not check the integrity of the wall. Nothing threatens my life. Or if it does, let it.

I pull the engineering pad from the cupboard. So many kinds of roads. In the margin, pale graphite estimates the TARE WEIGHT and PAYLOAD. Ring Road, built as the foundation of the capital, built to last. A cross section occupies the lower third of the sheet—aggregate base, asphalt concrete, wearing surface, seal coat . . . and sidewalk. Obuasi road, built to carry the strain of all that is not said, will never be articulated between a multinational corporation and the peoples of the land. Unquantified parameters in block lettering: AXLE LOAD and DESIGN LIFE. A path submerged beneath a reservoir whose impact civil engineers misjudged, resurrected as an impenetrable equatorial forest illumined by the lithe movements of the guard priest, like Kofi assaying the dense tropical vegetation that once prohibited passage along the ridge of the open pits in search of herbs that heal. I tear the sheet from the pad. So much comes from a road of unknown destination. I crumple the paper and throw it away.

Pressing my palms into the grain of the wood, I am possible.

Sebastian claimed *me*. He knows we are kindred souls. Not "he." How to speak truth with this hand-me-down balderdash of a language?

I'm feeling much better this morning. As I enter the office, Takyi reports, "Doctor stopped by to see if you're coming up to Safety today."

"I go to Safety every day." I return a skeptical look.

"Doctor did not say, but it seems to me that he has something on his mind that he needs to discuss with you. I believe so, but

Doctor did not say this." Takyi has one finger raised for emphasis and speaks as if taking me into his confidence.

"What do you think it is?"

He takes a deep breath. "I cannot say. This, I cannot say. Perhaps you will learn, if you go to Safety."

"I'll go when we get back from the villages. Where're the others?"

"They are here," he says.

The office is empty, except for the two of us. The team has taught me that it's impossible to get everyone in the office at the same time to start the day. They may arrive early, on time, or late. It is a certainty that when I want to speak to one, he will have disappeared—to the Miner's Circle for breakfast, to the bank, down to the market, or on some undisclosed errand. I sit down at the long table to see what transpired on their village visits last Thursday. Folders are scattered all over the table. I gather them into a pile and sort through, finding Sodua and Old Edubiase.

"Where are Bobriase and Old Akrofuom?"

"Are they not there?" asks Takyi.

"No, only Sodua and Old Edubiase."

Takyi picks through the stack of files on the bookshelf.

"They're not here," he reports. "Are you sure they're not there?" He comes to the large table and begins to search my pile.

"We need a file cabinet," I say, with great irritation. That's an expensive item in the U.S. I don't want to begin to imagine what it would cost here.

Osei, Thomas, and Agyeman enter within a few moments of each other.

"Maakye, Akua," they greet.

"Maakye." I study Agyeman for a trace of acknowledgement of our encounter at the rally. He does not look at me.

Osei stands clutching his leather purse to his chest with both hands.

"Yes, Mr. Osei?"

"Akua, I am sorry, I am afraid I cannot stay. I have a call from my company's regional office. I am to make a report in Kumasi today." His fast, choppy speech truncates several breaths.

"Okay." I feel winded, just listening.

"I am afraid I cannot go with you to the villages today, as I must go to Kumasi."

"Yes." I nod. "You are for Kumasi. Safe journey."

"Thank you, Akua." Osei bids the others farewell and exits with his anxiety. Thomas smiles after him. I smile, too.

"Is Kwabenakwakrom . . ." I abandon the question, noticing how Thomas and Agyeman both stare at the chaos on my head. I feel embarrassed that my agony is on display.

Thomas turns a knowing look to Agyeman and says, "German." Agyeman nods his concurrence.

There is nothing for it but to pretend I don't care. "Is Kwabenakwakrom in the Adansi West District?"

"Just," replies Thomas. "It's the last village on that road that's in the district."

"A man came to my house this weekend from Kwabenakwakrom . . ."

We're interrupted by honking from behind the Old Council. Takyi checks and calls me to the balcony. It's Anthony, leaning half out of the cab.

"Kwasi would like you to meet him at nine this morning. Can you do that?"

"Do we have the truck today?"

"Yes, as soon as I return from Stores. Can you make the meeting at nine this morning?"

"Do you think you can get a driver?" I ask Takyi.

"I will try. I'll go with him. He can drop me at Transport."

I yell down to Anthony, "If we get a driver, I can stay for the meeting."

"Wait, I'm coming," Takyi adds.

I return to Thomas and Agyeman.

"You're not going to the villages with us today?" asks Thomas.

"No, Kwasi wants to see me. Takyi said he came by the office on his way to work."

"What's it about?"

"I don't know," I say, raising my eyebrows.

Thomas asks, "What about this man from Kwabenakwakrom?"

Thomas's lead signals that Agyeman has not moved beyond the debtor's silence. "Yusuf Salihu," I reply. "He would like us to come for an introductory durbar Thursday night. I told him I'd have to see if all of you can make it."

"We can," Thomas says.

I look at the strong line of Agyeman's jaw, the rich texture of the skin of his cheek. "Good," I say to Thomas. "I told him we'd leave a note in his village tomorrow."

"Yusuf Ch . . . ?"

"Salihu. He's from Wa. Just started working in the mine and moved to Kwabenakwakrom. He doesn't like the stream water they drink." I look at Agyeman not looking at me.

"Kwabenakwakrom has money all right," says Thomas. "That's a new village. They're all miners. The village is growing fast. They may be too large to help with dug wells."

I don't miss his point. Another borehole will mean more money to raise, and we haven't even begun fundraising, yet. "Does the village have unity?" I ask.

"We shall discover this when we go."

Agyeman studies some papers. He has not met my eye once. I no longer care. I do not want what is not given. I ask Thomas, "Where could we get a file cabinet?"

He looks startled. "A file cabinet?"

"Yes."

"Why do we want a file cabinet?"

"To put our files in."

Nothing registers with Thomas.

"So we can find them, instead of having to search through every file in the office."

"Are you having difficulty finding a file?"

As if this is rare. "Bobriase and Old Akrofuom. They're not here and they're not on the shelf."

Thomas looks at the files Takyi had been sifting through, then walks the perimeter of the room. At the far end of the table, he lifts a short stack of books, revealing more folders. "They're here, Akua. We were going to update them. I don't think we've finished, yet."

"A lot of these files are out of date," I respond. "You guys have to get in the habit of writing the village records daily. You should do it at the end of the day, before you go home, while it's still fresh in your mind."

Thomas says nothing. I know the impossibility of what I'm saying. We get back from the villages at irregular hours. Often we've spent six to eight hours in the heat, lurching over rough roads, repeating the same conversations in different villages with little to eat or drink. No one is going to stay in the office at the end of the day.

"Do you understand that these village files are the only record we have of what we're doing? No one's going to read your pocket diaries."

Thomas and Agyeman look at each other.

"Don't worry, Akua, we're doing it," says Thomas.

They're not doing it. They don't see the value in it. They see it as tedious paperwork necessary only because I say so, which is not sufficient. "We need the information to be accessible in these village files." I cannot control the rising pitch in my voice. "This is the only thing that shows we're doing our job, that we actually went to the villages, that we didn't just chop the money."

"My friends, are you ready to go to the villages with me?"

I look over my shoulder to find Takyi prancing.

He transforms our office into a stage. "We have a driver and we have a truck." His step is light, his hand raised in flourish. "A driver and a truck are waiting for us, my friends. Are you ready?"

Agyeman, Thomas, and I cannot help laughing.

"We have a driver and a truck and the time is just eight forty-five. Do you think this funny?" Takyi asks in mock incredulity. He adds, with a raising of his brows, "Mr. Mensah gave me his best driver. He was to drive for the Managing Director, himself, but the Managing Director cancelled his trip from Accra. Our driver was to have driven for the Managing Director today."

"Let us not delay. Our driver can take us on a survey of our holdings." Thomas giggles, almost in tears.

"Yes! He can take us to survey our holdings." Takyi laughs, tapping a playful foot in my direction before following the others out.

Takyi, my illiterate one. Takyi, my beatific spirit. I need you the most. The tap of your foot code that you know you rescued me.

CHAPTER FIFTY-THREE

I throw my duffel bag over my shoulder and lock up. Out on the baking tarmac, I pause before trudging up the incline to Safety. By the time I reach the top of the hill, I feel feverish.

Kwasi meets me in the hall and I follow him to Finn Harrigan's office. Finn stands behind his desk lighting a cigarette. His eyes narrow and follow me to my seat. Kwasi takes up the right Fu lion position. Obeng, the left Fu lion, sits mesmerized by the chop job of my hair. I'm surprised he's not reveling in anticipation of my slaughter.

Finn places both hands on his desk and leans forward, his cigarette wagging from the corner of his mouth. "Who the hell do you think you are?" Our relationship has progressed. Finn no longer feels the need to lead with patronizing civility. "What do you think you're doing, shaking us down with the International Finance Corporation?" Finn glares. A bland stare conceals Kwasi's face. Obeng orients in my direction, vacant behind his rubbery mask. "You'd better explain yourself and fast."

I feel the heat in my face. A layer of sweat coats my belly, chest, and back. A chill sends an involuntary shudder down my body. "I didn't . . ."

"You damn well did. You know you did. What have you to say for yourself?"

Feeling the roil of my gut, I squeeze my cheeks. When the crisis passes, I say, "I didn't mean to put any negative light on West Africa Gold." I reach for my water bottle.

"You told them the Advocacy only works in Adansi West District."

Finally, I realize that WAG's push to have us work in all WAG-impacted villages, even those outside the district, must be to comply with the terms of the loan. Perhaps it should have been obvious, but I hadn't put it together. "I have been sick. I was not clear-headed that day. And the auditors were not listening to me. They wanted to interpret things in a certain way. Kwasi was there."

Finn looks to Kwasi, who nods. "She was sick."

I wipe away the sweat dripping down my cheek. Where is the air conditioning?

Finn bears down, leaning further over his desk. "I told you always to present a united front. It doesn't matter if you were sick. I don't care if you're dying. You and Kwasi always stand united."

"I told them that Kwasi was not limiting our use of the truck. They wouldn't believe me. Ask Kwasi."

Finn looks at Kwasi, who responds, "The auditors asked me to leave. I wasn't there."

Finn turns to me with a smug expression, as if Kwasi's words prove my guilt. "Louisa, if WAG cannot count on you when it matters most, I don't know why we're funding you. I'll be recommending to the General Manager that we terminate our funding. We can perform these functions much more effectively with our own personnel."

A spasm wrenches my gut. Am I relapsing? I take a swallow of rehydration salts. "I wish you well. The villagers threaten to beat up my staff for riding in a white truck that looks like a WAG truck. Imagine what they will do when a real WAG truck arrives without the Advocacy logo. The villagers berate us for not coming to their aid in dealing with WAG. At least, we can claim some independence from West Africa Gold. We can explain that we are not responsible for WAG's actions. What do you think will happen to actual WAG staff cut off in some remote village that isn't even on a map?"

"Are you threatening us? Do you think you can threaten WAG?"

"Excuse me, I must use the restroom." Squeezing my cheeks, I make my slow way out of the office and down the hall. I never want to leave the immaculate, tiled floor and porcelain toilet. I sit a long time, heaving, cramping, submitting to the violence in my gut.

When I return, Finn asks, "How long have you been ill?"

It is difficult for me to imagine time. "A week?"

"What do you have?"

"I'm not sure. It may have been street chop. It may have been the epidemic in Gyimiso Kakraba. Sebastian—my small boy—was very ill the last time we went."

"*Your* small boy?" Finn scoffs. "Ya kaffir boetie. It's cholera in Jimmy Kakra, now, isn't it, Kwasi?" I don't flinch at Harrigan's mispronunciation or his transparent effort to terrify me.

"There are two confirmed cases, of course, that is confidential." Kwasi warns. The Advocacy knows of the cholera via the talking drum.

"You ought to know better than to kiss the kaffirs." Finn looks pleased. "I knew a woman in South Africa who was aiding the kaffir wives, always meeting with them in the villages. She got very ill and didn't seek proper medical attention. She died."

Finn would love for me to remove myself due to illness. But, should I have gone to Accra by now? This morning my fever was down to ninety-nine. Now, it feels like it's spiking. The duration of the illness is most troubling. A virus would have run its course by now. The intermittent perception that I'm improving has kept me from seeking antibiotics.

"She thought local doctors were enough, but they didn't have the expertise or the resources."

"Your concern is touching." I didn't mean to say that aloud.

Finn pulls back, his knuckles digging into the edge of his desk. "You're on borrowed time, Louisa. Your stunt with the auditors was one too far. The General Manager has less patience for this than I do."

I feel I might vomit. Grateful for a belch that passes accompanied only by the sting of bile, I find it impossible to grasp the significance of decorum. Clutching my belly, I say in a low, slow tone, "If you and Madame Tettey are all out, you could borrow from the inexhaustible trove of patience you seem to possess when it comes to villagers contracting cholera as a direct result of WAG's dam, and the mine's shamefully inadequate response to the water problem in Gyimiso Kakraba. These are people's lives.

"Go ahead, pull our funding. When Bediem and Gyimiso Kakraba come with guns, don't call us. And don't send Obeng," I flick a finger toward the automaton who seems to have shrunk smaller than his already unimposing build. "Don't send Kwasi." I look at the miserable man who should have been my colleague. "You go. You and Madame Tettey, go answer to the people whose lives you have ruined. If you're patient enough, you may even have taken some lives, by then." I unscrew the cap on my water bottle. "Who the hell am I? Who the hell are you? Who the hell is Madame Tettey?" Both Fu lions cringe at this challenging of authority. I take a swig. "The Government of Ghana granted you a mining concession, not a license to kill. What the hell have you done? And for what? The cedis it would take to remedy this are inconsequential relative to WAG's profits. You're looking at three hundred dollars per ounce. You're mining a million ounces this year. The money is so small, that cannot be your motive. Where is your humanity?"

Finn has remained still, his knuckles frozen to the desk. I pick up my duffel bag and throw it over my shoulder. "As for the auditors, I answered their questions honestly and without any intent to impugn WAG." I pause at the door. "If WAG needs coverage outside of Adansi West, perhaps your staff could begin to work the adjoining districts. Perhaps the steering committee could permit your people to shadow the team for a while to learn the programme."

I listen for Finn's growl at my impudence to leave without his dismissal, but the hollow rumbling of the door closing behind testifies to my deliverance. After retching in Safety's toilet, I feel much better, though light-headed. I walk the empty hall feeling that I could be cut down in a single swath and knowing the inconsequence of it.

Slow steps take me past the Lab and along the edge of the parking lot. "Jim!" I wave to Jim Hansen and head for his truck. I had seen him loading a box and realize by the time I get down to the parking lot, that the bed is half full.

Jim offers a grim smile and the firm shake of a camarade who cannot evade his fate. "Louisa, good to see you. Saves me a trip. I want you to have this." He pulls his tennis racquet from the cab.

As he offers his gift, I feel space in my head. The Lord bequeaths to me his sword. "Thank you." I squeeze the grip to pull my thoughts closer to the earth. "Won't you need it?" I ask, dreading the answer.

"I'll get a new one. Promise me you'll use it."

Jim's appeal lands with the weight of death. "I will," I say, to honor that depth of kinship evoked by a man I know from a few conversations, who lives larger in my imagination than in outer life. "Where are you going?" My heart dives into a sea of sorrow.

"To Zimbabwe for a few weeks, then London."

"Why?" I hope he cannot hear me whimper.

"They sacked me. They say I've worked myself out of a job. My subordinates are trained and proficient to handle Environmental. It's the highest compliment." Jim tugs his van dyke.

I set the racquet on the tailgate, asking, "And the real reason?" I suppress an irrational anger at his abandonment.

Jim looks over his shoulder and steps closer. "You should know. I'm not one to divulge private matters, but you should know. They know about the ceremony."

My mind races to the day of the ceremony. What did I see in Jim's eyes?

"They know about our roles."

Jim's role? He procured me on behalf of Gyimiso Kakraba.

"You will get away with it. It's too damning for me, a WAG senior staff."

It comes too fast, learning that he played me, buried by the comprehension that he laid his livelihood on the line.

"Louisa, I'm sorry if you feel misled . . ."

I let my gaze fall to the neat squares of catgut. He would have wanted to dance.

"You understand I could not speak of it." He was not confused about the drill rig. He knew where he was sending me.

It was Lynn's survey conducted at Jim's behest that established the need for better water in the villages and that ultimately led to West Africa Gold funding the Advocacy. Gyimiso Kakraba would trust Jim. But it was too big of a risk. He needed a proxy.

"You were fired because of the ceremony?" Instead of taking me out, Finn is cutting me off. "Why now? Is it because of my interview?"

"Listen, you're safe, for now. They're under scrutiny from the International Finance Corporation. It would attract attention to dismiss you, or to pull funding from the Advocacy. Keep your head down. You're accomplishing more than we'd ever hoped. Steady on."

I extend my hand and hold his for a moment. "Jim, it's been an honor. Thank you for everything. Is there anything I can do?"

"Don't let them take you out of here in a straitjacket. Get yourself out on the court."

"I will." I mean it. "Take care."

CHAPTER FIFTY-FOUR

I feel weak and opt to take the road back to the Miner's Circle, a less challenging proposition than the steep slope of the golf course. Jim. Gone. I try to wipe a river of sweat from my nose, and discover the racquet in my hand. I hook my fingertips in the tight squares. As a penance for my contribution to Jim's dismissal, in tribute to a good man, and as a promise of change from my circumscribed life, I vow to take up tennis.

A sudden cramp has me squeezing my cheeks. I almost drop the racquet. After the wave passes, I limp over to the steps of the Old Council and lean against a pillar. Sweat pours off of me. I must be sick. Why does it come and go?

I feel scared and exhausted.

"Give ya a lift?" Ned Clyde's weathered face tilts in my direction.

"Hey." I step up to the open window, encouraged by the sight of the Old Man.

"I can drop you at the courts." Seeing my confusion, Ned juts his chin toward the racquet.

"Ah, thank you. That's not my destination."

"Where to?"

"Zongo."

"Hop in."

"That's out of your way."

"Not at all, luv," he says, leaning his head to the side and stretching the sound, as if to pull me in.

After I'm settled, Ned pulls round the Miner's Circle. He flicks ashes off his cigarette, and says, "You're puttin' a lot of miles on those feet. I see you walkin' about."

"Well, today, I'm grateful for the lift. I'm feeling poorly."

He peers at me from beneath brown, sun-faded bangs, allowing his gaze the briefest rest upon the riot of my hair. "How're things?"

"Crazy as hell. You?"

He takes a drag. "Always the same," he says in a voice soft as smoke.

I brush the tips of my fingers across the taut catgut. Jim is gone. "Say, Ned . . ."

"Yeah?"

I ignore Matt McKenna sitting at his desk, shaking his head. "I don't know the right way to say this." *A well unattended is a desecration.* Words of the guard priest ring in my ear. His clear, quiet tone cuts through smoke and chaos. "I know you don't owe me any favors."

"Wudya need?"

Do not interfere . . . McKenna's prohibition. "It's not me. It's a village." Sebastian. Don't tell me I'm violating the order by doing the one thing of which I'm capable. "Really, it's WAG." I pause at an uncomfortable wringing of my gut. Sweat pours down my face.

"You don't look good. Are you sure you don't have malaria?"

"No. My fever tops out at one-o-two. It comes and goes."

"What werya needin', luv."

I can't remember. McKenna stares at me in stony silence. "A file cabinet . . ."

"What?"

I drop my head into my hand. *We need the consecration to come from one who moves in both worlds.* The chief in his adornments, standing in the realm of myth—gold and finery, his royal court, the sage queen mother with whom one does not trifle—speaking to a desperate people who clamor for dignity. "Pumps." Surely McKenna, who loves Ghana, would not discredit the old ways. The African way has to be every bit as valid as the dealings of WAG and the District. The villagers are not helpless. They have invoked their gods . . . and they have tied a cord to my heart.

"Handpumps for Gyimiso Kakraba." I raise my head to meet his eyes. "They haven't had good water since the dam."

Ned scratches the line of his jaw with the joint of his thumb, the ember of his cigarette glowing between his fingers.

We must never forget what it means to be African, to be Ghanaian, to be human, to be decent. "Cholera is spreading." Has Sebastian contracted cholera?

Ned takes a long drag, looking far beyond the windshield.

I try to wipe away sweat, which keeps pouring down.

"Maybe you need a new thermometer." Stopping behind a dead taxi, Ned puts his hand on my brow. I almost cry. I'm unaccustomed to touch and moved that he cares. Returning his hand to the wheel to maneouver around the taxi, he asks, "What size?"

What size thermometer?

"What's the diameter of the borehole?"

I told you to stay out of it.

"Two boreholes. Both four-inch." He's thinking it through. Sebastian will have water.

Ned pulls to the roadside in front of Idrissu's place and extends his hand. One purple-black nail hangs from the bruised bed, swollen from the blow. Scaly knuckles reveal a preference for leather gloves. The unnatural angle of his index finger echoes some long ago horror. I see the hands of men I have known, rough, calloused, broken. Men who taught me how to be an engineer. Men who stake their integrity on a firm grip. I take his hand knowing the value of what is offered.

Idrissu opens my door and helps me down.

"Get some rest." Ned flicks his cigarette out the window and checks traffic. As he pulls away, Idrissu calls for Laila, who pops her head out from the home hidden behind Idrissu's sewing niche. She takes my hand and we queue up at the curb. A haul truck hurtles past and Idrissu's arm deploys in the way my mother's instinct shot her arm over the passenger seat when slamming the brakes.

One-o-two-point-five. I squint at the thermometer. Which line is the mercury crossing? I rummage in my Peace Corps medical kit for the pill bottle. Taking the anti-malarial means I'll have to race to Accra while the harsh effects of the drug take hold. I don't want to be out in the world in such a state.

One-o-two-point-five. What is the accuracy of a thermometer? Perhaps half a degree falls within the margin of error. *You ought to know better than to kiss the kaffirs.* Has Sebastian's illness continued to worsen? This One cannot die.

Maybe I should test for cholera at the Obuasi clinic. But the diarrhea improves and worsens; I think cholera would mean a steady decline. *She thought local doctors were enough . . . She died.* I open the pill bottle. Would everything get better if I just swallowed these two pills? Should I have gone to Accra already? Finn wants me gone.

I pass the day sleeping and sipping rehydration salts amid frequent trips to the toilet. Fantasies blur with dreams—Gladys quarantines me in the med unit. My disease is rare, something she's never seen. Steve Simmons's fungus coats my tongue. I'm med-evaced to Germany. I've lost so much weight by then, they keep me on a constant intravenous drip. I'm too ill to travel. Carol comes and holds my hand. As I take my last breath, she whispers, "You changed the world, Isa. They have water."

The women on my wall roll their eyes at my melodrama. The only danger I'll meet in Accra is McKenna's wrath for my insubordination. Barbara and Bessie insist in unison, "Rules don't apply to you." Their fierce independence anchors me. I didn't do it to prove my character. I did it because every human being deserves water. Because humble service in the provision of the most basic need is the heart of a civil engineer. I did it as a measure of gratitude for what cannot be said.

I cap the thermometer and press my palm into the blank page.

> What cannot be said?
> Righteous judgement of WAG engineers
> Dishonoring the mantle—*Civil Engineer*
> Degrading water—Sacrilege
> *Who am I to interfere?*—Travesty
>   *. . . a well unattended is a desecration*
> My forsaken identity—*Tender of Wells*
> Gyimiso Kakraba, do you know . . .
> In saving yourselves, you saved me?

CHAPTER FIFTY-FIVE

The abrupt cut of the mason's trowel streaks the plaster in a manner reminiscent of the paint shaved across Barudi's canvas. Barudi. Strange that I never knew the artist's name, never thought of it. But I knew much more than a name.

Every day I came home from school to Barudi's painting. I lay on the couch and studied her face. The Libyan woman. Weathered, observant, beautiful, shrewd, waiting for her moment. Her emotions changed with mine. Sometimes I learned what I felt by reading it in her face.

The ceiling seems inadequate. Nothing can compare to Barudi's woman.

I take the paper from the cabinet and smooth the Muslim against the grain of the table. My Muslim. What is in his eyes? What did I see in his eyes? What did he see?

The Muslim is silent.

I study the sketch, ignoring the corner of the table where Carol's letter lies. I try to find the truth in shading the Muslim's glasses. Distress flutters in my belly. Haven't I known from the beginning that graphite can't hold? My gaze falls to the ridge of Carol's envelope. Panic constricts my breath. There will be no undoing it.

The Rifleman walks into the center of Main Street. He stands tall, jaw strong. One hand on the butt of the gun, one on the barrel slanted across his hips. My finger feathers the envelope, the crease that tears a little more with each return of the letter. The Rifleman kneels in the dirt. As I remove the onion paper, the cursive etched by the nib of Carol's ballpoint grazes my fingertips. I pause at her touch. The Rifleman spreads a handkerchief before him. Carol speaks words I've memorized: "Truth, Isa. There is nothing else. Honor your Muslim."

The Rifleman bows. My fingers dig in the bottom of the envelope. Extending his arms, the Rifleman lays his weapon on the cloth above his head. I grasp Carol's gift, a fine artist's marker. The long black sheath as thick as a cigarette glides into balance in my hand. A sacred instrument. I smooth the blueline paper against the grain of the wood. Anything is possible.

Black flows from the coped tip, swathing the frame. The delicate laying in of the heavy line that benchmarks the rest of the Muslim, the felt stroking a way of loving this holy man, of cupping a moment in an Obuasi street. The way a humble man's strong palms cup fruit, offer bare flesh.

Tap tap. The rapping at my open shutter is followed by Idrissu's voice. "Agoo."

"Amee." I pull my eyes from the Muslim and go to the window. "Ɛte sɛn, Idrissu?"

"Ɛyɛ, Akua. You are writing?"

"Dabi. . . . I'm drawing."

"Eh? You are drawing?"

"Yes."

"Show me."

My throat clamps. I hadn't anticipated such a request. He's never asked about what I write. How can I show the Muslim? He belongs to no one but me. Aware of the extended silence, I let escape from my heart the question, "How?"

"Ei, Akua!" Idrissu sounds surprised. "Dat's right," he says in resolution, his voice fading as he turns to go.

433

I'm confused. I don't know why he left. It's possible he heard the Twi, "ɔhaw," meaning, "trouble."

My Muslim. The imperative in his eyes. Stark. Clear. What did he see? Can I read myself in his face, as I did in the Libyan woman's? I stare for a long time, waiting for the Muslim to answer.

It's better, perhaps, if I close my eyes and relive that moment. The stunning white cloth, elegance draped down the length of the man. The straight black line of the cane measuring his stride. The hand upon the cane—the only flesh visible other than his face. The rich brown tone of his skin framed by the cowl of white and the agal of red diamonds, cut by the heavy black glasses and the narrow black moustache.

A cleanness and boldness too good for the grit and stench of an Obuasi street. A clarity of vision. Urgency in his eyes. I look up in the only possible moment. Our eyes meet. I feel . . . seen. The Muslim sees—not a woman or an engineer or a buroni. The Muslim sees . . . me.

Solid black frames. Vivid. Bold. Imperative. Obvious now that the moustache and cane cry out for black. I brush the color onto paper that drinks the ink, yearns for blackness to be whole. Frames, moustache, cane. This is right. The frames. Everything else references off this line. The paper now seems dirty. The dull cast of the old blueprint paper cannot carry the pureness of the Muslim's gown. I will ask Carol for white pastel. And red for the Muslim's humanity.

I roll up the paper and glide the looped string over the end. At the last step down to the road, I mark a haul truck, hastening across after it passes. Without speaking, I point at the ironing table. Kwadwo removes the cloth and steps aside. Idrissu squeezes out of his niche while I unroll the drawing.

Idrissu and Kwadwo look at the sketch. Their eyes meet. Kwadwo shakes his head, removes his glasses, and puts his palm over his eyes, grimacing. Idrissu slips his hand under the parchment, lets the tip of his finger glide along the edge. The slow, gentle gesture may be deference or hesitation. He rolls up my Muslim and places him in my arms.

In a voice I've never heard, Idrissu says, "You show dis to nobody, Akua, nobody."

Idrissu doesn't look at me. He brushes his fingers across the smooth surface of the ironing table. He scratches the side of his beard. "You've seen Him." He raises his eyes. "You have seen Kofi."

Idrissu and Kwadwo exchange a glance. Kwadwo restores his cloth and iron. Idrissu resumes his sewing.

I pull myself up to my full height. Staring at Idrissu, who focuses on his needle, I scan my meager repertoire for an appropriate idiom. In a slow, clear voice, I say, "Meda wo ase."

Neither Idrissu nor Kwadwo responds. I step up to the gutter to await my moment. As I move into the wake of a carbon-spouting taxi, I hear the words, "Dat's right."

EPILOGUE

Agyeman, Thomas, Osei, and Takyi joke amongst themselves as they depart to the villages. I skim the pages of my pocket notebook for the men's signatures confirming their receipt of cash. Nothing kills my enthusiasm like preparing a budget report.

"You are in." Mr. Illiasu steps into the Advocacy office.

I slide my pen between the pages of my notebook and step around the desk, puzzled at his unexpected visit. Illiasu never comes here. "Akwaaba." He comes no further than across the threshold, so I stop short, uncertain of the etiquette.

Illiasu wears a Western business suit and tie. His sad eyes carry a spark today. The rumble of a passing haul truck invades through the open window. By silent agreement, we wait for the noise to recede.

"Congratulations, Akua." Illiasu throws his hands wide, then snaps his wrists to punctuate the slightest bow of his head.

"Medaase."

"You don't know?" he asks.

I shake my head.

"Your pumps arrived in Gyimiso Kakraba! Gyimiso Kakraba has water! There will be a commissioning ceremony."

"Ah, West Africa Gold finally delivered . . ."

"Not West Africa Gold," Illiasu interrupts. "Congratulations, Akua, for seeing something other than a construction site. Every volunteer before you quit, except Lynn, and she lived at the mine. She didn't have to live in our world. But you stayed in Obuasi town and you really feel the people." Illiasu's hips might be swaying. I've never seen him so free. "Gyimiso Kakraba will never forget what you have done."

"Thank you, but it was WAG's choice to give them the boreholes . . ." My voice trails off, as it is clear from Illiasu's cocked head and raised brows that he knows more than he ought. It's impossible to keep a secret in this town.

"Akua, I commend you. You have learned well. It is not to be spoken of—as some things are not to be written in letters. You see, there are ways, the old ways, African ways still very much alive in this world."

His words touch my heart and the memory of one no longer alive. "They killed Ken Saro-Wiwa." My voice comes out anguished. I don't know why I said it. Illiasu and I have never spoken of the situation in Nigeria. Although I trust him, there is too much that I will never know. He could be part of a Ghanaian state apparatus that stifles those who would speak. I don't care. I want acknowledgement of what is lost.

Illiasu holds my gaze for a long while. The spark softens into sorrowful intelligence. His arms fall to his sides. "Yes." He lets out that high-pitched giggle that reminds me Ghanaian men claim much more range for themselves than my Rifleman. "Yes. We used to imagine that atrocities occur because there is no one to bear witness. Now, the whole world watches on the Internet . . . and does nothing. Atrocity is now a sport for a world of voyeurs.

"But you did something. Woayɛ adeɛ. You have tried! O!"

I would like to run to him and bury my face in his breast and cry. But he is a man of high station who does not muddle boundaries. Coming to the Advocacy office is transgression enough.

"Akua," Illiasu raises his hand toward me as if acknowledging a daughter. "Wobɛtena ase."

I bow my head to receive the honor.

"You must wear a fine dress for the commissioning. I will talk to Helen Boateng."

Takyi's elusive boss does seem one for celebration. Every meeting she misses is due to a funeral or a wedding or a naming ceremony. With one small step, Illiasu crosses the threshold and makes his exit. From the hall, I hear his endearing giggle, ". . . she is an engineer . . ."

VILLAGES AND CHARACTERS

Villages

Gyimiso Kakraba	Asasebomebosia
Bediem	Adubensasu, aka Mile 9
Sansu	Nyameso
Mamiriwa	Kwabenakwakrom

Characters

Adansi West Rural Water, Sanitation, and Health Advocacy

TEAM MEMBERS	SECONDED FROM	BOSS ON STEERING COMMITTEE
Charles Yaw Takyi	Dept of Community Development	Helen Boateng
Mr. Osei	Ghana Water and Sewerage Corp	---
Thomas Anyidoho	Ministry of Health	Mr. Osabutey
Agyeman Isaac Theodore	Dept of National Mobilization	Mr. Preko

ADDITIONAL STEERING COMMITTEE MEMBERS

Robert Obeng	Jr. Environmental Officer, West Africa Gold
Mr. Abubakar	Jr. Administrative Officer, Adansi West District

COORDINATOR

Louisa Lehmann, aka Akua	Peace Corps Volunteer

Adansi West District

Mr. Abubakar	Junior Administrative Officer
Mr. Illiasu	District Administrative Officer
Mr. Kofi Kwegyir Ankrah	District Secretary

West Africa Gold Company Limited

Terry	Pilot
Robert Obeng	Jr. Environmental Officer
Kwasi, aka Dr. Kwarteng-Badu, aka Doctor	Sr. Environmental Officer

Jim Hansen	Sr. Environmental Officer
Finn Harrigan	Head of Safety Department
Madam Dzodzi Akyineba Tettey	General Manager
Anthony	Safety Administrator
Ethan Acquah	Safety Inspector
Mr. Mensah	Transport Officer
Jeff Fogerty	Former Head of Exploration
Peter Clayton	Metallurgist
Kwadwo	Driver, Friend of Idrissu
Ned Clyde	Superintendent

Peace Corps

Louisa Lehmann, aka Akua	Peace Corps Volunteer, Obuasi
Lynn Lubic, aka Abena	Former Peace Corps Volunteer, Obuasi
Lionel	Guard, Accra
Ozwald	Mailroom Handler, Accra
Genevieve Garnier	Associate Peace Corps Director, Education
Matt McKenna	Associate Peace Corps Director, Rural Development
Gladys	Peace Corps Medical Officer
Doc Macey	Peace Corps Doctor, West Africa Region
Bai	Peace Corps Volunteer, Walewale
Lorne	Peace Corps Volunteer
Amy	Peace Corps Volunteer, Chereponi
Steve Simmons	Peace Corps Volunteer
Uncle Ryan	Ghanaian Trainer of Peace Corps Volunteers

World Bank/United Nations Water and Sanitation Programme

| Tao Bronson | Manager, West Africa Region |
| Jim Kelly | Manager, Africa |

Nongovernmental Organizations

| Don Welsch | WaterCore |
| Wilberforce Wiafe | Water Vision |

Elizabeth	WomenCare
Fortunato	Hope Together In Love
Candace Issahaku	WomenCare

Obuasi

Idrissu	Akua's Neighbor
Fathia	Idrissu's Wife
Hasna and Laila	Idrissu's and Fathia's Daughters
Yam Chip Lady	Street Chop Vendor
Amadu al-Attar, aka Kofi	Folk Hero
Old Woman	Produce Seller

Construction

Gary	Laborer
Bob Drucker	Superintendent
Antoine	Old Man on Bridge Job

America

Mother	Louisa's Mother
Art	Louisa's Brother
Lou	Louisa's Father
Carol	Louisa's Friend

Other

Sebastian	Small in the Village of Gyimiso Kakraba
Ken Saro-Wiwa	Environmental Justice Activist, Nigeria
Kwabena	Egg Man, Accra
CDR Chairman	Chairman of the Committee for the Defense of the Revolution in the Village of Gyimiso Kakraba
Jerry John Rawlings	Ghana's Head of State
Mr. Moses	Chief Hydrologist, Ghana Water and Sewerage Corp, Kumasi
Michael Vaughn	Managing Director, Shell Oil, Nigeria
Barudi	Libyan Artist, Painter
Yusuf Salihu	Miner, Kwabenakwakrom

GLOSSARY

37	Akuafo Circle (traffic circle)
aane	yes
aduane	food
agal	cord that holds a man's headcloth in place (Arabic)
agoo	call at neighbor's door; as American "knock, knock"
akan	the largest ethnolinguistic group in Ghana
akwaaba	welcome
akye	is fried; "a"—is/has/have; "kye"—to fry
akyerɛmma	drummers
akyire yi	see you later; literally, "later"; shortened form of "akyire yi yɛbɛhyia"—we shall meet later
amee	general response to "agoo"
anaa	or
aswad	black (Arabic)
awuraa	madam; miss
bayerɛ	yam; a large, local root that serves as a staple, often boiled or fried or pounded into fufu; with bark similar to thin tree bark and meat that is denser than an American potato
bayerɛ a yɛakye	yam that we have fried
borehole	a well; small-diameter hole drilled into the ground and fitted with a pump to serve as a source of drinking water
bra	come (imperative form)
buroni	a white person; Caucasian; short form of "oburoni"
buroni waawu clothes	second-hand Western clothes; literally, "a white person has died clothes"
(the) castle	Osu Castle; Christiansborg Castle; seat of government
CDR	Committee for the Defense of the Revolution
cedi	currency of Ghana, symbolized as "₵"
chale wote	a pair of foam sandals; flip flops; literally, "dude, let's go"
chop	(v) to eat; to squander/spend or consume, as in "he chopped the money"; (n) food, as in "street chop"
CIP	Capital Investment Programme

445

circle	Kwame Nkrumah Circle (traffic circle)
da	to sleep; literally, "to lie down"
dabi	no
da yie	sleep well; good night (imperative form)
district	the ten regions of Ghana are subdivided into districts
durbar	a meeting in a village
expatriate	foreign national; also "expat"
ɛnna ase	no need to thank; do not thank; literally, "do not lie down"
ɛte sɛn?	how is it?; how are you?; how's it going?
ɛyɛ	good; it's good; it's well; literally, "it is"
fie	home
football	the sport of soccer; a soccer ball
fufu	plantain and cassava or yam, pounded into a sticky ball, usually served in soup
garden egg	vegetable with shape, size, and color of an egg, and the texture of an eggplant
gari	dried, ground cassava
GG shot	gamma globulin shot
ghibli	storm winds arising in southern Libya and moving north carrying large quantities of sand (Arabic)
grasscutter	cane rat; a sweet bushmeat considered a delicacy
groundnut paste	peanut butter
groundnuts	peanuts
gye nyame	except for God
-hene	suffix to designate royalty or high office; appended to the name of a village to refer to the chief of the village
haw	(n) worry or trouble; short form of "ɔhaw"
how?	how are you doing?
ice kenkey	"kenkey" is a staple dish of the Ga and Fanti people of Ghana made of fermented corn dough; "ice kenkey" is mashed kenkey sweetened with sugar and milk
inshallah	if Allah wills; God willing (Arabic)
jellabiya	pullover wide-cut gown with no collar and wide sleeves (Arabic)
kaffir	crude pejorative reference to black-skinned person (Afrikaans)
kaffir boetie	crude pejorative reference to friend of a black-skinned person (Afrikaans)

kaftan	a pullover men's robe worn with matching drawstring pants (Arabic)
kɔ	to go
kyɛ me sika	gift me money
maadwo	good evening; "I give you the cool"
maaha	good afternoon; "I give you weariness" (from the heat)
maakye	good morning; "I give you the dawning"
m'adamfo	my friend
mɛbo wo	I'll beat you
medaase	thank you; shortened form of "meda wo ase"
meda wo ase	thank you; literally, "I lie down (prostrate myself) before you"
me ho nyɛ	I'm not good; I'm not well; literally, "my body is not good"
mepa wo kyɛw	I beg you; please
merekɔda	I am going to sleep; Louisa uses unconjugated verb, "mekɔda, I go to sleep"
merekɔ fie	I am going home; Louisa uses unconjugated verb, "mekɔ fie, I go home"
merekɔnoa aduane	I am going to cook food; Louisa skips the verb "to go," "menoa, I cook"
me ti yɛ me ya	my head hurts
milo	a popular brand of cocoa powder
mineral	soda pop
na	and
nana	a title given to chiefs/kings or their courtiers; it may also form part of an individual's name
nananom	elders; plural form of "nana"
nante	to walk
nante yie	walk well (imperative form)
na wo nso ɛ?	and you also?; and how about you?
nkontommire	cocoyam leaves
nkwanta	junction
nkyenam	fried fish
noa	to cook
ntoosi	tomatoes
o	a clean and precise pronunciation, there is no drawing out of the sound as in the American "oh"; a wide variety of emotion can be expressed depending on the valence given to the sound; "o, I am sorry"
oburoni	a white person; Caucasian; plural "aborɔfo"

onyame	God
oral rehydration solution	oral solution taken to counter loss of electrolytes
ɔbaa	woman
ɔbarima	man
ɔhaw	(n) worry or trouble; also, "haw"
ɔkyeame	royal linguist through whom communications are made to and from chiefs
ɔkyeame poma	the staff of office of a linguist
pa	good
pa ara	very good; well; very much
palaver	predicament, trouble, incident (British)
political suit	Ghanaian adaptation of a Western man's business suit
presby	Presbyterian
queen mother	ancestral head woman
red red	fried ripe plantain and beans served in palm oil
saa	is that so?; really?
samosa	fried dough filled with meat or vegetables (Indian)
shotgun	the passenger side of a vehicle (American)
small	child; (pl) smalls; also, "a little" as in "to walk small"
solid	(n) favor (American)
stool land	land under a supreme chief; the stool is the symbol of chieftaincy
trotro	passenger lorry
WAG	West Africa Gold Company Limited
watsan	water and sanitation
well	hand-dug well or borehole
woayɛ adeɛ	you have done something
wobɛtena ase	you will sit down, meaning "you will stay"; compliment or expression of welcome to visitor
wopɛ ahe?	how much do you want? (Fanti Twi)
worekɔ he?	where are you going?
wote?	do you hear?
wote aseɛ?	do you understand it?
yɛnkɔ	let's go
yɛbɛhyia bio	we shall meet again
yɛfrɛ wo sɛn?	what is your name?; literally, "we call you what?"
zongo	the Muslim neighborhood of a town; variant of "zango"; literally, "a settlement of Hausa speaking traders"; vernacular, "stranger quarters" (Hausa)

ACKNOWLEDGEMENTS

In 1996, while driving from San Francisco to Santa Rosa, I heard a radio program on the one-year anniversary of the death of Ken Saro-Wiwa. Despite diligent efforts, I have been unable to find a record of that broadcast. To the best of my memory, the comments of the Acting Managing Director of Shell Oil and the environmental advocate working in Ogoniland and the Niger Delta, which are fictitiously attributed to an article in *Newsweek*, are direct quotations from that radio program.

Across the span of twenty-five years, many people influenced the writing of *The Advocacy*. Recalling their names invokes a parade of relationships, many of them loving, some with people whose presence has faded, all with fierce supporters of me as a writer or vital contributors to the evolution of the story.

Thank you to Marie Ross and Sharon Wun—who read my first attempt at a novel, who were the first to treat me as a writer; to the Adansi West Water and Sanitation Health Team—Meda wo ase pa ara!—Mr. Obeng, Vincent Nusenu, Adu-Gyamfi Luke Bartholomew, the late Samuel Kofi Frimpong, and Kim Koporc; to Tom Long, Dena and Ed Mortensen, Tamarah Knapp Hancock, Stu Bahen, Thurston Seaton-Majahara II, Annette Robinson, Lee Sloca, Erin Baker, Gabe Brandt, Mohammed Obeng and Amalia, David Ketchum, Larry Batson, Jerry and Ginny Howe, Laura Peters, C.J. and Ming Shin, Chris Arnold, Kwabena Mate, Jeff and Gerrie Stanton, Lucy Blake-Elahi, Martin Staples, Madeleine Mader, Kimlin Johnson, David Bachtel, Ray Castellino, Sarah Theismann, Uncle Henny, Bronwyn Chambers, Colin Speirs,

Barb Ketchum, anonymous Ghanaian civil engineer, Jaime Badia, Frances Squire, Patrick LoBrutto, Kay Martin, Doug Daher, Richard Kish, Mica Tanabe, Mo Bina, Greta Hilde, Whitney Weddell, Mary-Ann Tirone Smith, Jan Petersen, Pauline Nguyen, Don Drorbaugh, Anne Carayon, Chris Halaska, John Morash and Sabra Wohlenberg; to Beyond Baroque; to Writers & Books, especially, Joe Flaherty and Judith Kitchen; to the open mic gang at the Midnight Special Bookstore of bygone days and the Rapp Saloon, with special thanks to Rev D; to the Southern California Writers' Conference, especially, Judy Reeves, Rick Anderson, Jennifer Silva-Redmond, Marla Miller, Matt Pallamary, Janis Thomas, Maralys Wills, Jean Jenkins, Wes Albers, and Michael Steven Gregory. A special thanks to my writing partner, Kelley Gusich.

Thank you to the professionals who gave of their time and offered guidance—the reference librarians, Harrison Behl of the Library of Congress and Laura Schnitker of Special Collections at the University of Maryland; Sheryl Seitz of Mapbox; the agents of rightsholders administering permissions—Robert Shatzkin, Dana Francoeur, Austin Mueller, Diane Grosse, Yessenia Santos, Patricia Zline, Jillian Sims, Ivan Babanovski, Rachel Reeder, Hannah Stokes, Louise Henderson, Jim Fleming, Giovanni Boccardi, Rochelle Roca-Hachem, Diana _____ at UNESCO, Sabrina Brockman, Diana Reeve, Robert Dunkin, Pankaj A., and Kassahun Checole.

Thank you to the epigraph authors—your work inspires me!—for your generous consent to my quoting of your words—William Abraham, Ute Luig, Heike Behrend, Dympna Ugwu-Oju, Maliqalim Simone, David Hecht, and Ato Quayson.

Thank you to Gillian Stead Eilersen and Evelyn Fox Keller for writing the biographies of Bessie Head and Barbara McClintock, respectively. Your compassion and objectivity did them justice and provided me, as a writer and as a woman, with invaluable inspiration.

Thank you to my parents, Margaret Barker and Mel Fischer, for giving me this life. You always encouraged me to read and write.

Thank you to Ann Williams, my English teacher at West Bakersfield High School, who wrote in the margin of my journal, "Like most people's . . . [your talent] . . . will probably be wasted." May *The Advocacy* serve as my answer, in no small measure due to your encouragement and thorough proofreading of numerous drafts. All remaining errors are mine alone. *Once can last a lifetime.* Rest in peace.

Thank you to Stephen Awiba (Yaw) for your passion for language, your diligent research when bona fide source documents were not always extant, and your professional expertise applied to proofing the Twi language. All remaining errors are mine alone.

Thank you to Gabriel Brandt for naming the phenomenon of "white as gender."

A special thanks to Theresa Dodge for your friendship of more than twenty years, the many furtive late night talks after babies and boys, your perceptiveness and wondrous artistic sensibility.

Thank you to Kilometer Thirteen; Ali Shaw, Vinnie Kinsella, and Jenny Kimura of Indigo Editing; and Jessie Glenn, Julie Swearingen, and Kristen Ludwigsen of Mindbuck Media—for helping me bring it home.

BIBLIOGRAPHY

Abraham, W. E. *The Mind of Africa*. Chicago: A Phoenix Book, University of Chicago Press, 1966.

Aidoo, Ama Ata. *Changes: A Love Story*. New York: The Feminist Press, 1993.

———. *No Sweetness Here and Other Stories*. New York: The Feminist Press, 1995.

———. *Our Sister Killjoy: or Reflections from a Black-eyed Squint*. Essex: Longman Group Limited, 1994.

Armah, Ayi Kwei. *The Beautyful Ones Are Not Yet Born*. Oxford: Heinemann, 1988.

———. *Two Thousand Seasons*. Chicago: Third World Press, 1987.

Ayensu, Edward S. *Ashanti Gold: The African Legacy of the World's Most Precious Metal*. Accra: Ashanti Goldfields Company Limited, 1997.

Behrend, Heike and Ute Luig, eds. *Spirit Possession: Modernity & Power in Africa*. Madison: University of Wisconsin Press, 1999.

Boateng, E. A. *A Geography of Ghana: Second Edition*. Cambridge: Cambridge University Press, 1967.

Buivenga, Jos. "Fontin." Font conversion by Charles Dye, "Fontin TrueType," 2006. *Fontsquirrel*. 26 July 2019. https://www.fontsquirrel.com/fonts /Fontin?q%5Bterm%5D=fontin&q%5Bsearch_check%5D=Y

Conrad, Joseph. *Heart of Darkness & The Secret Sharer*. New York: The New American Library, 1950.

Cook, Alfred W. and Kenneth D. Matthews, Jr. *Cities in the Sand: Leptis Magna and Sabratha in Roman Africa*. Philadelphia: University of Pennsylvania Press, September 1963.

Crisp, Jeff. *The Story of an African Working Class: Ghanaian Miners' Struggles 1870-1980*. London: Zed Books, Ltd., 1984.

Edelman, Marian Wright. *The Measure of Our Success: A Letter to My Children and Yours*. Boston: Beacon Press, 1992.

Eilersen, Gillian Stead. *Bessie Head: Thunder Behind Her Ears – Her Life and Writing*. Portsmouth: Heinemann, 1996.

Garamantes. Wikipedia contributors. *Wikipedia, The Free Encyclopedia*, 09 July 2019 13:25 UTC, https://en.wikipedia.org/wiki/Garamantes.

Gere, James M. and Stephen P. Timoshenko. *Mechanics of Materials* (Second Edition). Belmont: Brooks/Cole Engineering Division, 1984.

Great Wall of China. Wikipedia contributors. *Wikipedia, The Free Encyclopedia*, 22 June 2019 17:46 UTC, https://en.wikipedia.org/w/index .php?title=Special:CiteThisPage&page=Great_Wall_of_China&id=902976788.

Gyasi, Yaa. *Homegoing*. New York, Alfred A. Knopf, 2016.

Harden, Blaine. *Africa: Dispatches from a Fragile Continent*. Boston: Houghton Mifflin Company, 1991.

Head, Bessie. *A Gesture of Belonging: Letters of Bessie Head, 1965-1979* (Randolph Vigne, Ed.). London: SA Writers; Portsmouth: Heinemann, 1991.

———. *A Question of Power*. Oxford: Heinemann, 1974.

———. *Maru*. Oxford: Heinemann, 1995.

Hecht, David and Maliqalim Simone. *Invisible Governance: The Art of African Micropolitics*. New York: Autonomedia, 1994.

Hives, Frank and Gascoine Lumley. *Ju-Ju and Justice in Nigeria*. New York: Ballantine Books, 1930.

Hughes, John. *The New Face of Africa: South of the Sahara*. New York: Longmans, 1961.

imagestockdesign. "Map of Africa on gray with red Ghana vector – Vector." *Shutterstock*. ID: 376561081. https://www.shutterstock.com/image-vector /map-africa-on-gray-red-ghana-376561081?src=d83oushpiuM_3ss-dwmLiaQ-1-0&studio=1.

Keller, Evelyn Fox. *A Feeling for the Organism: The Life and Work of Barbara McClintock*. New York: W. H. Freeman and Company, 1983.

Leptis Magna, Libya - Ancient Roman Civilization. *Waymarking*, fi67, WMMTJM, 03 November 2014, http://www.waymarking.com/waymarks /WMMTJM_Leptis_Magna_Libya.

Lewis, Paul. "BLOOD AND OIL: A Special Report.;After [*sic*] Nigeria Represses, Shell Defends Its Record." *The New York Times*, The New York Times Company, 13 February 1996, https://www.nytimes.com/1996/02/13/world /blood-and-oil-a-special-report-after-nigeria-represses-shell-defends-its -record.html.

Lindqvist, Sven. *Exterminate All The Brutes*. New York: The New Press, 1996.

Lock, Charles. "Ken Saro-Wiwa, or 'The Pacification of the Primitive Tribes of the Lower Niger.'" *Ken Saro-Wiwa: Writer and Political Activist*. Craig W. McLuckie and Aubrey McPhail, eds. Boulder: Lynne Rienner Publishers, Inc., 2000. Page 4. *Google Books* Web. 20 July 2019.

MacDonald, Jean. "Denkyem." *West African Wisdom: Adinkra Symbols and Meaning*. http://www.adinkra.org/htmls/adinkra/denk.htm.

———. "Hye Won Hye." *West African Wisdom: Adinkra Symbols and Meaning*. http://www.adinkra.org/htmls/adinkra/hyew.htm.

———. "Nsaa." *West African Wisdom: Adinkra Symbols and Meaning*. http://www .adinkra.org/htmls/adinkra/nsaa.htm.

———. "Osram Ne Nsoromma." *West African Wisdom: Adinkra Symbols and Meaning*. http://www.adinkra.org/htmls/adinkra/osra.htm.

Murray, Stephen O. and Will Roscoe, eds. *Boy-Wives and Female Husbands: Studies of African Homosexualities*. New York: St. Martin's Press, 1998.

Na'Allah, Abdul Rasheed, ed. *Ogoni's Agonies: Ken Saro-Wiwa and the Crisis in Nigeria*. Trenton: Africa World Press, Inc., 1998.

Naipaul, V.S. *A Bend in the River*. New York: Vintage International, Vintage Books, a Division of Random House, Inc., March 1989.

Noah, Bob. "Instant look in real life water ripples in a park pond during a beautiful morning sunrise - Image." *Shutterstock*. ID: 240002395. https://www.shutterstock .com/image-photo/instant-look-real-life-water-ripples-240002395?studio=1.

Nugent, John Peer. *Call Africa 999*. New York: Coward-McCann, Inc., 1965.

Ojike, Mbonu. *My Africa*. New York: The John Day Company, 1946.

Pilkington, Ed. "14 years after Ken Saro-Wiwa's death, family points finger at Shell in court." *The Guardian*, Guardian News & Media Limited, 27 May 2009, http://www.theguardian.com/business/2009/may/27/ken-saro-wiwa-shell-oil.

Quartey, Kwei. *Gold of Our Fathers*. New York: SoHo Press, Inc., 2016.

——. *Wife of the Gods*. New York: Random House, 2009.

Quayson, Ato. *Oxford Street, Accra: City Life and the Itineraries of Transnationalism*. Durham: Duke University Press, 2014.

Roscoe, Will. *Changing Ones: Third and Fourth Genders in Native North America*. New York: St. Martin's Press, 2000.

Sarton, May. *Journal of A Solitude*. New York: W.W. Norton & Company, 1992.

Schwabenblitz. "Map – Ghana, Ashanti – Vector." *Shutterstock*. ID: 433611979. https://www.shutterstock.com/image-vector/map-ghana-ashanti-433611979?src=ZJWQVgFu9f3eM0Ef5RpwZg-1-8&studio=1.

Severan Basilica at Leptis Magna. United Nations Educational, Scientific, and Cultural Organization (UNESCO), 28 March 2011, https://www.facebook.com/unesco/photos/a.10150138085998390.301089.51626468389/10150142369658390/?type=1&theater.

Shomo, Jared. "Sankofa Bird Hand Drawn Adinkra Symbol – Vector." *Shutterstock*. ID: 164020862. https://www.shutterstock.com/image-vector/sankofa-bird-hand-drawn-african-adinkra-164020862?src=HtUcYRCqNAntfC2Hb5UQhA-1-8&studio=1.

Sidhe. Akoko Nan adinkra symbol is from "seamless pattern with adinkra symbols for your design – Vector." *Shutterstock*. ID: 510241876. https://www.shutterstock.com/image-vector/seamless-pattern-adinkra-symbols-your-design-510241876?studio=1.

The Rifleman. Los Angeles: American Broadcasting Company, ABC, 1958-1963. Television.

Turnbull, Colin M. *The Forest People: A Study of the Pygmies of the Congo*. New York: A Clarion Book, Simon and Schuster, 1961.

Ugwu-Oju, Dympna. *What Will My Mother Say: A Tribal African Girl Comes of Age in America*. Chicago: Bonus Books, Inc., 1995.

van der Post, Laurens. *The Dark Eye In Africa*. New York: William Morrow & Company, Inc., 1955.

Wästberg, Per. *Assignments in Africa: Reflections, Descriptions, Guesses*. New York: Farrar, Straus & Giroux, 1986.

Wellard, James. *The Great Sahara*. New York: E. P. Dutton & Co., Inc., 1965.

Woodman, Marion with Rita Greer Allen, Kate Danson, and Mary Hamilton. *Leaving My Father's House: A Journey to Conscious Femininity*. Boston: Shambhala, 1993.

Zongo settlements. Wikipedia contributors. *Wikipedia, The Free Encyclopedia*, 21 May 2019 13:42 UTC, https://en.wikipedia.org/w/index.php?title=Zongo_settlements&oldid=898115136.

ABOUT THE AUTHOR

Melissa Fischer was born and raised in Southern California. They earned bachelor's and master's degrees in Civil Engineering from Stanford University. Fischer has lived five years in Africa, including two in Ghana, where they managed a water and sanitation agency in a region impacted by gold mining. Fischer has worked over thirty years as a civil engineer in construction, public works, development, and relief work.